THE LADYBIRDS (COCCINELLIDAE) OF BRITAIN AND IRELAND

An Atlas of the Ladybirds of Britain, Ireland, the Isle of Man and the Channel Islands

HELEN E. ROY

PETER M.J. BROWN

ROBERT FROST

REMY L. POLAND

In celebration of
PROFESSOR MICHAEL MAJERUS

Cover image Eyed ladybird, *Anatis ocellata*.
Photo: Remy Poland

Reprinted with corrections (2012)

Published for: Biological Records Centre
NERC Centre for Ecology and Hydrology
Maclean Building
Benson Lane
Crowmarsh Gifford
Wallingford
Oxfordshire
OX10 8BB

By: FSC Publications
Unit C1, Stafford Park 15
Telford
TF3 3BB
www.field-studies-council.org

ISBN: 978 1 906698 20 1

Contents

Dedication to Professor Michael Majerus

We dedicate this book to our friend and mentor, the late Professor Michael Majerus. Mike was Professor of Evolution at the University of Cambridge and organiser of the Coccinellidae Recording Scheme from the late 1980s until his premature death in early 2009, after a short but extremely severe illness.

Much of what we know about ladybirds, we learnt from Mike. He was a PhD supervisor to Remy Poland and Peter Brown, and Helen Roy first met him whilst working on her PhD in the 1990s; he welcomed her into his lab for a few months of experimental work, offering much help and guidance. Robert Frost first met Mike at a weekend ladybird course which Mike was leading. Mike was a wonderfully friendly source of guidance to all four of us, and his New Naturalist 'Ladybirds' book (Majerus, 1994) is a rich resource for all.

Mike was a splendid public speaker, lecturer and tutor to his students. He seemed to find public speaking very easy – at least, he made it look that way. He would enthuse his audience by making his science both clear and exciting. He undoubtedly had an eye for the sensational; 'Sex Wars' (Majerus, 2003) is the title of one of his books, and a press release announcing the arrival of 'the most invasive ladybird on Earth!' had a ring of the flamboyant. But Mike chose his words carefully and always had sound scientific ideas behind the bold phraseology. His predictions on the rapid rate of spread of the harlequin ladybird have already been borne out, including the arrival of this species in Scotland in 2008. Mike was never afraid to put forward a theory, sometimes controversial, in order to stimulate thought and research. To quote him directly: "I also enjoy speculating... if my ideas and theories are subsequently put to the test by others who are caught up in a fascination of ladybirds... I will be delighted, whether my ideas are verified or refuted." (Majerus, 1994).

Mike was an unpretentious character who made time for people of all ages and levels of knowledge. Through his positions of responsibility, especially as President of the Amateur Entomologists' Society (a society which he joined as a teenager, as soon as membership rules allowed!), he encouraged interest in insects in as wide a range of people as possible. He was a dedicated father and had an especially good manner with children, to whom he seemed to enjoy talking as much as to experienced scientists. His own love of butterflies from a very early age undoubtedly led to this; Mike began collecting insects at the age of four, and was once quoted as saying that he considered the first four years of his life to have been wasted! Mike owned E.B. Ford's New Naturalist titles on butterflies (Ford, 1945) and moths (Ford, 1955) at the age of ten and was delighted and honoured to himself write a new version of 'Moths' (Majerus, 2002) as well as the earlier 'Ladybirds' (Majerus, 1994).

Some of our fondest memories of Mike are from days spent with him in the field. He had a passion for fieldwork and over his lifetime made meticulous observations of a huge variety of moths, butterflies and ladybirds in the field. Most years Mike would disappear for a month or two to a far-off land – perhaps Rwanda or Ecuador – to study insects in their natural environments. He developed a large network of overseas friends and collaborators. Our fieldwork with him was usually rather less exotic, but always enjoyable – involving days in Surrey and especially King's Forest in Suffolk. This is a rich habitat for ladybirds and we would invariably find many species, and as we went along, learn new aspects of their ecology from Mike.

Mike's sudden illness was a great shock, but he would not want us mourning his death, rather celebrating his life. If he were alive today, he would of course be first author of this book. We have tried our hardest to do justice to Mike's work here, and we hope that he would be pleased with the book. He was our inspiration, and we hope that some of his enthusiasm for insects comes across in the pages that follow.

Helen Roy, Peter Brown, Robert Frost and Remy Poland.

Foreword

It was Gilbert White, the eighteenth-century naturalist and curate of Selborne in Hampshire, who suggested that one could usefully spend a lifetime studying the natural history of a single parish. Some people may look no further than their own private gardens, while my own studies of ladybirds were initially restricted to the small town of Horley in Surrey, and were only extended to cover the whole county with the help of many other people and a great many country rambles. But no matter how narrow or broad one's own area of study, it is both important and interesting to place one's local observations within a wider picture – hence the need for a national distribution atlas. At a glance one can see whether the creature one has found is common or rare, or at the edge of its range, or, most exciting of all, a new record for the region.

But this atlas offers so much more than distribution maps. Using photographs and text it helps with the identification of all ladybird species, from the largest to the very smallest, and in all their stages: egg, larva, pupa and adult. There is information on life histories, behaviour, host plants and prey, and details of the enemies of ladybirds, especially their parasites. And it comes at a critical moment in the story of ladybirds in Britain and Ireland. The native species, so carefully mapped and studied over the last thirty years or so, must now compete with hordes of alien ladybirds from the east. The invading species, *Harmonia axyridis*, has been given almost as many English names as it has varieties of pattern, but has now conclusively been named the harlequin ladybird. It originated in the Far East and has come to us on a devious route through North America and the Low Countries. Fortunately, it was spotted almost as soon as it arrived in Britain in 2003. Its spread over the last seven years has been studied carefully and is documented here. Now the commonest ladybird in many areas, it competes with the native species both for food and by direct predation. Some familiar and common native species, the 2-spot, 10-spot and cream-spot ladybirds, live on deciduous trees and are in the front line of these ladybird wars. The 2-spot is already showing a decline in its numbers. It remains to be seen whether these species can survive alongside the harlequin, perhaps in a particular habitat niche or area of country. So, although this atlas gives the story so far, the need to observe and record ladybirds throughout this period of change is even greater than before.

Roger Hawkins.

Acknowledgements

First and foremost we would like to thank the thousands of people who have contributed ladybird records to the Coccinellidae Recording Scheme, Harlequin Ladybird Survey, UK Ladybird Survey and Ladybirds of Ireland project. The enthusiasm of people across Britain has been inspirational; each and every record contributes to our understanding of the ecology of ladybirds in Britain, and we are enormously grateful for the dedication to wildlife recording of so many people. We also owe a debt of gratitude to many county Coleoptera recorders, other beetle recorders, and local record centre staff, for sharing their coccinellid records with us, including: Keith Alexander, Roy Anderson, Sam Bosanquet, Dave Bentley, Steve Bolchover, Sheila Brooke, Martin Collier, Phil Cook, Michael Darby, Jonty Denton, Scotty Dodd, Arthur Ewing, Garth Foster, Peter Garner, Bill Grange, Neil Gregory, Roger Hawkins, Kate Hayward, Peter Hodge, Dave Hodges, David Iliff, Trevor James, Steve Lane, Derek Lee, Nick Littlewood, Derek Lott, Bob Marsh, Graham Maynard, Ken Merrifield, David Nash, Phil Northing, Brian Ribbands, Wolfgang Schaefer, Matt Smith, Don Stenhouse, Ian Thompson, Fiona Walker, Richard Weddle, R. Colin Welch, Derek Whiteley, Steve Woodward, Richard Wright, Sheila Wright, staff at Buckinghamshire & Milton Keynes Environmental Records Centre (BMERC), Environmental Record Centre for Cornwall and the Isles of Scilly (ERCCIS) and Sussex Biodiversity Record Centre. We also thank the Centre for Environmental Data and Recording (CEDaR), National Museums Northern Ireland and the Ladybirds of Ireland project for permission to include provisional data from Ireland.

We thank John Muggleton, organiser of the original Coccinellidae Recording Scheme. We also thank Paul Mabbott, particularly for his work in the early tracking of the harlequin ladybird and for providing thousands of records. We thank Roger Hawkins not only for his records, but for reviewing the text and for providing many helpful suggestions.

Various organisations have helped us promote the ladybird surveys in recent years, and we particularly thank the Amateur Entomologists' Society, BBC, British Trust for Ornithology, Buglife, Butterfly Conservation, National Trust, Rothamsted Research, Royal Entomological Society, Royal Horticultural Society, Royal Society, RSPB, Wildlife Trusts and the Zoological Society of London. Ladybird Clothing and Ladybird Books have also supported the UK Ladybird Survey with prizes and promotional materials for events. Many records were provided by local natural history societies across the country, including: Bedfordshire Natural History Society, Benson Environment Survey Team, Cambridge Natural History Society, Derby and Notts Entomological Society, Essex Field Club, Harrow Natural History Society, Isle of Wight Natural History & Archaeological Society, London Natural History Society, Milton Keynes Natural History Society, Rutland Natural History Society, Sorby Natural History Society, Southampton Natural History Society and Yorkshire Naturalists' Union.

We are also grateful to Andrew Branson for publishing our annual wildlife report on ladybirds in *British Wildlife*. Ian McLean has kindly invited us to contribute ladybird workshops for the British Entomological and Natural History Society. The welcomes we have received from the Natural History Museum (London), Oxford University Museum of Natural History (Darren Mann) and University Museum of Zoology Cambridge (William Foster and Russell Stebbings) have been immensely appreciated and useful. We are particularly grateful to the latter for allowing us access to the Crotch ladybird collection and entomology library.

We thank many recorders who have provided not only records, but useful insights, including: Derek Bateson, Mike Bidwell, Paul Brothers, Phil Budd, Dennis Dey, Barry Dickerson, Ken Dolbear, Gary

Farmer, Maria Fremlin, Jean Geiger, Lucy Hulmes, John Llewellyn-Jones, Steven Pascoe, Trevor Pendleton, Bill Phillips, Chris Rawlings, Brian Reid, Jon Shanklin, Penny Shorter and April Zobel. We are very grateful to Jeremy Milne, a very knowledgeable coleopterist, who has passed on his understanding of ladybird habitats, helped with recording ladybirds and assisted in the identification of inconspicuous ladybird species. We would like to thank Andrew Frost for his time spent in the field hunting for and identifying ladybirds. We also thank coleopterists Max Barclay, Roger Booth and Andrew Duff.

We thank the photographers (many of whom have also provided records) for their generosity in sharing their stunning images of ladybirds. The photographs are fantastic assets for assisting in species identification, but also often provide unique insights into the ecology and behaviour of these beautiful insects. We are particularly grateful to Gilles San Martin, Jo Bogaert and Richard Comont for providing many superb images.

The production of this atlas was supported by the Biological Records Centre (BRC), which is co-funded by the Natural Environment Research Council (through the Centre for Ecology & Hydrology) and the Joint Nature Conservation Committee (JNCC). We are particularly grateful to Chris Cheffings (JNCC) for many useful discussions over the last few years. We also thank Trevor James and Jim Munford (National Biodiversity Network Trust), who were instrumental in securing funds for the rejuvenated recording scheme in 2004 (funding from Defra through the NBN Trust).

Chris Preston (Head of Botany in BRC) provided guidance throughout the development of this atlas and kindly agreed to review the final text. We have had the pleasure of many insightful discussions with him, and have benefited both from his editorial experience and his expertise in understanding the distribution patterns of species. Mark Bailey (Director of Biodiversity), Mark Hill (Head of BRC until retirement in July 2010), Richard Pywell (Science Section Head) and David Roy (Head of BRC from July 2010) have been hugely encouraging and supportive throughout this atlas project. David Roy has, on many occasions, assisted us with transferring data and with mapping species distributions.

We are very grateful to Jim Bacon (BRC web developer) for his dedication in advancing the technological aspects of the survey, without which we could not have engaged so many people in biological recording. We also thank former BRC staff Francis Rowland (developer of our original website and online recording system) and Gavin Broad.

Colin Harrower, Stephanie Ames, Cassie Hoyland and Henry Arnold (BRC) were instrumental in ensuring the effective flow of ladybird data into the BRC database and ultimately the NBN Gateway. Their ability and patience in producing maps on demand, often urgently, is much appreciated. Nick Isaac (along with Belgian collaborators Tim Adriaens, Dirk Maes and Thierry Onkelinx) developed the methods to analyse the distribution trends presented for the conspicuous ladybirds. We thank Barnaby Smith and the Knowledge Transfer team at the Centre for Ecology & Hydrology for their enthusiasm and support in promoting the UK Ladybird Survey so widely. Indeed there are many, many people within CEH who have enthusiastically supported our activities over the years and this is enormously appreciated.

Over the years we have had the pleasure of working with staff and volunteers who have helped in compiling ladybird data from many different sources and in many different guises. We are grateful to them all, but Val Burton, who worked for BRC for over 40 years, is particularly thanked. Her aptitude for inputting paper records and compiling data is incredible. Gemma Baron, Björn Beckmann, Charlotte Coombes and Richard Comont have also assisted in the production of this atlas.

Members of the University of Cambridge Genetics Field Station contributed a huge amount to this project, both in terms of records and expertise. Special thanks go to Ian Wright (whose harlequin sighting led to the launch of the Harlequin Ladybird Survey), and to Emma Rhule, L-J Michie and Richard Hall for an impressive commitment to ladybird recording and uploading public records to the database. Thanks go to Lori Lawson-Handley and Cathleen Thomas at the University of Hull for their time spent processing records. In addition, we thank Julian Doberski, Dawn Hawkins and Alison Thomas (all Anglia Ruskin University) for support and encouragement.

We thank Rebecca Farley-Brown and Simon Norman at the Field Studies Council for production of the field chart *Guide to Ladybirds of the British Isles* (recently revised), and for supporting us in our endeavours to produce a forthcoming field chart for ladybird larvae and pupae. The FSC's generosity in allowing the free download of the field chart through an iPhone app and throughout the BBC Breathing Places Ladybird Survey is also appreciated. Finally we thank the FSC, particularly Rebecca, for ensuring the final publication of this atlas.

Our families and friends (particularly David, Katy and Ella Roy, Penny Shorter, Faith Frost, James Frost, Guy Poland, Clare Walker, Cameron and Jodie Brown, Tina Majerus) have been endlessly patient and supportive of our (obsessive) passion for ladybirds. For all the times they have listened to our ladybird tales and stood patiently while we have scoured favourable ladybird habitats while 'just out walking' (and, indeed, often joined us in our quest for records), we are extremely grateful.

Finally we would like to thank Mike, who inspired us beyond words.

Introduction

"Biological science must stand on its foundations in basic observations of organisms in the field: what they do, when they do it, why they do it, and how they have come to do it." Majerus, 1994.

The family Coccinellidae comprises a diverse group of beetles. Some species are brightly coloured and these are colloquially termed 'ladybirds'. Others are small and inconspicuous, although these, on close inspection, are just as attractive as their charismatic counterparts. There are 47 species of Coccinellidae resident in Britain and Ireland (and more than 4500 species described worldwide). Of these, 26 are easily recognisable as ladybirds and 21 are not. The life histories of the latter, termed 'inconspicuous coccinellids', have received less attention than the true ladybirds, with the exception of a notable few that have been used as biological control agents. Hereafter we refer to all the Coccinellidae as 'ladybirds'.

Undoubtedly, the popularity of ladybirds is, in part, a consequence of their role as predators of pest insects. However, the affectionate attitude of people towards ladybirds goes far beyond gardeners and biological control practitioners. Many books, toys and clothes feature ladybirds as lovable creatures, quite the opposite of voracious predators! The word 'ladybird' has been used as a term of endearment in classical literature. For example, Juliet's nurse in Romeo and Juliet (Act 1: Scene 3) uses the word ladybird synonymously with sweetheart, calling: *"What, lamb! What, ladybird! God forbid! Where's this girl? What, Juliet!"* In many parts of the world, ladybirds are regarded as lucky omens and fortune-tellers. They are attributed with the ability to predict the weather, crop yield, fertility and romance. Reference to the association between ladybirds and love is common, particularly in Europe.

The derivation of the word ladybird is linked to religion, ladybird being a dedication to Mary, Our Lady. The elytra (wing cases) of the common 7-spot ladybird, *Coccinella septempunctata*, are thought to depict the red cloak of Mary, and the seven spots are linked to Mary's seven joys and seven sorrows. The association of ladybirds with Mary spans many languages, and many other names are dedications to God. Interestingly, in Verona, the common name for some species of Coccinellidae is Galletto del Diavolo, meaning The Devil's Cockerel. There are two conflicting theories on the derivation of the word Coccinellidae. One attributes the name to the Latin *coccinatus*, meaning clad in scarlet (Majerus, 1994). The other derives from *cocci*, meaning small and spherical (Hodek and Honěk, 1996). Both are logical explanations linking the family name to key attributes.

Figure 1. 7-spot ladybird foraging for aphids on borage. Photo: Helen Roy.

In this atlas, we describe the distribution of ladybirds in Britain and Ireland (including the Channel Islands) using data collated through the Biological Records Centre Coccinellidae Recording Scheme (including the UK Ladybird Survey and provisional data from Ladybirds of Ireland) since 1964. Ladybirds are charismatic beetles with fascinating life histories. Their interactions with natural enemies, particularly parasites, are intriguing and we hope that this atlas will encourage further recording of ladybirds, and also the natural enemies associated with them. This publication is also a celebration of the work of Mike Majerus and the many ladybird recorders he inspired.

Key features of British and Irish ladybirds

All the British and Irish species have a number of physical attributes in common. They are small to medium-sized beetles (1.3 mm to 8.5 mm in length) and characteristically have a hemispherical or oval body shape. The slightly clubbed antennae generally have 11 segments and are attached to the inner edge of the large compound eye. The mouthparts consist of large, strong mandibles with four-segmented maxillary palps (terminal segment axe-shaped) located behind them. The labium (lip) is divided into the pre-labium and post-labium, three-segmented labial palps and the labrum. The head can be partly withdrawn under the pronotum, which is broader than long, and has anterior extensions at the margin. The short legs can be retracted under the body and end with four-segmented tarsi (although only three in *Nephus* species); however the third segment is small and hidden by the second segment. The abdomen is comprised of ten segments.

Taxonomy

The family Coccinellidae is within the Cucujoidea, a superfamily within the Coleoptera. It is a member of the phylogenetic branch of Coleoptera referred to as the Cerylonid complex of families (Cerylonidae, Discolomidae, Alexiidae, Corylophidae, Endomychidae and Lathridiidae). Six subfamilies of Coccinellidae are generally recognised worldwide: Sticholotidinae, Chilocorinae, Scymninae, Coccidulinae, Coccinellinae and Epilachninae. However, an alternative phylogeny suggests a seventh subfamily, Ortaliinae (Kovář, 1996). Three of these subfamilies dominate the European fauna: Scymninae, Chilocorinae and Coccinellinae. There are very few European Sticholotinae, very few Coccidulinae and only three species of Epilachninae (Iperti, 1999). There are no members of the Sticholotinae currently in Britain or Ireland.

Table 1: Number of genera and species within each subfamily of the Coccinellidae (adapted from Duff, 2008) in Britain and Ireland (number in brackets). It should be noted that, in the Checklist of the British Beetles (Duff, 2008), Coccidulinae and Scymninae are combined into the Coccidulinae. Furthermore, the checklist contains all species that have been recorded as residents, an additional five species to the list of 42 species resident to Britain published by Majerus & Kearns, 1989. There are 27 species of ladybird in Ireland.

Subfamily	Genera	Species
Coccidulinae and Scymninae	7 (5)	20 (9)
Chilocorinae	3 (1)	4 (1)
Coccinellinae	14 (13)	21 (16)
Epilachninae	2 (1)	2 (1)
TOTAL	**26 (20)**	**47 (27)**

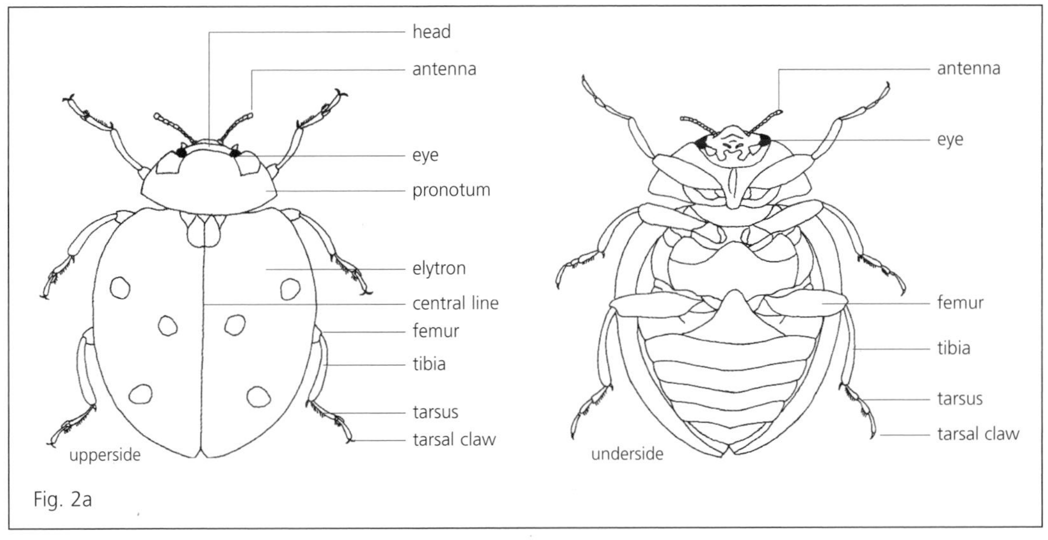

T1-T3 = thoracic segments 1-3

A1-A8 = abdominal segments

O = outer row of tubercles

M = middle row of tubercles

I = inner row of tubercles

Mid = midline

Fig. 2b

T1-T3 = thoracic segments 1-3

A1-A8 = abdominal segments
(N.B. 8-9 not always visible)

O = outer row of tubercles

M = middle row of tubercles

I = inner row of tubercles

Mid = midline

Fig. 2c

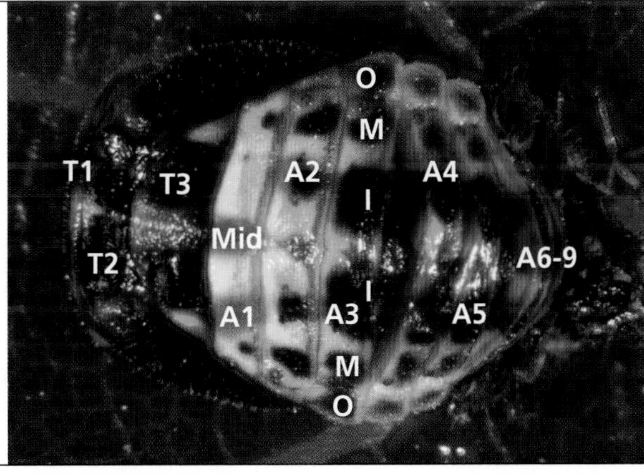

Figure 2. Anatomy of ladybirds (a. adult; b. fourth-instar larva; c. pupa). Photos: Remy Poland.

Species of Coccinellidae resident in Britain and Ireland
(all species found in Britain and *indicates those species also found in Ireland)

Order Coleoptera

Superfamily Cucujoidea

Family Coccinellidae

Subfamily Coccidulinae Mulsant, 1846

Coccidula rufa (Herbst, 1783) — marked *
Coccidula scutellata (Herbst, 1783)
Rhyzobius chrysomeloides (Herbst, 1792)
Rhyzobius litura (Fabricius, 1787) — marked *
Rhyzobius lophanthae (Blaisdell, 1892)
Clitostethus arcuatus (Rossi, 1794)
Stethorus punctillum (Weise, 1891)
Scymnus suturalis Thunberg, 1795 — marked *
Scymnus auritus Thunberg, 1795 — marked *
Scymnus frontalis (Fabricius, 1787)
Scymnus haemorrhoidalis Herbst, 1797
Scymnus femoralis (Gyllenhal, 1827)
Scymnus schmidti Fürsch, 1958 — marked *
Scymnus nigrinus Kugelann, 1794 — marked *
Scymnus limbatus Stephens, 1832 — marked *
Scymnus interruptus (Goeze, 1777)
Nephus redtenbacheri (Mulsant, 1846) — marked *
Nephus quadrimaculatus (Herbst, 1783)
Nephus bisignatus (Boheman, 1850) (thought to be extinct in Britain)
Hyperaspis pseudopustulata Mulsant, 1853 — marked *

Subfamily Chilocorinae Mulsant, 1846

Platynaspis luteorubra (Goeze, 1777)
Chilocorus bipustulatus (Linnaeus, 1758) (Heather ladybird) — marked *
Chilocorus renipustulatus (Scriba, 1791) (Kidney-spot ladybird)
Exochomus quadripustulatus (Linnaeus, 1758) (Pine ladybird)

Subfamily Coccinellinae Latreille, 1807

Anisosticta novemdecimpunctata (Linnaeus, 1758) (Water ladybird) — marked *
Tytthaspis sedecimpunctata (Linnaeus, 1761) (16-spot ladybird)
Myzia oblongoguttata (Linnaeus, 1758) (Striped ladybird) — marked *
Myrrha octodecimguttata (Linnaeus, 1758) (18-spot ladybird) — marked *
Propylea quattuordecimpunctata (Linnaeus, 1758) (14-spot ladybird) — marked *
Calvia quattuordecimguttata (Linnaeus, 1758) (Cream-spot ladybird) — marked *
Halyzia sedecimguttata (Linnaeus, 1758) (Orange ladybird) — marked *
Psyllobora vigintiduopunctata (Linnaeus, 1758) (22-spot ladybird) — marked *
Anatis ocellata (Linnaeus, 1758) (Eyed ladybird) — marked *
Aphidecta obliterata (Linnaeus, 1758) (Larch ladybird) — marked *
Hippodamia tredecimpunctata (Linnaeus, 1758) (13-spot ladybird) — marked *

Hippodamia variegata (Goeze, 1777) (Adonis' ladybird)
Coccinella hieroglyphica Linnaeus, 1758 (Hieroglyphic ladybird)
Coccinella magnifica Redtenbacher, 1843 (Scarce 7-spot ladybird)
Coccinella quinquepunctata Linnaeus, 1758 (5-spot ladybird)
Coccinella septempunctata Linnaeus, 1758 (7-spot ladybird)
Coccinella undecimpunctata Linnaeus, 1758 (11-spot ladybird)
Adalia bipunctata (Linnaeus, 1758) (2-spot ladybird)
Adalia decempunctata (Linnaeus, 1758) (10-spot ladybird)
Harmonia axyridis (Pallas, 1773) (Harlequin ladybird)
Harmonia quadripunctata (Pontoppidan, 1763) (Cream-streaked ladybird)

Subfamily Epilachninae Mulsant, 1846

Henosepilachna argus (Geoffroy in Fourcroy, 1762) (Bryony ladybird)
Subcoccinella vigintiquattuorpunctata (Linnaeus, 1758) (24-spot ladybird)

Life cycle

The Coccinellidae belong to the Endopterygota, meaning they undergo complete metamorphosis, passing from the egg to larval, pupal and adult stages.

Figure 3. Harlequin ladybird laying eggs.
Photo: April Zobel.

Figure 4. 7-spot ladybird larva.
Photo: Gilles San Martin.

Figure 5. Harlequin ladybird pupa (left) and pre-pupa (right). Photo: Ken Dolbear.

Figure 6. 2-spot ladybird adult.
Photo: Michael Kilner.

Ladybird eggs are smooth, oval, elongate and yellow (ranging from off-white and pale in the case of the orange ladybird to dark orange for the kidney-spot ladybird). The chorion (outer shell) of ladybird eggs is thicker than in other beetles. Most species of ladybird lay their eggs upright in groups ranging from two to 100 eggs.

The fully developed larva has specialised cuticular structures on the head or thorax, called egg-busters, which are used to penetrate the tough chorion. Egg-busters are only found on first-instar larvae. The larval stage comprises four instars (stages). At the end of each stage the larva sheds its skin (ecdysis) by attaching itself to a substrate using the anal cremaster. The skin is then shed backwards and left attached to the substrate along with the cuticular linings of the fore-gut, hind-gut and tracheal system. Ladybird larvae have elongate bodies which are covered in bumps called tubercles (and are sometimes distinctly spiky). The head capsule is hard and often dark and has antennae of up to three segments. Ladybird larvae, unlike many beetle larvae, eat the same food as the adult stage and their mouthparts reflect this. The mandibles have one or two teeth at the tip. The three-segmented maxillary palps and one- to two-segmented labial palps are also visible. Ladybird larval legs vary in length; the legs of the 14-spot ladybird larvae are notably long. Most larvae can be identified to species on the basis of their colour patterns but only at late instars. The larva enters a period of quiescence prior to the final larval moult called the pre-pupal stage. During this phase it attaches to a substrate for the final time, its body becomes hunched and it remains so for several days.

The pupal stage of ladybirds appears to be a continuation of the quiescent pre-pupal phase, but pupae are not entirely immobile. Predator or parasitoid attack causes the anterior end of the pupa to move rapidly up and down in a flicking movement, in which the pupa acts like a heavily armoured jaw (so called 'gin trap'); this could deter some natural enemies such as parasitoids. The external surfaces of ladybird pupae are highly variable depending on the degree to which the larval skin is shed. In the Coccinellinae, the larval skin is attached at the base and the pupa is left exposed. Pupae of the subfamilies Chilocorinae and Coccidulinae are partially covered by the larval skin which splits open and is not completely shed; an exception is the pupa of *Coccidula scutellata* which is almost entirely exposed. Pupae also vary in colour and markings both between and within species. The variation in pupal colour form is, in part, inherited, but also dependent on temperature and humidity. Developmental structures called imaginal discs are present throughout all the immature life stages and these give rise to the adult organs.

The adult stage emerges from the pupa in a process termed eclosion. The pupal skin breaks open at the anterior end and the adult ladybird climbs out onto the pupal case, where it remains for several hours. The colours of the pronotum are fully developed in the newly emerged adult but the elytra are soft and pale-coloured. Haemolymph (tissue fluid) is pumped into the wings facilitating expansion over a few hours; however the colour takes much longer to develop. Pigments are laid down over several days, resulting in the characteristic markings of the particular species.

Winter in Britain and Ireland is an adverse time for ladybirds, because food is scarce and the weather conditions are unfavourable. So they enter a dormant state and overwinter as adults, usually in groups (aggregations). Some aggregations comprise more than one species. Some species – including the 16-spot, 22-spot, kidney-spot and harlequin ladybird – tend to form very large aggregations, and the same overwintering sites may be used year after year. The exact timing of the onset of overwintering varies between species and depends on environmental cues

Figure 7. 7-spot ladybirds aggregate in preparation for winter.
Photo: Leslie Hebdon.

(temperature and light). Many become dormant in the latter part of September. It is usual to see clusters of 7-spot ladybirds on fence posts at this time, preparing to move into the leaf litter where they will reside for the winter months. 2-spot ladybirds begin to enter houses, forming aggregations around window frames and in attics. Some species remain active into November. Orange ladybird larvae can be found in September because this species feeds on mildews, which generally form in late summer, and development is slower than in aphid-feeding species. Harlequin ladybirds are also active late in the season, and the UK Ladybird Survey has reports of larvae still present in late December. It is highly unlikely that these harlequin larvae will complete their development but is an indication of the opportunistic life style of this invasive alien. There are many records of ladybirds throughout the winter months but most of these now relate to harlequin ladybirds, which arrive in domestic dwellings in extremely high numbers; it is not unusual to receive reports of 1000 individuals in one house.

Mortality of ladybirds during the winter is high. Most species can survive long periods at sub-zero temperatures but they are less able to cope with dramatic fluctuations in the temperature over short periods of time; for example, late frosts are particularly detrimental. Fungal pathogens, such as *Beauveria bassiana*, are a major mortality factor during winter, and high numbers of infected individuals can be recorded in wet winters.

Overwintered adult ladybirds begin to emerge from February onwards. They form conspicuous groups as they slowly appear from their overwintering locations. 16-spot ladybirds can be seen in spectacularly high numbers at this time, particularly on fence posts in damp locations. Pine ladybirds are generally the first species to mate (early February) and lay eggs (early March). They find early food sources on evergreen, needled conifers and the trunks of certain deciduous trees. April is usually the time that adult ladybirds, particularly the species that feed on aphids on herbaceous plants, begin to disperse to locate food and mates. The species that rely on the aphids of deciduous trees begin to feed and mate in early May, although they may use alternative food sources (such as pollen and nectar) earlier in the season.

The reproductive behaviour of ladybirds has received considerable research attention from both ecological and evolutionary perspectives. Most species are highly promiscuous and this has led to lengthy mating bouts in which the male essentially guards the female. Mating can last up to eight hours, and a 2-spot ladybird will have in excess of 20 partners in its life time. Repeated mating is essential to maintain a high level of egg fertility. Larvae hatching from a ladybird egg batch are minute (approximately 1-2 mm) and the first-instar is a critical stage; if they do not feed rapidly, they will starve. For many predatory species the first-instar larva is approximately the same size as its prey, or even smaller. It is perhaps not surprising that first-instar larvae are highly cannibalistic and will feed on unhatched siblings, after first consuming their own egg shell. The larval stage lasts for about three weeks (predatory species) to five weeks (non-predatory species) depending on environmental conditions and food availability. The larvae pupate from mid-May and the adults emerge after about one week.

Some species are univoltine, *i.e.* they go through only one generation per year, regardless of environmental conditions or prey availability. The ovaries of 7-spot ladybirds will not mature until they have been through a period of dormancy called diapause. Therefore, 7-spot ladybirds are univoltine. In contrast, other species are multivoltine and can reproduce immediately after pupation, if conditions are favourable. Indeed, it is not uncommon to see newly emerged 2-spot and 10-spot ladybird adults copulating before the pigment has developed in the wing cases. The harlequin ladybird is a multivoltine species, and, in Britain, two and, exceptionally, three generations have been recorded in one year.

Long-distance flight

Ladybirds usually disperse over relatively short distances during their reproductive period, in search of food. However, periodically long-distance flights of 'swarms' of ladybirds are observed. This is thought to be the result of the hypermobility of starving adults of a new generation (Hodek *et al.*, 1993). Large groups of 7-spot ladybirds have been observed in summers when good weather conditions and high aphid numbers resulted in large populations and an eventual depletion of aphids. In 1976 and 2009 contributors to the survey reported 'swarms' of ladybirds, particularly along the east coast of Britain. It is thought that this is a consequence of ladybirds

Figure 8. 7-spot ladybirds on a ferry from Denmark to England.
Photo: Paul Sopp.

dispersing widely in search for food and arriving at the coast. It has also been speculated that the large numbers of ladybirds observed are in part due to immigration from other European countries. Reports of large numbers of ladybirds on ships indicate the propensity for ladybirds to undertake long-distance flights across the sea. On one day in April 2009, several thousand 7-spot ladybirds were reported to arrive in a Moroccan port on a cruise ship (Minchin, 2010). The ship was fumigated but the 7-spot ladybirds were still present fourteen days later. Other species of ladybird, such as harlequin ladybirds, have been reported on ships, and this is undoubtedly one introduction pathway for this species.

Ladybirds also engage in long-distance flights when preparing for dormancy; diapausing ladybirds migrate to overwintering sites, and after dormancy they disperse to breeding sites. Aggregations of ladybirds are common in autumn, as many individuals move to the same overwintering site. 2-spot and harlequin ladybirds favour sheltered overwintering locations above-ground and often at elevated positions. These two species are found in very large numbers in houses and other buildings.

Figure 9. Pine ladybird larva (centre) feeding on scale insects (coccids).
Photo: Richard Comont.

Feeding relationships

There has been considerable research attention on the feeding behaviour of ladybirds. This is, in part, because of interest in the potential for biological control by species that consume economically important, primarily pest insects such as aphids. There have been a number of reviews on the feeding ecology of ladybirds. Recently an entire issue of the journal *Biological Control* (volume 51) was devoted to the trophic ecology of ladybirds. Many people distinguish between essential (promoting development and reproduction) and alternative (enabling survival) foods (Hodek and Honěk, 2009) although there is still much to be elucidated in this regard. In Table 2 the principal (essential) foods are listed with notes on other foods (some of which are likely to be essential foods). It is important to note that we have used colloquial terms for the different prey and that the taxonomy of these groups is complex. Further information on many of the prey species is available at www.britishbugs.org.uk.

Table 2: Principal foods of British and Irish ladybirds and notes on other foods (adapted from Majerus, 1994; Klausnitzer and Klausnitzer, 1997; Hodek and Honěk, 2009). In summary, 28 species consume aphids (greenfly/blackfly); 9 species consume coccids (scale insects); 1 species consumes Acari (mites); 4 species consume adelgids (conifer woolly aphids); 3 species consume mildew; 3 species consume pseudococcids (mealybugs); 1 species consumes aleyrodids (whiteflies); 1 species consumes phylloxera; 1 species consumes chrysomelid larvae (heather leaf beetle); 2 species consume diaspidids (armoured scale insects); 1 species consumes psyllids (jumping plant lice) and 2 species consume plants. Blank = not known.

Species	Principal foods	Other foods
Coccidula rufa	Aphids	
Coccidula scutellata	Aphids	
Rhyzobius chrysomeloides	Coccids	Aphids
Rhyzobius litura	Aphids	
Rhyzobius lophanthae	Coccids/Diaspidids	
Clitostethus arcuatus	Aleyrodids	
Stethorus punctillum	Acari	Aphids, honeydew, pollen
Scymnus suturalis	Adelgids especially *Pineus pini*	Aphids, coccids, pollen
Scymnus auritus	Phylloxera	Pollen
Scymnus frontalis	Aphids	Pollen, nectar, mildew
Scymnus haemorrhoidalis	Aphids	Coccids
Scymnus femoralis	Aphids	Pollen, nectar
Scymnus schmidti	Aphids	Pollen
Scymnus nigrinus	Aphids/Adelgids	Coccids, pollen
Scymnus limbatus	Aphids/Coccids	
Scymnus interruptus	Pseudococcids/Diaspidids	Aphids
Nephus redtenbacheri	Pseudococcids	Aphids
Nephus quadrimaculatus	Coccids	
Nephus bisignatus	Coccids/Pseudococcids	
Hyperaspis pseudopustulata	Aphids	Coccids, honeydew, pollen, nectar
Platynaspis luteorubra	Aphids	
Heather ladybird	Coccids	Aphids, adelgids
Kidney-spot ladybird	Coccids	Diaspidids, aphids, adelgids, mites
Pine ladybird	Coccids/Adelgids	Aphids, mites, honeydew, pollen, nectar
Water ladybird	Aphids	Honeydew, pollen, nectar
16-spot ladybird	Mildew	Thrips, mites, pollen, nectar
Striped ladybird	Aphids	Coccids, adelgids, honeydew
18-spot ladybird	Aphids	Adelgids, pollen
14-spot ladybird	Aphids	Coccids, adelgids, mites, honeydew, pollen, nectar, mildew
Cream-spot ladybird	Aphids/Psyllids	Mites, honeydew
Orange ladybird	Mildew	Aphids, honeydew

Continued overleaf

Table 2 (continued).

Species	Principal foods	Other foods
22-spot ladybird	Mildew	
Eyed ladybird	Aphids	Coccids, adelgids, honeydew, pollen
Larch ladybird	Adelgids	Aphids, coccids
13-spot ladybird	Aphids	Pollen, nectar
Adonis' ladybird	Aphids	Coccids, honeydew, pollen, nectar
Hieroglyphic ladybird	Aphids/Larvae of heather leaf beetle	
Scarce 7-spot ladybird	Aphids	Coccids, adelgids, honeydew, nectar
5-spot ladybird	Aphids	Coccids, adelgids, honeydew, pollen, nectar, mildew
7-spot ladybird	Aphids	Coccids, adelgids, mites, honeydew, pollen, nectar, mildew
11-spot ladybird	Aphids	Coccids, adelgids, mites, honeydew, pollen, nectar, mildew
2-spot ladybird	Aphids	Coccids, adelgids, mites, honeydew, pollen, nectar, mildew
10-spot ladybird	Aphids	Coccids, adelgids, mites, honeydew, pollen, nectar
Harlequin ladybird	Aphids	Coccids, adelgids, aleyrodids, psyllids, various insect larvae, honeydew, pollen, nectar
Cream-streaked ladybird	Aphids	Coccids, adelgids, honeydew, pollen, nectar
Bryony ladybird	White bryony	
24-spot ladybird	Campion, false oat grass	Nectar

Most predatory ladybirds feed on either aphids or coccids and a few feed on both. In addition, the following prey are eaten by some ladybird species: mites, adelgids, aleyrodids, chrysomelid larvae, cicadellids (leafhoppers), pentatomids (shieldbugs), phylloxera, and psyllids. The biogeography of the major prey of ladybirds, *i.e.* aphids and coccids, provides interesting insights into the distribution of ladybird species. Temperate zones are characterised by an abundance of aphids, and grasslands in these regions contain ladybirds from the subfamilies Coccidulinae and Coccinellinae (such as *Coccinella* spp., *Adalia* spp.). Open deciduous and coniferous forests in this temperate zone contain other genera of Coccinellinae (such as *Anatis* spp., *Myrrha* spp., *Myzia* spp.). In contrast, tropical zones in central and southern Africa, South America, India and China, where Coccidae are abundant, are dominated by ladybirds from the tribes Chilocorinae (such as *Chilocorus* spp., *Exochomus* spp., *Brumus* spp.) and Coccidulinae. Aphids and coccids are found together in Mediterranean regions of Europe and here the ladybird fauna is typified by species from both the temperate and tropical zones.

Ladybirds as biological control agents of pest insects

The role of predatory ladybirds for the biological control of pest insects has been recognised for almost two centuries; in 1815, Kirby and Spence noted the importance of ladybirds in controlling hop aphids. However, it was not until the 1880s that the vedalia ladybird, *Rodolia cardinalis*, was released intentionally to control the cottony cushion scale *Icerya purchasi* (a coccid) that was threatening the citrus industry of California. The release of the vedalia ladybird (native to Australia) as a classical biological control agent is widely quoted as marking the advent of modern biological pest control. Both the cottony cushion scale and the vedalia ladybird are present in Californian citrus groves today, but the ecological balance between predator and prey ensures that the pest is no longer a problem (Majerus, 1994). The vedalia ladybird has been introduced into 32 countries and yielded complete control of cottony cushion scale in 26 of them, with substantial or partial control in six others.

The success of the vedalia ladybird in controlling cottony cushion scale resulted in a period, colloquially referred to as the 'ladybird fantasy', in which more than 40 species of ladybird were introduced to North America (Dixon, 2000) although only four of these species became established. Dixon (2000) noted that, worldwide, there have been 155 attempts to control aphids and 613 to control coccids through the introduction of Coccinellidae. The control of aphids by ladybirds has been largely unsuccessful (only two, approximately one percent, of the attempts against aphids exerted any level of control); this has been attributed to the mismatch between the reproductive and development rates of these ladybirds and of their aphid prey. Ladybirds have a lower reproductive capacity and considerably slower development rate than aphids. Coccids develop more slowly than aphids and so it is not surprising that approximately nine percent of the releases against coccids were deemed successful (Dixon, 2000). Unfortunately, there are a few cases in which the introduced ladybird species has had far-reaching, unacceptable impacts on biodiversity and so has been deemed an invasive species. The harlequin ladybird is the only such example in Britain (Brown *et al.*, 2008b) although there is no evidence that this species has yet established in Ireland.

Alien ladybirds in Britain

Approximately 90% of ladybirds are predators, and the movement of ladybirds between countries worldwide can largely be attributed to their role in biological control strategies. The 11 alien ladybirds in Europe have all been intentionally released as biological control agents of pest insects. The vedalia ladybird was the first ladybird species to be introduced as a predator of cottony cushion scale in 1888 (Portugal), 1901 (Italy) and 1912 (Italy and France). This species was subsequently released through the mid to late twentieth century to many other countries: Israel, Spain, Malta, Britain, Albania, Cyprus, Switzerland and Ukraine. *Cryptolaemus montrouzieri*, native to Australia, was released to control the mealybug *Planococcus citri* (Pseudococcidae) in Italy (1908), Spain (1926), Corsica (1970), France (1974), Portugal (1984) and Sweden (2001). This species has established in all of these countries except Sweden (where its status is unknown). *Rhyzobius lophanthae*, native to New Zealand, was introduced to control armoured scale insects (Diaspididae) in Italy (1908), Portugal (1930 and 1984), Spain (1958), Sardinia (1973), France (1975), Greece (1977) and Germany (2000). It has recently been reported as established in London (Barclay, 2007). Other species introduced to Europe for the control of coccids include *Rhyzobius forestieri*, *Nephus reunioni*, *Chilocorus nigritus* and *Chilocorus kuwanae*. Of these, only *C. nigritus* (native to the Indian sub-continent) has been introduced to Britain for the control of Diaspididae, Pseudococcidae and Coccidae. More than 50 species of ladybird attack the eggs and immature stages of whitefly pests in glasshouses. *Serangium parcesetosum* (native to Asia and the Indian subcontinent) and *Delphastus catalinae* (native to North America) were introduced across Europe (but not to Britain). Two species of ladybird have been introduced for the control of aphids in Europe: the convergent ladybird (*Hippodamia convergens*) (native to North America) and the harlequin ladybird. Neither has been documented as intentionally released in Britain, but both have been widely available in Europe. The harlequin ladybird is now widespread across Europe.

The arrival of the harlequin ladybird in Britain

'Ladybird knocks spots off the squirrel's migration' (*The Times*, 7th February 2008); 'Invading ladybirds breed up ecological storm for UK species' (*Guardian*, 30th June 2009); 'Harlequin ladybird threat to 1000 species' (*Mirror*, 30th June 2009); 'Beware the plague of smelly ladybirds' (*Daily Express*, 27th October 2009).

These are just a few of the many headlines for stories about the arrival and spread of the harlequin ladybird in Britain. Indeed, the press has been instrumental in highlighting research on the harlequin ladybird; in 2009 there were more than 300 press items about the species. But what is the story behind the headlines?

It would be fair to say that the ecological and economic impacts of most introductions of ladybirds have not been well documented. However, from the scant information available, most appear to have been unsuccessful in regulating target pest insects. The notable exceptions are the vedalia ladybird and C. *montrouzieri*; these two species have irrefutably been economically valuable.

Aphidophagous ladybirds have almost universally failed as biological control agents and, as stated, this has been attributed to the asynchrony between the reproductive and development rates of ladybirds and their aphid prey. Equally, most of the intentional releases have not caused ecological or economic problems. However, a small number of ladybirds are documented as having non-target effects such as consuming or competing with other beneficial insects (other ladybirds, hoverflies, lacewings, pathogenic fungi and pollinators). *Cryptolaemus montrouzieri* is reported to lower the effectiveness of an introduced natural enemy (*Dactylopius opuntiae*) for weed control. The most infamous ladybird introduction causing ecological and economic problems is undoubtedly the harlequin ladybird.

The harlequin ladybird was released as a classical biological control agent in North America from as early as 1916. Europe followed 70 years later, with harlequin ladybirds commercially available from the 1990s. This species has many attributes that contribute to its economic viability as a biological control agent, not least its polyphagous nature. Harlequin ladybirds are known to have a wide dietary range and consume a variety of tree-dwelling aphids, psyllids, coccids, adelgids and other insects. In North America, harlequin ladybirds have been successful in achieving effective control of target pests in many crop systems (e.g. pecan, apple, citrus fruits, sweetcorn, alfalfa, cotton, tobacco, winter wheat and soybean). Therefore, it can be argued that the spread of the harlequin ladybird throughout Europe could prove to be beneficial, by reducing aphid numbers below economically damaging levels and reducing the use of chemical pesticides.

It was predicted that the polyphagous nature of harlequin ladybirds would result in negative impacts on non-target prey species. The UK Ladybird Survey collaborates with a group of over 120 European scientists working on harlequin ladybirds, with a key focus on assessing the effects of this species on native biodiversity. Laboratory studies indicate that harlequin ladybirds are a

Table 3: Summary of release dates and records of the harlequin ladybird in Europe. Adapted from Roy and Migeon (2010); Brown *et al.* (2012).

Country	Earliest year of release (blank if not released)	Year of first record
Belarus	1968	Unknown
Portugal	1984	
France	1982	1991
Greece	1994	1998
Germany	1997	1999
Belgium	1997	2001
Netherlands	1996	2002
England		2003
Switzerland	1996	2004
Luxembourg		2004
Italy	1990s	2006
Denmark	2000s	2006
Czech Republic	2003	2006
Austria		2006
Norway		2006
Poland		2006
Wales		2006
Spain	1995	2007
Liechtenstein		2007
Northern Ireland		2007
Scotland		2007
Sweden		2007
Croatia		2008
Hungary		2008
Serbia		2008
Slovakia		2008
Slovenia		2008
Ukraine	1964	2009
Bulgaria		2009
Latvia		2009
Romania		2009
Ireland		2010

predator of immature monarch butterflies, *Danaus plexippus*, immature small tortoiseshell butterflies, *Aglais urticae*, lacewing larvae and other ladybirds (Pell *et al.*, 2008). Harlequin ladybirds are large, aggressive, polyphagous ladybirds and as such have the potential to dramatically disrupt native guilds in Europe.

Majerus *et al.* (2006a) stated 'The negative effects of *H. axyridis* on other aphidophages are likely to be the result of a complex range of interactions, with *H. axyridis* in general having a competitive edge through resource competition, intraguild predation and a more plastic phenotype. A more rapid development rate, continual breeding ability and lack of diapause requirement, efficient chemical defence and relatively large size would provide *H. axyridis* with a significant reproductive advantage over many native British species.' The pattern is anticipated to be widespread throughout Europe.

Figure 10. Harlequin ladybird larva observed consuming moth eggs in the field. Photo: Bill Phillips.

The UK Ladybird Survey is actively engaged in a number of research projects across Europe. We are particularly interested in two key themes, focussing on community dynamics:

- Interactions with other aphidophagous insects in natural and managed habitats;
- The population dynamics of harlequin ladybirds and effects of climate, habitat and natural enemies.

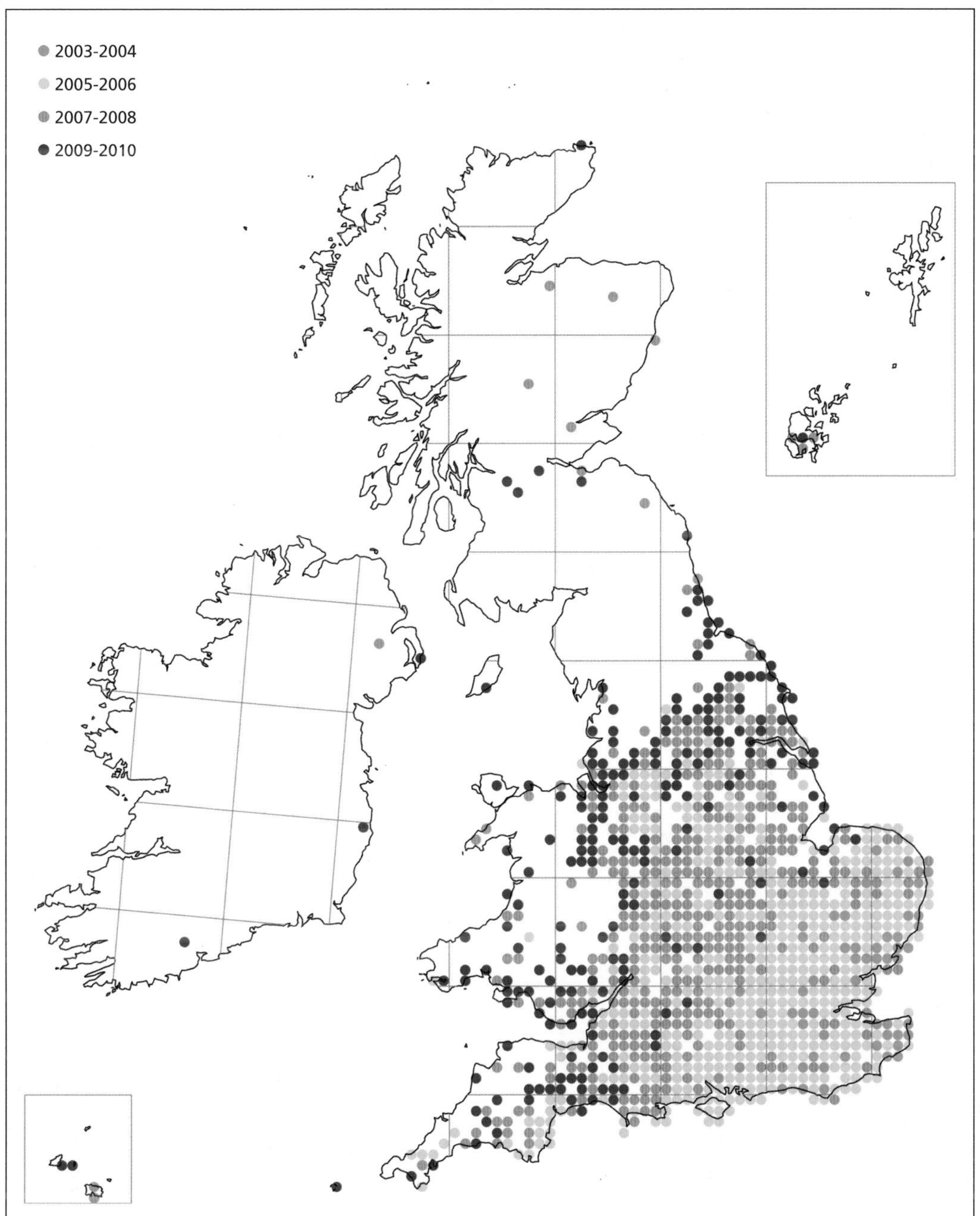

Figure 11. Spread of the harlequin ladybird in Britain and Ireland. The coloured dots indicate 10km squares in which the harlequin ladybird has been first recorded in different time periods from arrival in 2003 to present.

Verified ladybird records, through the UK Ladybird Survey, provide a foundation on which to base this research. The atlas data enable us to address many key questions on the distribution and range of ladybird species across Britain and Ireland. In addition, records and recorders' meticulous observations provide inspiration for new research directions.

Ladybird recording schemes

National surveys

The long tradition of biological recording in Britain and Ireland led to the establishment, in 1964, of the Biological Records Centre (BRC – www.brc.ac.uk). BRC (within the Centre for Ecology & Hydrology) receives data from over 80 national recording schemes for lower and higher plants, invertebrates and vertebrates, and the Coccinellidae Recording Scheme is one such scheme. Launched in 1968, it collates and analyses records of ladybird species found in Britain and Ireland, and maps their distributions.

The Coccinellidae Recording Scheme was led for many years by Dr John Muggleton, with Professor Michael Majerus taking over from the late 1980s. In the early years, participants tended to be experienced naturalists, so to draw others in, Majerus set up the Cambridge Ladybird Survey (a national survey, so named because Majerus was based at the University of Cambridge). Running from 1984 to 1994, this was a very successful public participatory scheme. As a way of making ladybirds more accessible to non-entomologists, Majerus assigned English names to the 26 conspicuous species. This was a small but important step. For many entomologists, the Latin binomials are a preferable way of referring to each ladybird species; however, for someone new to recording, *Exochomus quadripustulatus* is more difficult to remember than pine ladybird. The Cambridge Ladybird Survey generated a large number of biological records and associated natural history observations which contributed hugely to the New Naturalist 'Ladybirds' book (Majerus, 1994). For example, new information on overwintering habitats, phenology and inter-generational matings of ladybirds was compiled. Beautifully illustrated, detailed and informative Cambridge Ladybird Survey newsletters were produced with interesting findings received by the survey, along

THE CAMBRIDGE LADYBIRD SURVEY

NEWSLETTER 15
SEPTEMBER 1992

It has been another busy summer for the Survey, with WATCH again becoming involved, and much of our time in Cambridge being spent on a series of tortuously detailed experiments into the ecology, behaviour and likelihood of survival, of ladybird larvae in their first hours after hatching

Figure 12. Cambridge Ladybird Survey Newsletter.

with Majerus' insights and summaries of some of his research. At the end of the Cambridge Ladybird Survey, a provisional distribution atlas for the conspicuous ladybird species was produced (Majerus, 1995). Up to now this is the only published atlas of ladybird species in Britain and Ireland.

For a period of ten years from 1995, the collation of ladybird records was limited, although the Coccinellidae Recording Scheme continued to tick over. This situation changed drastically with the arrival of a new species! The first record of the harlequin ladybird in late 2004 was met with trepidation by Majerus, but he recognised the potential for involving the public in a unique opportunity to study the spread of an invasive animal from the start of the invasion process. Majerus, Helen Roy, Trevor James and David Roy devised an on-line recording scheme to engage the nation using digital photographs for verification of records. Funding, to develop the on-line recording scheme and associated websites, was rapidly granted by the Department for Environment, Food and Rural Affairs (Defra) via the National Biodiversity Network (NBN) Trust. Collaborative work between Majerus, Helen Roy and staff at the Biological Records Centre enabled the Harlequin Ladybird Survey (www.harlequin-survey.org) to be launched in early 2005 at the Natural History Museum, London. It was one of the first online wildlife surveys in the Britain and Ireland. Soon afterwards, a re-branded Coccinellidae Recording Scheme, the UK Ladybird Survey (www.ladybird-survey.org), was also launched. The Harlequin Ladybird Survey and UK Ladybird Survey have been very successful thanks to extremely enthusiastic support from the public and the media.

Recording in Ireland

Recording of ladybirds in Ireland is organised on an all-Ireland basis by the Centre for Environmental Data and Recording (CEDaR), National Museums Northern Ireland, through the Ladybirds of Ireland project. The information gathered by this project is shared with the National Biodiversity Data Centre (Waterford) and the statutory nature conservation agencies in both parts of the island, the Northern Ireland Environment Agency and the National Parks and Wildlife Service. The Ladybirds of Ireland project has a comprehensive website (www.habitas.org.uk/ladybirds) which includes a photo gallery, a ladybird key, a section on recording ladybirds in Ireland, and an appeal for harlequin ladybird records. The distribution of all the Irish species is shown, the records all having been validated by the site author Roy Anderson. Recording of ladybirds in Ireland is not complete and the data presented in this publication is provisional. The distributions shown are very influenced by recorder effort. Readers should consult the website for up to date information and anyone recording ladybirds in Ireland should submit their records to the appropriate data centre.

Technology

In recent years, modern technology has provided new opportunities for recording schemes, including the ladybird surveys. The internet has made it much easier to engage a far wider audience than was previously possible. Lots of information, images and maps were put on the ladybird survey websites, and colour identification sheets made available for download. Digital photography made the verification of specimens much faster; at least with the conspicuous ladybirds, as there is usually no need to see a specimen if a photo is available. Affordable digital cameras have been available for the last few years, making it easy to send an image electronically. Additionally the UK Ladybird Survey recording form can be accessed using a mobile phone web browser and photos taken from such a device can be uploaded. The quality of the images received from both digital cameras and mobile phones has improved markedly. We are lucky in this regard; for many schemes with a larger array of similar species, digital photography is not necessarily such an effective tool. On-line recording has made the receipt of records and replying to recorders an efficient process. Our on-line recording system has evolved thanks to innovative work by Jim Bacon in BRC. The ability to upload photos together with a species record was a major breakthrough, as the images and records in the database are automatically tied together. Automatic generation of emails to recorders was another advance, and replies to recorders could be customised automatically based on the determination of the species. We have always considered replying to recorders an essential part of the recording process, both to increase the knowledge level of recorders and to express our gratitude and encourage future participation. Some recorders send in many records and their identification skills progress rapidly.

All of these technological advances have enabled the ladybird surveys to deal efficiently with large volumes of data and verify and validate submitted records quickly. The request for photographs (and, to a lesser extent, specimens) to back up records from non-experts enabled more than 40% of records from the public to be verified.

In the forthcoming years the UK Ladybird Survey will be aiming to deliver on-line recording using the recording software Indicia, which was implemented successfully for the BBC Breathing Places Ladybird Survey. Indicia has many advantages including entry of information on the locality of a record using an interactive map, enhanced feedback to recorders and ease of sharing data through a website interface to the database (data warehouse).

The NBN Gateway and access to data

The NBN Gateway, Britain's on-line portal for accessing species maps and data, has been a further vital component to the success of the ladybird surveys in recent years; ladybird data is regularly fed from BRC to the NBN Gateway. By viewing maps on the NBN Gateway, recorders can easily spot where gaps in distributions are, look at changing distributions over time, and track the spread of new species such as the harlequin ladybird. Maps generated directly from the NBN Gateway, using Coccinellidae Recording Scheme and UK Ladybird Survey data, are fed back to the UK Ladybird Survey website.

Outreach

Tens of thousands of people have contributed to the Harlequin and UK Ladybird Surveys. Many events and talks have taken place to publicise ladybirds and their recording, and several high-profile campaigns have assisted enormously. National Insect Week, organised by the Royal Entomological Society, first took place in 2004 and aimed to heighten awareness and interest in insects through a targeted week of events and talks. Running biennially, National Insect Week has twice featured the ladybird surveys prominently.

The BBC has made a huge contribution in helping to raise awareness of ladybirds through various means, including the popular television series Springwatch and Autumnwatch, and an associated project, BBC Breathing Places. The idea of Breathing Places was to ask people to 'Do one thing' for nature in their local area. In 2010, recording ladybirds was the main Breathing Places survey, with schools particularly targeted alongside BBC Wild Days Out. Approximately 11 000 schools registered and received extensive teachers notes on both the UK Ladybird Survey and the new

Figure 13. UK Ladybird Survey participation in outreach events.

Ladybird Parasite Survey. Hundreds of schools carried out surveys in their grounds or nearby areas and provided their records to the UK Ladybird Survey. In addition to learning how to identify ladybirds, children could develop their knowledge of insect life cycles and ecology, particularly interactions with other species. Through the associated Ladybird Parasite Survey, also launched as part of Breathing Places, schools were asked to look for ladybird pupae and record and photograph parasitism by, for example, phorid flies and chalcid wasps. This was an important step in broadening the scope of the ladybird surveys and improving our understanding of some of the complex interactions of ladybirds. BBC Breathing Places led to the translation into Welsh of our Field Studies Council *Guide to the Ladybirds of the British Isles* (Majerus *et al.*, 2006b). The FSC kindly agreed to this guide being made available to all registered schools free of charge.

The ladybird survey team was privileged to contribute to the Royal Society Summer Science exhibition in 2009. A special ladybird exhibit, initiated by Michael Majerus, was a fitting tribute to his career. Over 5,000 visitors came to the exhibition and there were more than 200 press items associated with the UK Ladybird Survey and biological recording as a consequence of the exhibit. Visits to the Harlequin and UK Ladybird Survey websites escalated during the week of the exhibition. A version of our Royal Society exhibit was displayed at the 2010 Moscow Science Festival, which two of us attended.

Figure 14. Oldfield Park Infant School and Crowmarsh Gifford C of E School getting involved in the BBC Breathing Places Ladybird Survey.

Figure 15. Royal Society Summer Science Exhibition 2009: 'Ladybird, Ladybird: Unravelling the story of an alien invader'. Photo: Jim Bacon.

Other outreach events, including 'BioBlitzes', have helped encourage participation in the ladybird surveys. The idea behind the BioBlitz project is to involve the public, working with local wildlife experts, to record as many species as possible at a particular site over a 24 hour period. We have attended many such events and enjoyed the opportunity of encouraging participation in biological recording. In 2010 we were invited to participate in the BioBlitzes run under the auspices of the BBC Wild Days Out. Ladybird cards, based on top trumps, were produced for these events and provided an excellent means of promoting biological recording and the science behind the morphological characteristics of ladybirds.

Figure 16. Ladybird Cards – this simple game provides an opportunity to discuss biological recording and introduce some of the fundamental concepts behind species identification. Authors: Helen Roy and Peter Brown.

Regional surveys and atlases

There have been several local ladybird recording surveys, some with associated atlas projects. The London and Essex Ladybird Surveys, coordinated by Paul Mabbott and organised by the London Natural History Society and the Essex Field Club, respectively, are very active and have an informative website (www.ladybird-survey.pwp.blueyonder.co.uk/londonla.htm). *Ladybirds of Surrey* (Hawkins, 2000) was the result of Roger Hawkins' Surrey Ladybird Survey carried out over a 20-year period. The Surrey maps illustrate presence of ladybird species at tetrad (*i.e.* 2-km square) resolution. The Surrey atlas provides a wonderful insight into the natural history of ladybirds in southern England. The Cambridgeshire & Huntingdonshire Ladybird Atlas Project, led by Robert Frost, is largely modelled on the Surrey Ladybird Survey and, similarly, a tetrad resolution atlas will be published in the future. A ladybird atlas for Cheshire is also planned, and some local Biological Records Centres and museums, for example in Worcestershire and Cumbria, have published ladybird species maps. The amount of time and commitment from the organisers of these local projects cannot be overstated – comprehensive mapping of ladybirds at tetrad level is a huge task, even in relatively small counties: for example, Huntingdonshire (VC 31) has 299 tetrads.

Coverage

The records included in the present atlas are from many sources and we are very grateful to all contributors. Britain has a network of county Coleoptera recorders, many of whom have kindly contributed records from their regions. However, many counties do not have such recorders. Further data was received from local natural history societies and local Biological Records Centres. The Harlequin and UK Ladybird Surveys received records from members of the public and naturalists via on-line recording, postal records and spreadsheets of data. Verification of records received from the public was made by receipt of either a specimen or photograph of the ladybird. However, records of the 7-spot ladybird and 2-spot ladybird (typical form) were accepted without a specimen or photo although many were accompanied by a photo. Also, records received from coleopterists and experienced naturalists were regarded as accurate and have been included in the dataset without direct verification by the authors. Records from the literature were extracted from British entomological journals.

Some regions have been recorded more sparsely than others, for three main reasons. Firstly, the low density of people in some areas resulted in under-recording; clearly, on average there was more recording effort by members of the public in heavily populated regions. Secondly, there was a general lack of recorders in some regions, e.g. much of Ireland. Thirdly, there were areas of heightened recording due to activities of a county Coleoptera recorder or local ladybird project.

Furthermore, the recording effort was not equal across all the ladybird species. Some species are clearly more visible and easy to identify than others. However, whilst records of very common and obvious species tended to be over-represented in the records from the public, the situation was reversed in terms of records from some beetle experts (who tended to ignore the common species). The inconspicuous ladybird species were generally not well recorded by the public, and most records of these are from experienced naturalists. Due to the dedicated Harlequin Ladybird Survey and frequent media attention, the harlequin ladybird was very well recorded in relation to other ladybirds.

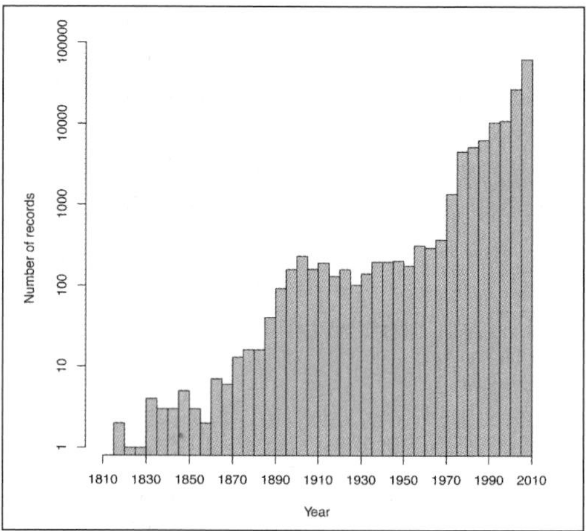

Figure 17. Number (log scale) of ladybird records received by the Biological Records Centre Coccinellidae Recording Scheme (comprising the UK Ladybird Survey) over time. Records from 1800 to 2010 grouped in five year time periods.

Finally, recording effort has varied over time due to particular efforts of the various scheme organisers over the years and the work of local recorders at different times, plus bursts of publicity and varying levels of interest in the surveys. In general, the volume of records received increased over time, and markedly so in recent years.

International collaborations

There are other excellent European surveys of ladybirds, most notably in Belgium, which has a network of recorders mapping ladybirds across the country. We are fortunate to have many opportunities to collaborate with international colleagues, particularly in Europe and especially following the heightened interest initiated by the harlequin ladybird. A meeting in Brussels in 2007 led to the formation of a working group under the banner of the International Organisation for Biological Control of Noxious Animals and Plants (IOBC). The working group, Benefits and Risks of Exotic Biological Control Agents, is led by Helen Roy and involves over 120 scientists from around the world. In 2008 a special edition of the journal *BioControl*, comprising research papers on the harlequin ladybird, was published as a book (Roy & Wajnberg, 2008a). The first conference of the IOBC working group was held in Switzerland in 2009 (Babendreier *et al.*, 2010). In 2011 the group will be publishing a further special issue of *BioControl* 'Invasive arthropod predators and parasitoids: an ecological approach' which will also be within the book series 'Progress in Biological Control' and will highlight the latest research on harlequin ladybirds alongside chapters on other predators and also parasitoids.

Surveying and recording ladybirds

There are three main techniques that tend to be used to find ladybirds: searching by eye, tree beating and sweep netting.

Searching by eye

Many ladybirds are conspicuous and colourful and so some people opt to search for them visually, using no equipment. Searching by eye through low vegetation, hedgerows or the lower branches of trees can be rewarding. However, visual searches will tend to bias what is recorded in favour of large and colourful species. In order to increase the chances of seeing more ladybirds, other techniques, principally sweep netting and tree beating, may be used.

Figure 18. James Frost searching by eye for 5-spot ladybirds, in typical habitat of unstable river shingle. Photo: Robert Frost.

Tree beating

A beating tray is used for surveying the lower branches of trees, bushes and hedgerows. It is basically a frame covered with cloth. The tray opens like a fan, usually rectangular in shape and with the handle in the middle of one of the longer sides. It is placed below a branch, which is struck briskly with a sturdy stick or rod. Any insects on the foliage will fall onto the tray and can then be identified. The material stretched across the frame is pale in colour, making the collected insects easier to see.

Figure 19. Tree beating is an effective method for sampling ladybirds. Photo: Guy Poland.

Beating trays can be expensive and there are two alternatives. A piece of material (perhaps an old sheet, folded up) about a metre square in area can be used. The material is either placed on the ground under the vegetation to be beaten, or (if there are at least three people), held beneath the branch by two people, whilst the third person beats. An even better substitute for a beating tray is an umbrella. The open umbrella is used in a similar way to the beating tray – it is held upside down under the branch. When the branch is beaten the insects will fall into the umbrella. The material of the umbrella should preferably be of a light colour, so that any insects caught can easily be spotted.

Figure 20. A beating tray is being used here to beat flood debris attached to scrub on unstable river shingle – 5-spot ladybirds tumbled out. Photo: Helen Roy.

Beating trays are difficult to use in windy conditions. Umbrellas, being smaller and having the handle in the centre of the frame, are slightly easier to control. It is not recommended to use these tools in winds greater than F4 on the Beaufort Scale.

Figure 21. An upturned umbrella makes an excellent substitute for a beating tray. Photo: Darren Frost.

Sweep netting

A sweep net is designed for sweeping low-growing vegetation. It is basically a canvas bag on a sturdy frame with a long handle, and is somewhat similar to a butterfly net, but with a stronger rim holding the net, which is usually made of a thicker material. The net is swept from side to side whilst walking forwards at a steady pace. With practice, the net can be swept to within a few centimetres of the ground, providing that the vegetation is not too low.

Figure 22. Sweep netting can be used for sampling ladybirds in low-lying vegetation. Photo: Trevor James.

As with beating trays, sweep nets tend to be fairly expensive to buy. Again, an umbrella may be substituted, particularly when searching taller vegetation, which can be tapped over the open umbrella. However, this isn't ideal; the shape of the upturned umbrella is a limiting factor in its use as a substitute for the sweep net; the point at the tip of the umbrella limits the minimum distance that it can be used from the ground. An alternative is to manufacture one's own sweep net from some simple household items (Appendix 1).

Where to look

All ladybirds are terrestrial, and vegetation is generally the best place to look for them (except perhaps in winter). Searching the undersides of leaves can be particularly productive, as this is often where aphids live. As with any group of organisms, different ladybird species occur in different habitats. Whilst some species are generalists and may occur on a very wide range of plants, others are specialists and may generally be limited to one or a few plant species. Good habitats for ladybirds include trees, hedgerows and low herbaceous vegetation such as nettles. Deciduous trees generally have a different suite of species to coniferous trees. Conifers, and Scots pine trees in particular, are home to several of our more specialist species. Please refer to the species accounts in this atlas for information on where to look for the different ladybird species.

When to look

Time of year

Adult ladybirds may be found at any time of year, although more tend to be seen between March and September. See Introduction (Life cycle) for further information.

Time of day

Ladybirds are diurnal insects, *i.e.* they are active during the day. Activity periods vary with the season and weather (and probably the species), but around 10am to 4pm is the best core time to carry out surveys.

Weather conditions

Warm, dry, sunny weather with low wind is best for maximising the chances of seeing ladybirds. Searching for ladybirds in the rain is likely to be unproductive, and using a sweep net or beating tray in wet conditions is inadvisable; once the material of the net or tray is wet, any insects caught will tend to get damaged. As mentioned above, using a beating tray (and to some extent, a sweep net) in windy conditions is problematic.

Risks

Recording ladybirds is a safe activity as long as common sense is used. However, there are dangers associated with any fieldwork. Special care is needed when surveying adjacent to roads, on uneven pathways and near ditches, ponds, canals, rivers and gravel pits. Long sleeves, trousers and closed-toed shoes should be worn when surveying nettle plants! Children are often very good at ladybird spotting but should always be supervised, especially close to roads or water. Occasionally ladybirds may bite, but the bite is nothing more than a small nip. However, a very small proportion of people are allergic to such bites.

Details for the recording form

The following information is useful when recording ladybirds (Appendix 2), particularly if the record is to be submitted to a survey such as the UK Ladybird Survey.

Date

Include the day, month and year. For site surveys (as opposed to incidental records), the survey start and finish times should also be noted.

Recorder

Include the name of the recorder, *i.e.* the person carrying out the survey.

Determiner

If someone other than the recorder has identified, or confirmed the species, then their name should be noted as the 'Determiner'.

Site

If possible, a site name as used on an Ordnance Survey 1:50 000 series map should be noted. For each site visited and if a site is revisited, then a separate recording form should be compiled.

Grid reference

A six-figure (*i.e.* resolution to a 100 metre square) OS grid reference for the survey site is preferred. The post code of the site may be used for sites in built-up areas.

Site description

A site description should be as full as possible. For example 'garden', 'deciduous woodland', or 'gravel pit', etc. is good, but if the ladybird was found on a known plant species, including this information is very useful.

Weather conditions

An indication of the weather conditions at the time of the survey can be useful.

Species

All species found on a site should be recorded. Records (especially of rarer species) are even more valuable if details of other species found in the same survey are also given. Species that cannot be identified should be photographed, or a specimen carefully placed in a plastic tube with screw top, for later identification. It is helpful to add a loose packing of tissue paper, to absorb moisture and protect the insect. No food or plant material should be added.

Figure 23. Ella Roy using a mobile phone for both taking a photograph of a ladybird and for submitting the record on-line. Photo: Barnaby Smith.

Abundance

Counts of the number of each species found are useful.

Life stage

Noting the ladybird life stage (larva, pupa or adult) is helpful.

Colour form

Some adult ladybirds have various colour forms. If known, noting the colour form(s) (and abundance of each) is useful.

Guide to species accounts

Species distribution maps

These show the recorded occurrence in Britain, Ireland, the Isle of Man and the Channel Islands for each species at 10km resolution. Each map displays three date classes: before 1990, before and after 1990, 1990 onwards. Records received without a date are plotted as before 1990. The maps are not a definitive statement of the distribution but represent our knowledge to the end of 2010.

Phenograms

Phenograms of numbers of records per species were generated from the BRC database and displayed as half-monthly counts.

Number of records

The total number of records for each species from the BRC Coccinellidae Recording Scheme, UK Ladybird Survey and Ladybirds of Ireland.

Species name

Taxonomic order and scientific names follow Duff (2008). Vernacular names follow Majerus & Kearns (1989) and Majerus *et al.* (2006).

Species account

A short introduction is provided for each species, often representing the authors' personal experience of the species. Further information is available in Majerus (1994), Hawkins (2000) and Hodek *et al.* (in press).

Identification

Length, background colour, pattern colour, number of spots (the range is shown, with the most common (modal) number in brackets), spot fusions (whether or not spots merge), melanic (black) forms, pronotum, leg colour and other characteristic features are provided for the adult. Further notes are provided for the fourth-instar larval and pupal stages. These are meant as a guide to identification but readers are encouraged to use published keys (Majerus & Kearns, 1989) and expert advice for reliable identification. Figures 2a-c provide a guide to the anatomy of adult, fourth-instar larval and pupal stages.

Ecology

Notes on the broad habitat, based on EUNIS categories (http://eunis.eea.europa.eu/), are given for each species. Some species are associated with particular plants, either as food or the food of their prey, and so host plants on which the species are commonly recorded are listed. Plant nomenclature follows Stace (2010) for native and naturalised species. Major food preference is given for each species. Notes on overwintering site are also provided.

UK conservation designation

The conservation designation in the UK is listed for each species where relevant. There has been a plethora of lists of conservation status produced over the last 30 years including Red Lists, Biodiversity Action Plan Priority Lists, species listed on European Directives, species listed on the Schedules of the Wildlife & Countryside Act and lists of rare and scarce species. JNCC has collated many of the current lists into a downloadable spreadsheet of species designations (www.jncc.gov.uk/page-3408). Eleven species of Coccinellidae appear in this spreadsheet because they have been assigned a conservation designation. It should be noted that there are no ladybirds on the UK Biodiversity Action Plan Priority Lists. It should also be noted that these designations apply to the UK and not Ireland.

Table 4: Conservation designations for the eleven species of Coccinellidae listed by JNCC (applicable to UK only). Endangered – occurring only as a single population or otherwise in danger of extinction; Vulnerable – declining or in vulnerable habitat and likely to become endangered in the near future; Rare – very restricted by area or by habitat or with thinly scattered populations, occurring in no more than 15 10km squares; Nationally notable – uncommon with two grades of rarity, Notable A occurring in between 16 and 30 10km squares and Notable B occurring in between 31 and 100 10km squares.

Species	Reporting category	Conservation designation
Clitostethus arcuatus	Red Listing based on pre-1994 IUCN guidelines	Endangered
Scymnus femoralis	Rare and scarce species (not based on IUCN criteria)	Nationally notable B
Scymnus schmidti	Rare and scarce species (not based on IUCN criteria)	Nationally notable B
Scymnus limbatus	Rare and scarce species (not based on IUCN criteria)	Nationally notable B
Nephus quadrimaculatus	Red Listing based on pre-1994 IUCN guidelines	Vulnerable
Nephus bisignatus	Red Listing based on pre-1994 IUCN guidelines	Extinct
Hyperaspis pseudopustulatus	Rare and scarce species (not based on IUCN criteria)	
Platynaspis luteorubra	Rare and scarce species (not based on IUCN criteria)	Nationally notable A
Hippodamia tredecimpunctata	Red Listing based on pre-1994 IUCN guidelines	IUCN (pre-1994) – insufficiently known
Coccinella magnifica	Rare and scarce species (not based on IUCN criteria)	Nationally notable B
Coccinella quinquepunctata	Red Listing based on pre-1994 IUCN guidelines	Rare

UK distribution status

A quantitative system has been devised, adapted from Hawkins (2000), Majerus et al. (2006) and Baldock (2008), for the 36 species of ladybird that do not have a conservation designation. The UK comprises 3028 10km squares. For each species the number of 10km squares was converted to a percentage of this total and categorised as follows:

Ubiquitous – found almost everywhere and in at least 35% of the 10km squares.

Very widespread – found in less than 35% but more than 25% of the 10km squares.

Widespread – less than 25% but more than 15% of the 10km squares.

Local – less than 15% but more than 5% of the 10km squares.

Very local – less than 5% of the 10km squares.

UK distribution trend (1990-2010)

UK Ladybird Survey data have provided the opportunity to explore trends in ladybird distributions over time. New ecological modelling techniques are allowing the exploration of observational (atlas) data, such as that collated by the UK Ladybird Survey, more robustly than ever before. The UK Ladybird Survey, with the support of BRC macroecologist Nick Isaac, has had the unique opportunity to link with Belgian scientists to analyse ladybird distribution trends pre- and post- arrival of the harlequin ladybird.

The main problem when analysing distribution data collated through recording schemes is the lack of absence data. People record the presence of a species but it is not feasible to accurately document the absence of every species in a field survey. To overcome this, Nick and our Belgian collaborators developed the concept of 'a well-recorded one-km grid cell' from which absence could be inferred for each year. A square is considered to be well recorded if more than two species have been recorded within it for three or more years across the time period. Mixed-effects models were applied to the extracted data.

Detailed results for eight species, including data from Belgium and Britain, have been submitted for publication in a peer-reviewed journal. Here we present an assessment of the trends in the data for all ladybirds in the UK over the last 20 years, based on the mixed-effects models, but summarised qualitatively as decreasing, stable or increasing.

Table 5: Number of 10km squares in which each ladybird was recorded in Britain and Ireland alongside the number of records. The distribution status and trends are provided for the UK only.

Species name	Number of 10km squares	Number of records	UK distribution status	UK distribution trend (1990-2010)
7-spot ladybird	1786	27166	Ubiquitous	Stable
10-spot ladybird	1272	7191	Ubiquitous	Decreasing
14-spot ladybird	1200	10146	Ubiquitous	Decreasing
2-spot ladybird	1192	16535	Ubiquitous	Stable (but decreasing since arrival of harlequin ladybird)
Harlequin ladybird	1099	25676	Ubiquitous	Increasing
Cream-spot ladybird	907	4329	Very widespread	Decreasing
11-spot ladybird	854	2664	Very widespread	Decreasing
Coccidula rufa	845	3371	Very widespread	Decreasing
22-spot ladybird	814	4985	Very widespread	Decreasing
Orange ladybird	797	4687	Very widespread	Increasing
Rhyzobius litura	715	2571	Widespread	Decreasing
Pine ladybird	632	5723	Widespread	Increasing
Kidney-spot ladybird	588	2130	Widespread	Stable
24-spot ladybird	578	3098	Widespread	Increasing

Continued overleaf

Table 5 (continued).

Species name	Number of 10km squares	Number of records	UK distribution status	UK distribution trend (1990-2010)
16-spot ladybird	528	2738	Widespread	Stable
Larch ladybird	519	1281	Widespread	Stable
Eyed ladybird	481	1425	Widespread	Stable
Water ladybird	477	2294	Widespread	Decreasing
Adonis' ladybird	295	918	Local	Stable
Cream-streaked ladybird	269	1009	Local	Stable
Scymnus suturalis	248	546	Local	Stable
18-spot ladybird	245	636	Local	Stable
Hieroglyphic ladybird	241	527	Local	Decreasing
Scymnus auritus	240	476	Local	Stable
Nephus redtenbacheri	226	393	Local	Decreasing
Heather ladybird	223	591	Local	Stable
Striped ladybird	202	397	Local	Stable
Scymnus haemorrhoidalis	195	348	Local	Stable
Scymnus frontalis	194	394	Local	Stable
Coccidula scutellata	144	332	Very local	Stable
Hyperaspis pseudopustulata	83	134	Very local	Stable
Scymnus femoralis	78	125	Very local	Stable
Stethorus punctillum	75	113	Very local	Stable
Scymnus schmidti	73	142	Very local	Stable
Scymnus nigrinus	67	110	Very local	Stable
Scarce 7-spot ladybird	55	177	Very local	Stable
Platynaspis luteorubra	55	109	Very local	Stable
Scymnus limbatus	51	77	Very local	Stable
Rhyzobius chrysomeloides	42	108	Very local	Increasing
Nephus quadrimaculatus	41	101	Very local	Stable
5-spot ladybird	39	151	Very local	Stable
13-spot ladybird	39	87	Very local	Stable
Clitostethus arcuatus	15	32	Very local	Stable
Bryony ladybird	14	146	Very local	Stable
Scymnus interruptus	9	20	Very local	Stable
Rhyzobius lophanthae	4	10	Very local	Stable
Nephus bisignatus	3	4	Extinct	

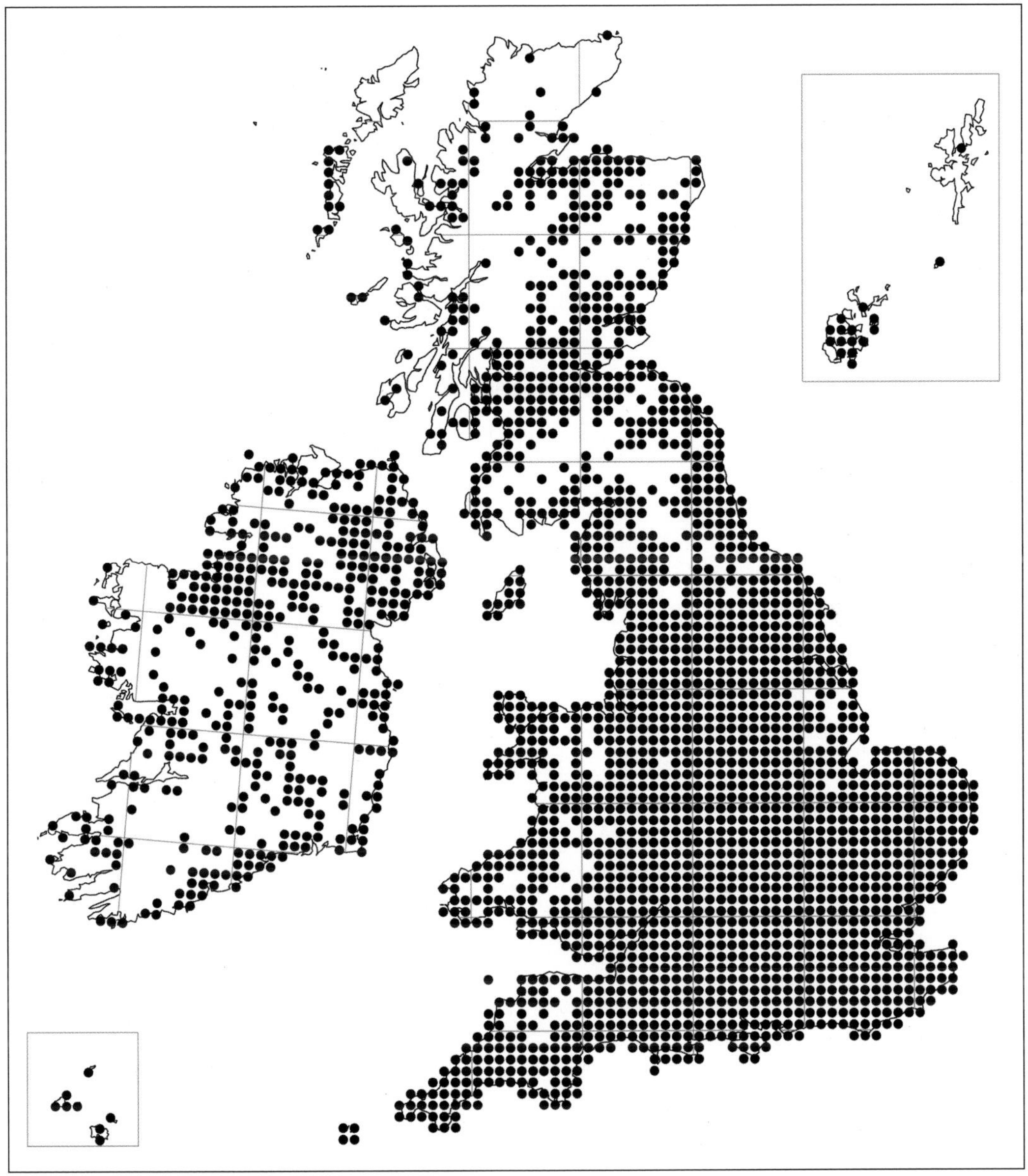

Map 1. Overall coverage map.

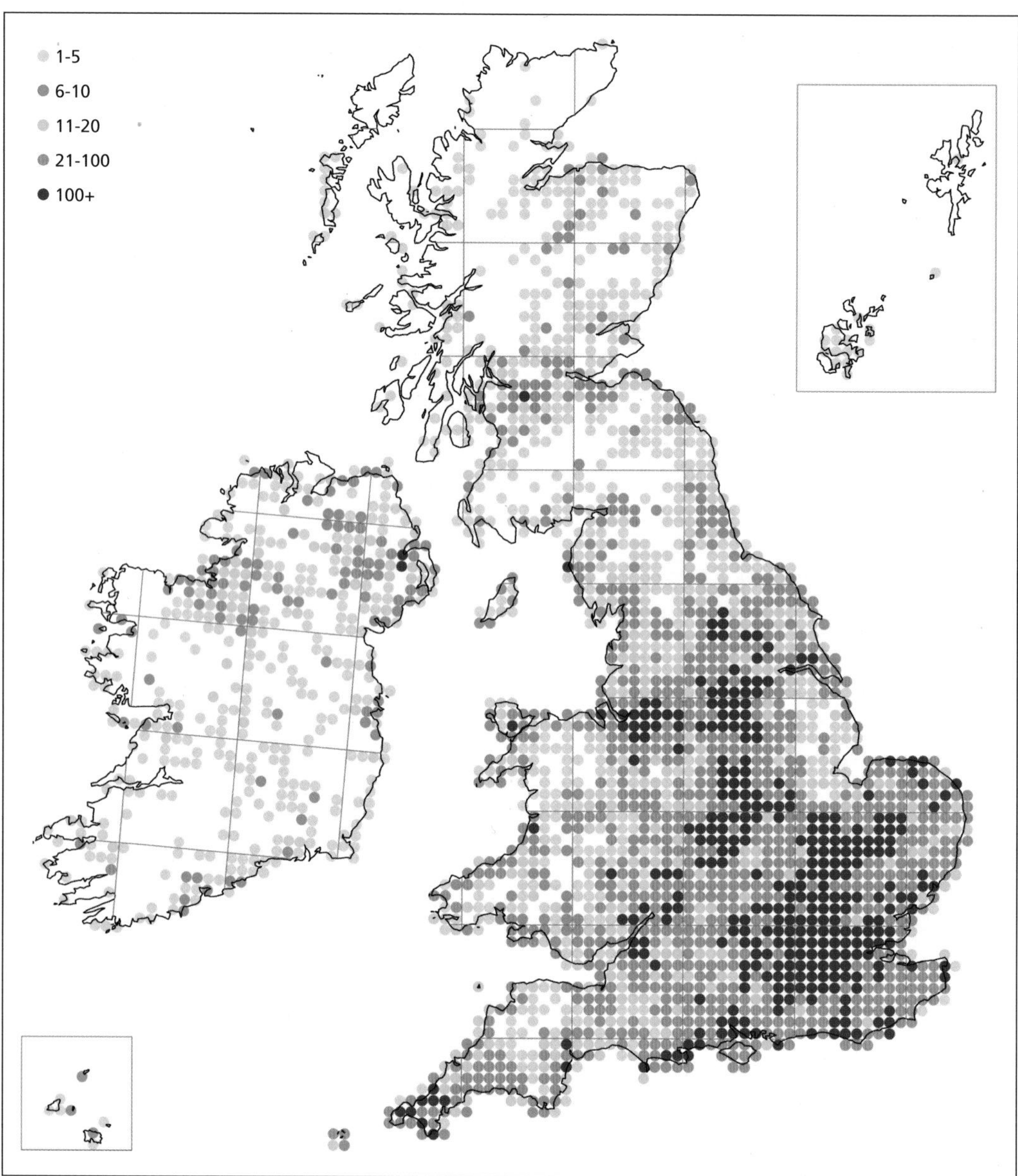

Map 2. Intensity of recording (number of records per 10km square).

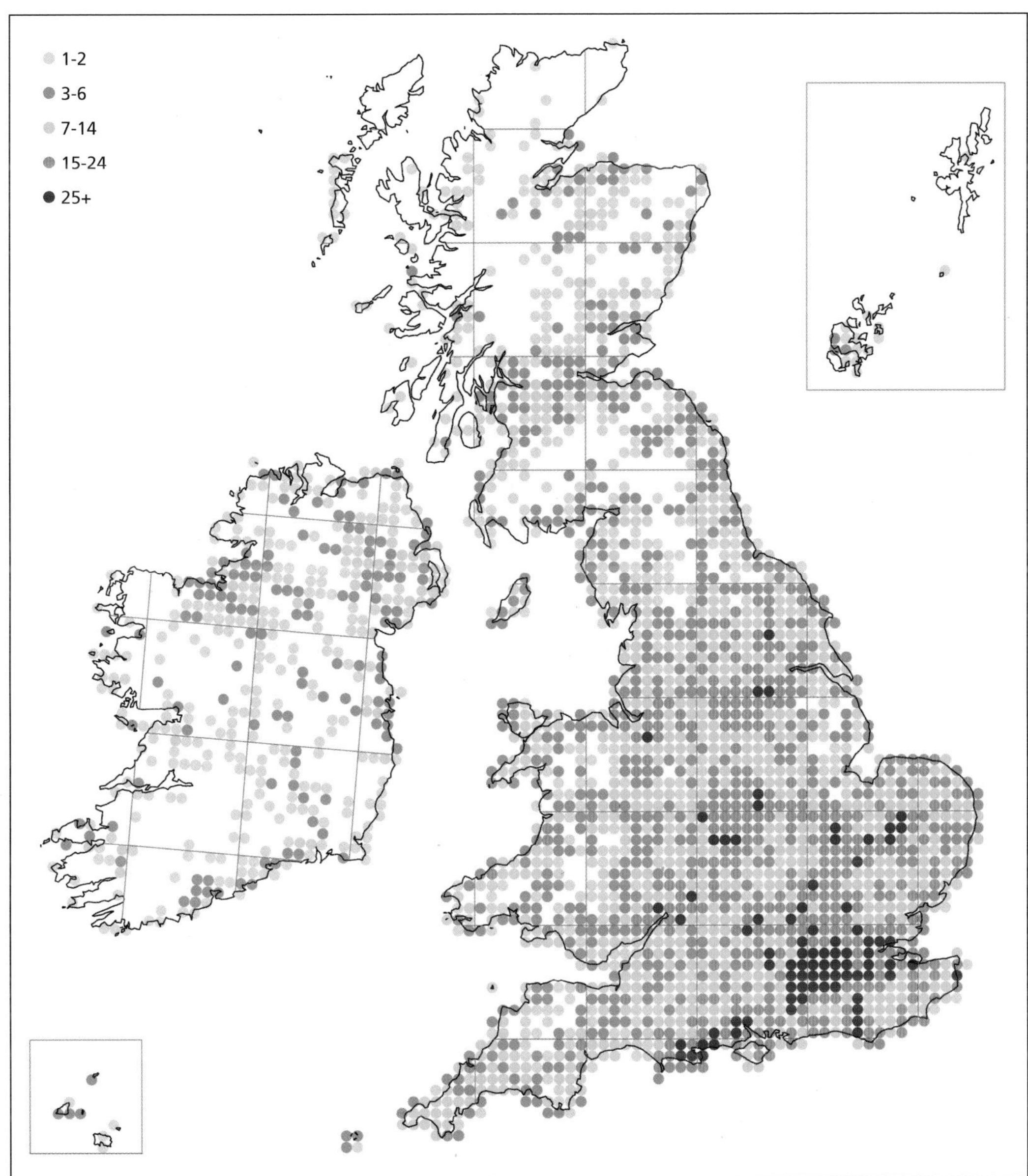

Map 3. Species richness (number of species recorded per 10km square).

Top recorders

We are extremely grateful to all who have provided records for this atlas. The following people have made especially significant contributions by providing large numbers of records.

Recorders providing 1000 or more records

Anderson, R.
Brooke, S.E.
Brown, P.M.J.
Budd, P.
Collins, G.A.
Daws, J.
Denton, J.H.
Ely, W.
Frost, R.
Hardwick, B.
Hawkins, R.D.
Hodge, P.J.
Iliff, D.A.
Lott, D.A.
Mabbott, P.R.
Marsh, B.
McWilliam, S.J.
Phillips, W.
Whiteley, D.

Recorders providing 100 to 999 records

Addey, J.
Albertini, M.V.
Alexander, K.N.A.
Allen, A.A.
Anderson, N.
Andrews, D.
Atty, D.B.
Benham, B.R.
Bentley, D.P.
Binding, A.
Binns, D.
Black, K.
Bolchover, S.P.
Booth, R.G.
Bosanquet, S.D.S.
Brackenbury, A.
Bratton, J.H.
Brothers, P.
Burden, C.
Burden, S.
Burton, G.
Callf, R.
Cawley, M.
Church, H.F.
Claxton, J.
Collier, M.J.
Collins, A.
Cooke, P.
Corney, C.
Cotton, D.
Creed, E.R.
Crittenden, M.
Curati, M.
Davies, J.
Dempsey, M.
Denton, M.
Devos, D.
Dickerson, B.
Dodd, S.G.
Dolbear, K.
Dolling, W.R.
Downer, V.
Drake, C.M.
Drane, A.B.
Everett, C.M.
Eyre, M.D.
Flanagan, J.
Foster, A.P.
Fowler, W.W.
Fowles, A.P.
Frankum, M.
Frost, A.R.
Frost, J.
Geiger, J.
Goddard, D.G.
Golding, G.
Grove, S.J.
Haines, F.H.
Halbert, J.N.
Hammond, P.M.
Harvey, M.
Harvey, P.
Hatton, W.
Hawgood, G.
Heath, P.J.
Hind, S.
James, T.J.
Jarvis, G.
Kenington, F.
Kerguelen, V.
Kirby, P.
Lane, J.
Lane, S.A.
Lazenby, A.
Lee, W.J.
Llewellyn-Jones, J.
Majerus, M.E.N.
Marshall, R.
McClenaghan, I.
Measday, A.V.
Menzies, I.
Merrifield, R.K.
Merrifield, R.M.
Merritt, R.
Muggleton, J.
Northing, P.
Owen, D.
Owen, J.A.
Parr, A.J.
Payne, R.M.
Pearson, P.
Pendleton, T.
Philp, E.G.
Plant, C.
Poland, R.
Proctor, J.
Rawlings, C.
Read, R.W.J.
Reid, C.
Robinson, K.
Roy, D.B.
Roy, H.E.
Sage, B.L.
Schaefer, W.
Shanklin, J.
Skidmore, P.
Smith, E.
Smith, E.J.
Smith, M.N.
Stenton, P.
Telfer, M.G.
Thickett, L.
Thompson, I.
Twigg, D.
Walker, B.
Weddle, R.
Welch, R.C.
Wilton, D.L.
Woodward, S.F.
Wright, R.J.
Wright, W.
Zobel, A.

Subfamily Chilocorinae Mulsant, 1846

Chilocorus bipustulatus (Linnaeus, 1758) (Heather ladybird)

Synonyms None

Number of records 591
Number of 10km squares 223

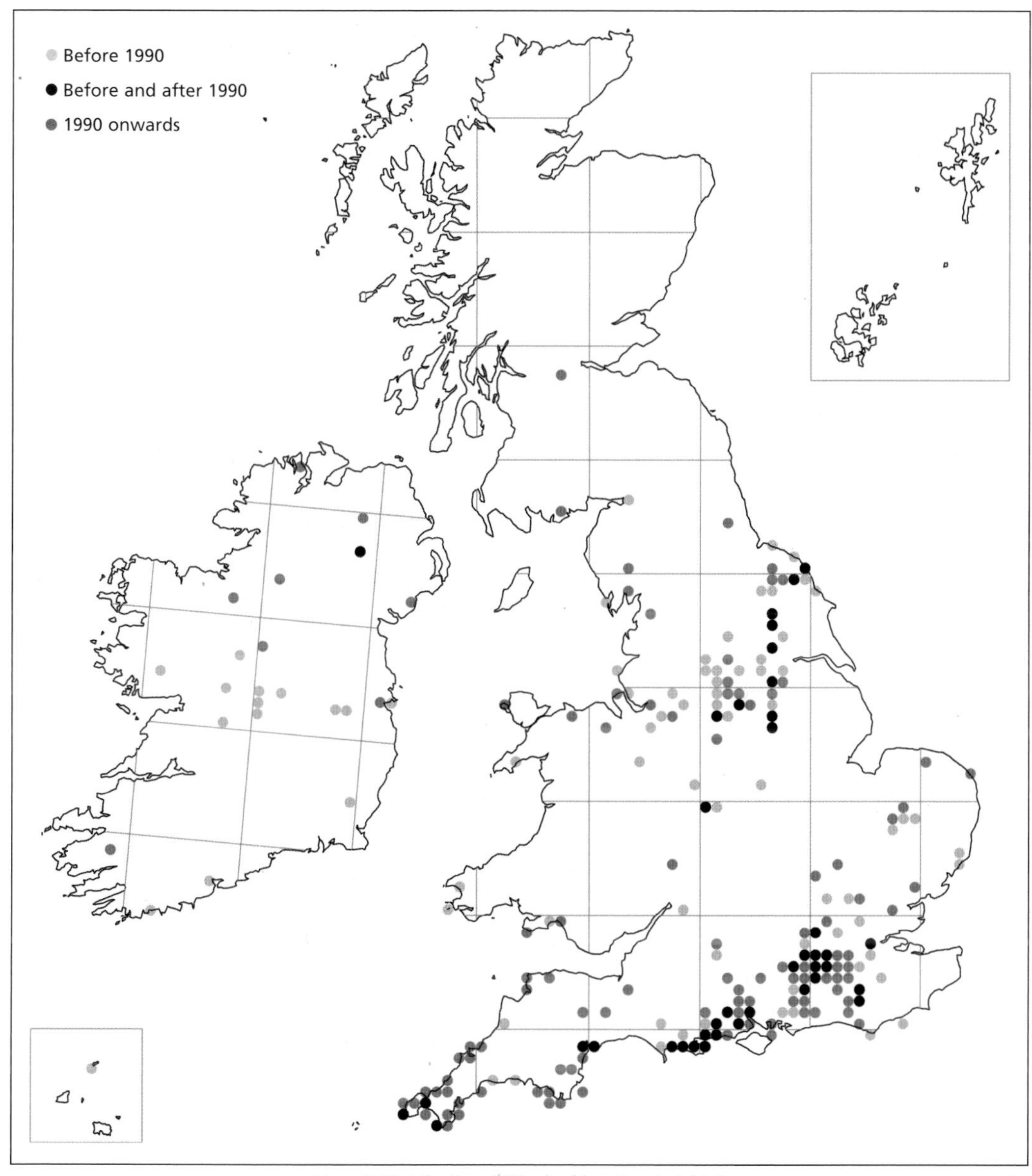

Map 4. Distribution (10km) of heather ladybird.

The heather ladybird is a small black ladybird with delicate spot patterning – the species name *bipustulatus* implies two red spots (or pustules) but actually what is visible is a transverse line of (usually six) red spots across the elytra. This species has rarely been recorded in Scotland, but recently the UK Ladybird Survey received records from two sites; including one via the 2010 BBC Breathing Places Ladybird Survey. These are exciting records, not only because of their locality, but also because this is a species rarely reported by members of the public. The heather ladybird is so-named because it occurs on heathland; however it can also be found on deciduous trees and increasingly on Leyland cypress. Majerus *et al.* (2006b) suggest that evergreen shrubs are common overwintering sites for this species and this may explain the records from cypresses. However, scale insects can be extremely abundant on cypress and this is also likely to explain the occurrence of heather ladybirds. It has also recently been speculated that the heather ladybird might comprise a species complex; what we regard as a single species might actually be distinct species or subspecies. There is clearly much to be revealed about this elusive ladybird.

Figure 24. Heather ladybird adult.
Photo: Michael Majerus.

Figure 25. Heather ladybird adult.
Photo: Gilles San Martin.

Figure 26. Heather ladybird late-instar larva.
Photo: Gilles San Martin.

Identification

Length: 3-4mm. *Background colour*: black. *Pattern colour*: red spots. *Number of spots*: 2-6 (6). *Spot fusions*: sometimes. *Melanic (black) forms*: not applicable. *Pronotum*: black. *Leg colour*: black. *Other features*: distinct rim around the edge of the elytra.

Fourth-instar larva: black, with tubercles bearing long black spines giving rise to hairs with extensive side-branching; with a diagnostic pale first abdominal segment. *Pupa*: larval skin encloses the lower part of the pupa.

Ecology

Habitats: this is a species commonly found on heathland. There are also a number of coastal records from dune systems and scrub. Heather ladybirds have also been recorded from marshy habitats.

Host plants: heather ladybirds have been widely reported from *Calluna*. However, they are also associated with plants typical of scrub habitats, including bracken, bramble and gorse. There are a growing number of records from Leyland cypress and occasionally other trees such as sallow, willow and Scots pine.

Food: coccids.

Overwintering sites: heather ladybirds overwinter in litter or in bark crevices (commonly conifers and gorse).

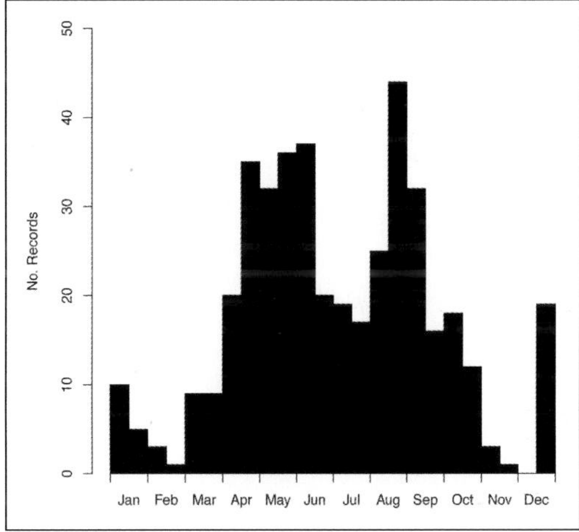

Figure 27. Heather ladybird phenogram.

UK distribution status Local

UK distribution trend (1990-2010) Stable

Chilocorus renipustulatus (Scriba, 1791) (Kidney-spot ladybird)

Synonyms *Chilocorus similis* (Rossi, 1790) non (Thunberg, 1781)

Number of records 2130
Number of 10km squares 588

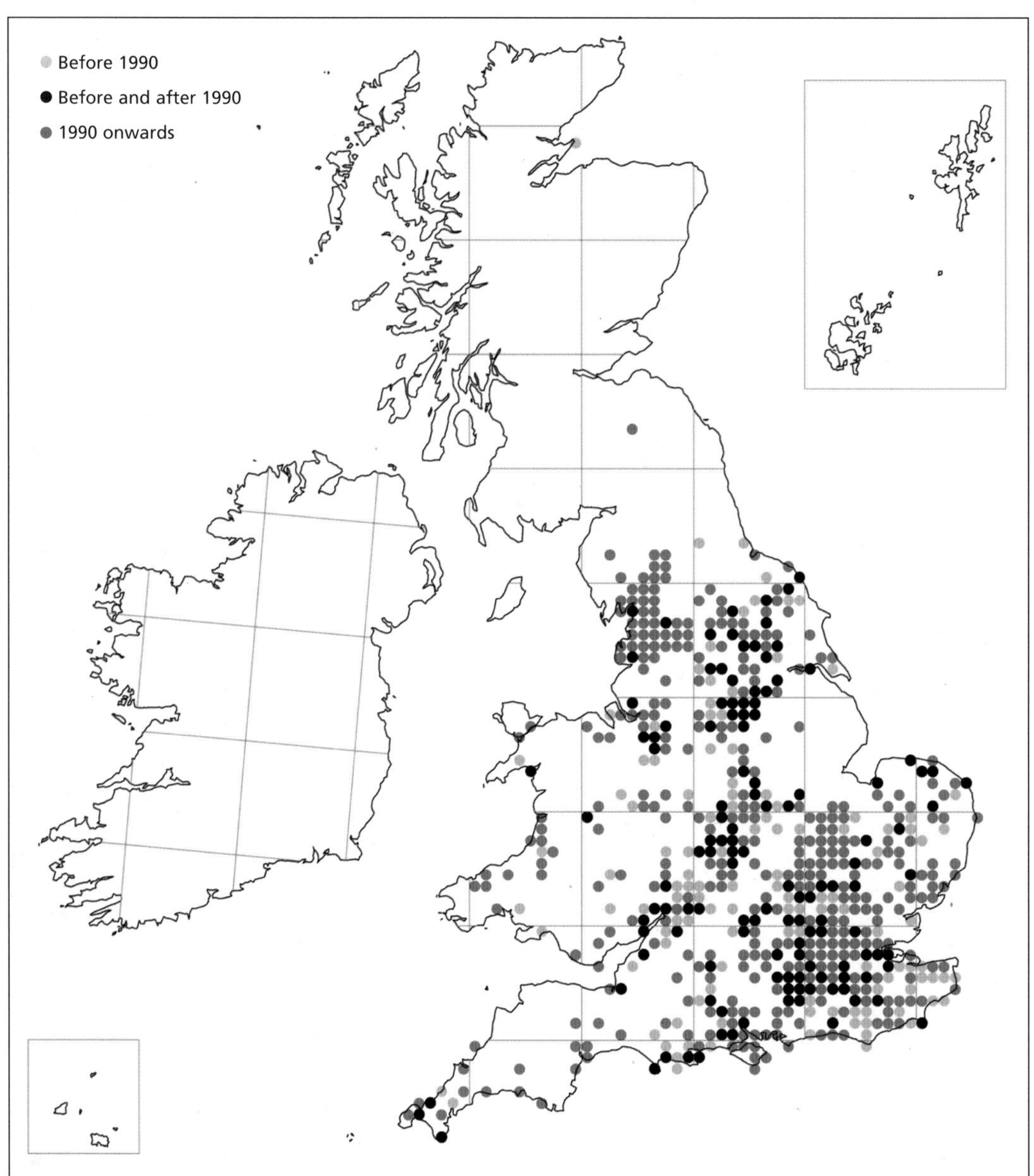

Map 5. Distribution (10km) of kidney-spot ladybird.

The black and shiny kidney-spot ladybird is commonly seen contrasted against the silvery bark of ash trees. It is a stunning ladybird with its two distinctive red spots. Interestingly, when this species emerges from its pupal cases, the elytra are bright red and the black pigmentation slowly appears over about 24 hours (a similar phenomenon occurs with other ladybird species). This is a species widely reported to the UK Ladybird Survey. It can be confused with the *conspicua* colour form of the harlequin ladybird, but the kidney-spot is notably smaller and has an entirely black pronotum and a very pronounced rim around the elytra. Indeed it has the appearance of a small bowler hat! Kidney-spot ladybirds feed on coccids. The feeding behaviour of this species was meticulously documented by Kirby (2008) who made observations of coccids (*Unaspis euonymi*) and kidney-spot ladybirds on spindle. Ladybirds of the genus *Chilocorus* have unique adaptations (including modified mandibles) that enable them to feed on armoured scale insects (small insects that live under a waxy scale for much of their life cycle). Kirby (2008) described the way in which kidney-spot ladybirds access the covered scale – 'the ladybird stands on the scale with its two hind pairs of legs, and with its front legs on the stem or another scale, flexing its abdomen and levering up the scale with its strong, pointed mandibles, rather like removing a crown cap from a bottle'.

Figure 28. Kidney-spot ladybird adult.
Photo: Ken Dolbear.

Figure 29. Kidney-spot ladybird late-instar larva.
Photo: Gilles San Martin.

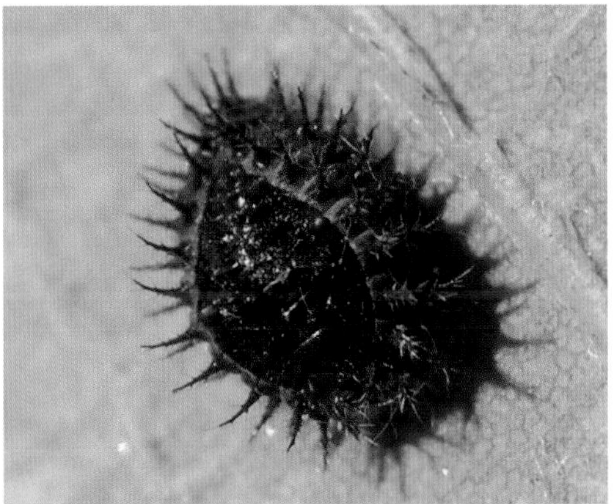

Figure 30. Kidney-spot ladybird pupa.
Photo: Richard Comont.

Figure 31. Kidney-spot ladybird pupae on a tree trunk.
Photo: Marion Hannaford and Sophie Benaiges.

Identification

Length: 4-5mm. *Background colour*: black. *Pattern colour*: red spots. *Number of spots*: 2. *Spot fusions*: none. *Melanic (black) forms*: not applicable. *Pronotum*: black. *Leg colour*: black. *Other features*: distinct rim around the edge of the elytra.

Fourth-instar larva: dark greyish-brown with distinctive long black bristles emerging from each tubercle; bristles bear extensive side-branches. *Pupa*: uniformly black and shiny; larval skin encloses the lower part of the pupa; bristles longer than those of the pine ladybird.

Ecology

Habitats: this species is commonly found in deciduous woodland. However, kidney-spot ladybirds have also been recorded from mixed woodlands, grasslands and scrub in the vicinity of deciduous trees.

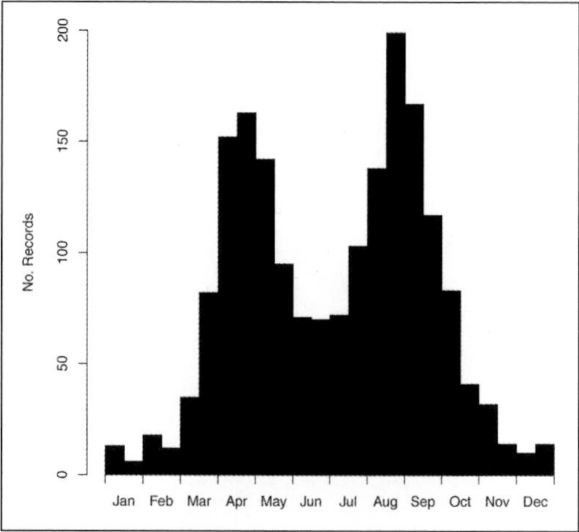

Figure 32. Kidney-spot ladybird phenogram.

Host plants: most kidney-spot ladybird records are from the trunks of ash and sallow trees. The species has also been recorded on a number of other deciduous trees including willow, oak, field maple, alder and birch, and also on Leyland cypress. Kidney-spot ladybirds are not uncommon on apple trees and on herbaceous vegetation such as thistles and nettle.

Food: coccids.

Overwintering sites: kidney-spot ladybirds overwinter in sheltered positions on deciduous trees, usually near the base.

UK distribution status Widespread

UK distribution trend (1990-2010) Stable

Exochomus quadripustulatus (Linnaeus, 1758) (Pine ladybird)

Synonyms None

Number of records 5723
Number of 10km squares 632

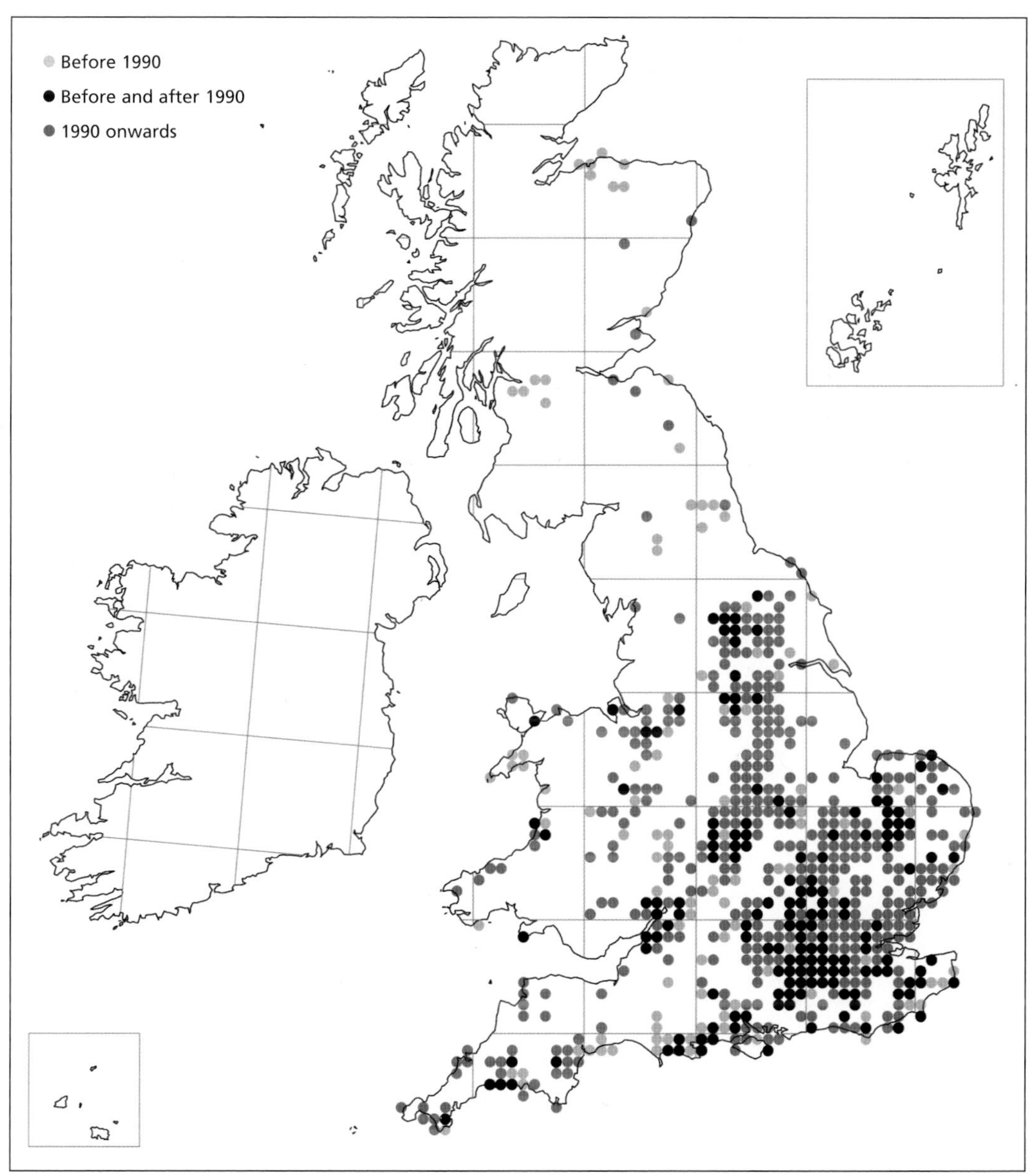

Map 6. Distribution (10km) of pine ladybird.

The pine ladybird is a commonly recorded species. The name 'pine' is a little misleading, because, whilst this species is commonly found on pine trees, it also occurs on various deciduous trees. In early spring, in urban environments, it can often be seen basking on tree trunks or on fences below a range of tree species. It can be easily confused with the *spectabilis* colour form of the harlequin ladybird, but is smaller, lacks any white markings and, as with the other species in the subfamily Chilcorinae, has a very pronounced rim around the elytra edge. The front two of the pine ladybird's four red spots have a characteristic 'comma' shape. The UK Ladybird Survey receives many records of this species in early spring. It is one of the first ladybirds to emerge from overwintering and is a welcome early indication of spring. Pine ladybirds show a distinct preference for prey insects that cover their bodies or their eggs with a mass of separate strands of waxy secretions or exudates (Hawkins, 2000). These include certain scale insects, adelgids and other woolly aphids. The wax covering appears to be consumed along with the prey (Hawkins, 2000). Pine ladybirds only produce one generation a year in Britain, but they have been observed mating in the autumn as well as, more usually, in the spring. It is quite possible that the sperm from autumn matings remains viable until the following spring, when conditions are favourable for egg production (Majerus, 1994). Many species of ladybird spend the winter months in aggregations containing other ladybird species and this is particularly the case with pine ladybirds. Pine ladybirds have been found overwintering with 17 different species of ladybird, including 16-spot, Adonis', larch and, notably, scarce 7-spot ladybirds (Majerus, 1994).

Figure 33. Pine ladybird adults.
Photo: Richard Comont.

Figure 34. Pine ladybird adults mating.
Photo: Richard Comont.

Figure 35. Pine ladybird late-instar larva.
Photo: Richard Comont.

Figure 36. Pine ladybird pupa.
Photo: Richard Comont.

Identification

Length: 3-4.5mm. *Background colour*: black. *Pattern colour*: red spots. *Number of spots*: 2-4 (4). *Spot fusions*: none. *Melanic (black) forms*: not applicable. *Pronotum*: black. *Leg colour*: black. *Other features*: distinct rim around the edge of the elytra.

Fourth-instar larva: grey and spiny but with shorter bristles than either the heather or kidney-spot ladybird; white patch on and around middle tubercle of first abdominal segment. *Pupa*: black and shiny with brown markings on thoracic region; larval skin encloses the lower part of the pupa; bristles shorter than those of the kidney-spot ladybird.

Ecology

Habitats: pine ladybirds can be found in a number of habitats including deciduous, coniferous and mixed woodland, grassland, coastal habitats (cliffs and dunes), heathland and marshy areas. This species is common in urban habitats. Pine ladybirds overlap with a number of other species of ladybird and are commonly found with pine-specialist ladybirds, plus 2-spot, 7-spot, 10-spot, 14-spot and harlequin ladybirds.

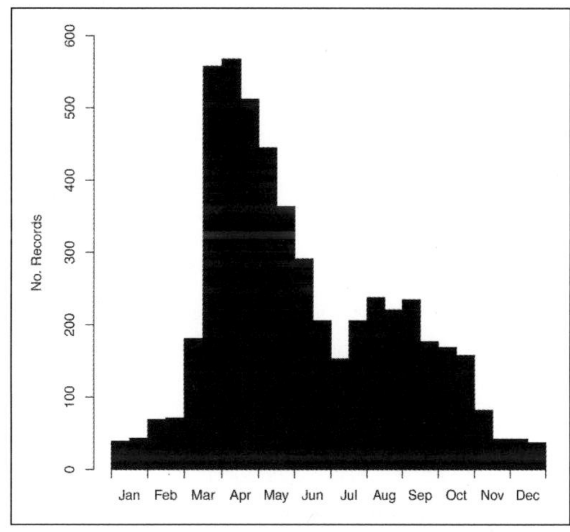

Figure 37. Pine ladybird phenogram.

Host plants: the pine ladybird is so named because it is the most common species of ladybird found on pines. Whilst its name suggests specialisation on pines, it is found on a very diverse range of plants. These include needled conifers (particularly Scots pine), scale-leaved conifers, yew and many deciduous trees such as ash, birch, sallow, willow, oak, beech, lime, hazel, sycamore, maples and horse-chestnut. It is also commonly found in gardens on plants such as thistles, nettle, camellia and firethorns.

Food: coccids, adelgids and other woolly aphids.

Overwintering sites: pine ladybirds overwinter in leaf litter, foliage and bark crevices of evergreen trees and shrubs.

UK distribution status Widespread

UK distribution trend (1990-2010) Increasing

Platynaspis luteorubra (Goeze, 1777)

Synonyms None

Number of records 109
Number of 10km squares 55

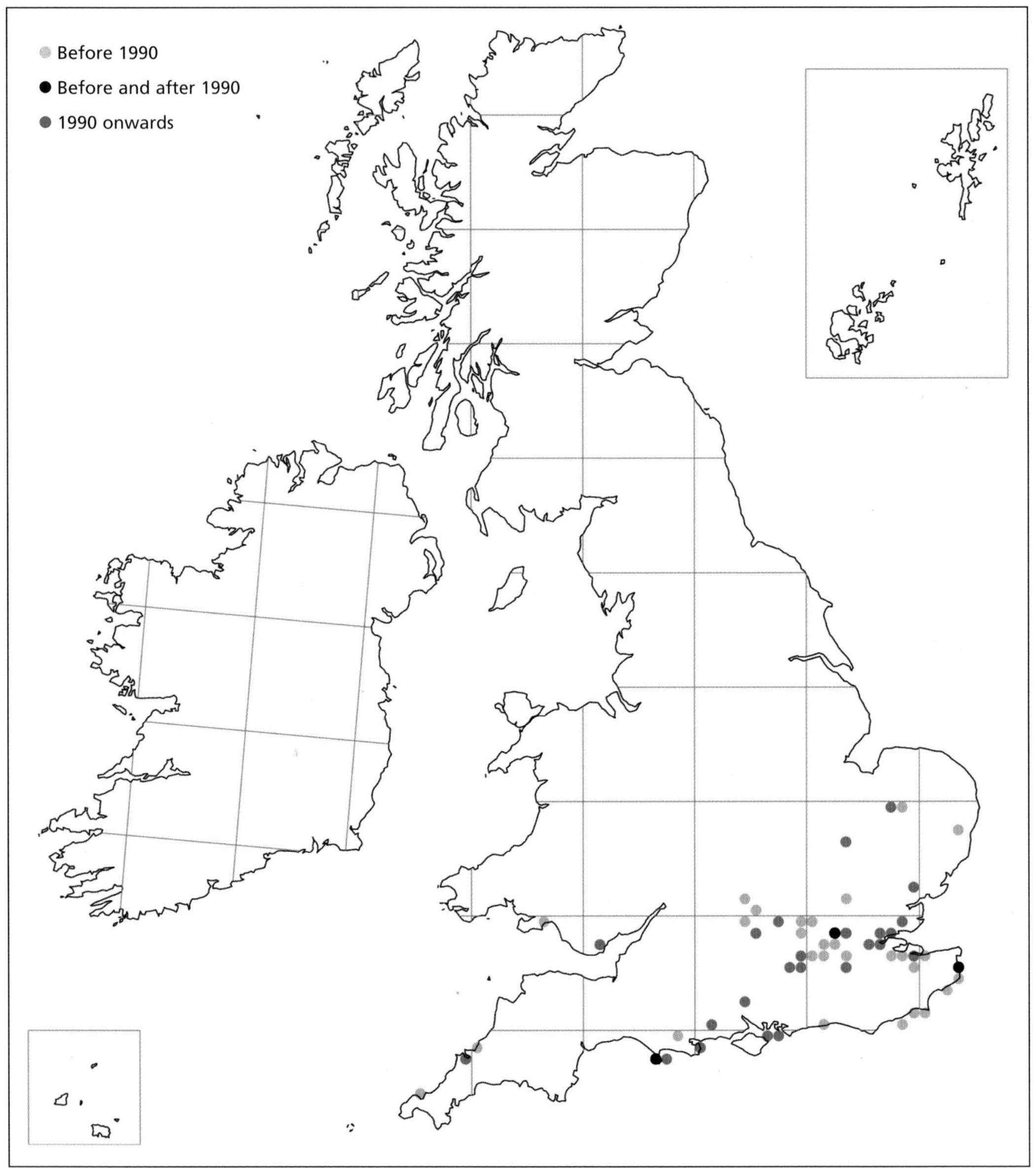

Map 7. Distribution (10km) of *Platynaspis luteorubra*.

Platynaspis luteorubra is one of the two myrmecophilous (ant-loving) ladybirds in Britain, and has a closer tie to ants than the other myrmecophile, the scarce 7-spot ladybird. Largely restricted to south-east England, *P. luteorubra* is found with ant species such as *Lasius niger* (Majerus, 1994). The pupa and especially the larva are unusual and very different in appearance from those of most other ladybirds, presumably because of a specialised lifestyle tied to the ants. Larvae may be found underground, feeding on subterranean aphids.

Figure 38. *Platynaspis luteorubra* adult.
Photo: Peter Brown.

Figure 39. *Platynaspis luteorubra* adult (head-on view).
Photo: Gilles San Martin.

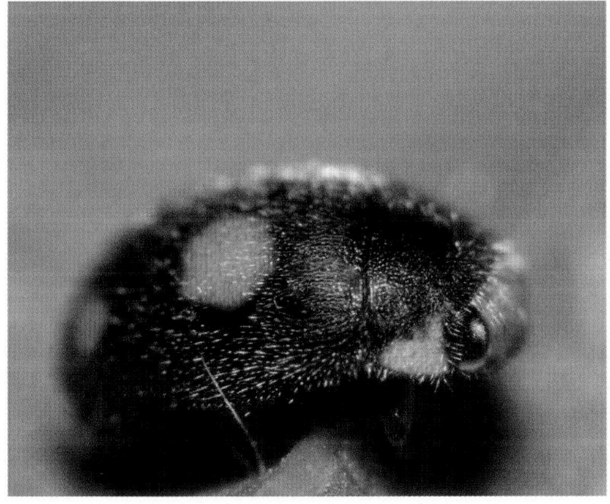

Figure 40. *Platynaspis luteorubra* adult.
Photo: Gilles San Martin.

Figure 41. *Platynaspis luteorubra* pupa.
Photo: Peter Brown.

Identification

Length: 2.5-3.5mm. *Background colour*: black. *Pattern*: four orangey-red spots. *Pronotum*: black with cream anterior margin. *Head colour*: pale (male); black (female). *Leg colour*: reddish brown with black femora. *Other features*: hairy.

Ecology

Habitats: dry sandy and chalky habitats occupied by ants.

Host plants: low-growing vegetation in association with ants.

Food: aphids.

Overwintering sites: unknown.

UK conservation designation Nationally notable A

UK distribution status Very local

UK distribution trend (1990-2010) Stable

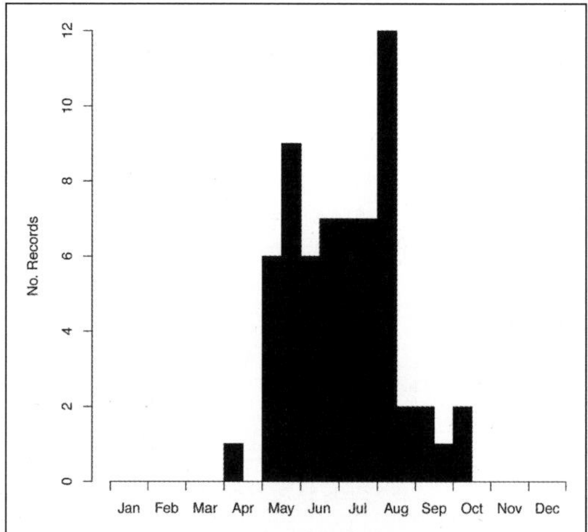

Figure 42. Phenogram for *Platynaspis luteorubra.*

Subfamily Coccinellinae Latreille, 1807

Anisosticta novemdecimpunctata (Linnaeus, 1758) (Water ladybird)

Synonyms None

Number of records 2294
Number of 10km squares 477

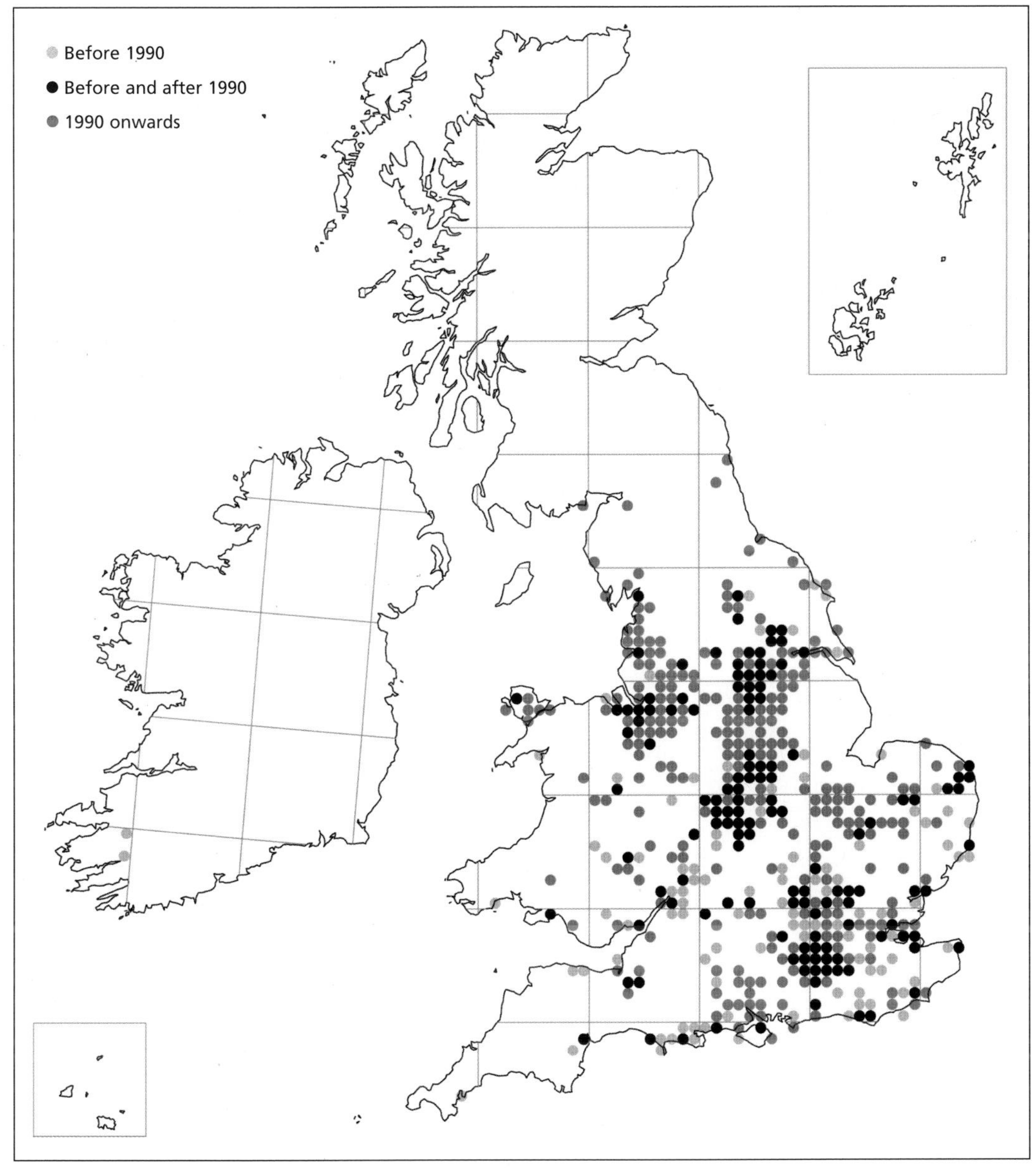

Map 8. Distribution (10km) of water ladybird.

The water ladybird (sometimes known as the 19-spot ladybird) is a fascinating species, owing to its specialist habitat requirements and remarkable ability to change colour during the year. It is found living on the water's edge, feeding on aphids on reed, reedmace and reed sweet-grass, growing alongside lakes and rivers. Water ladybirds spend the winter tucked down between the sheaths of dead reedmace leaves, and at this time are buff-coloured with 19 black spots. This colour pattern offers superb camouflage against their winter habitat. However, during the spring they disperse to new reeds in search of aphids and rapidly develop bright warning colours, the background colour of their elytra changing from buff to red. This change in colour is intriguing and unique among British ladybirds.

Figure 43. Water ladybird adult (summer colouration). Photo: Gilles San Martin.

Figure 44. Water ladybird adult (summer colouration). Photo: Alby Oakshott.

Figure 45. Water ladybird adult (winter colouration). Photo: Gilles San Martin.

Figure 46. Water ladybird adult (winter colouration). Photo: Gilles San Martin.

Identification

Length: 4mm. *Background colour*: July-April, buff/beige; April-June, reddish. *Pattern colour*: black spots. *Number of spots*: 15-21 (19). *Spot fusions*: sometimes. *Melanic (black) forms*: no. *Pronotum*: buff/beige or red with 6 black spots; rounded at the sides with greatest width in the middle. *Leg colour*: pale brown. *Other features*: distinctly elongate and flattened in shape.

Fourth-instar larva: thoracic region cream/white with dark patches; abdomen pale grey with alternating rows of black and white tubercles running longitudinally; fine hairs projecting from tubercles. *Pupa*: unknown.

Ecology

Habitats: water ladybirds are habitat specialists, occupying reed-beds and grassland in marshy or wet locations. This species can often be found on the emergent vegetation surrounding ponds. There are a few records from exposed riverine sediments.

Host plants: water ladybirds can be found on tall emergent plants including reeds, reedmace, reed sweet-grass and rushes.

Food: aphids.

Overwintering sites: water ladybirds overwinter between leaves and in stems of reeds, and in grass tussocks.

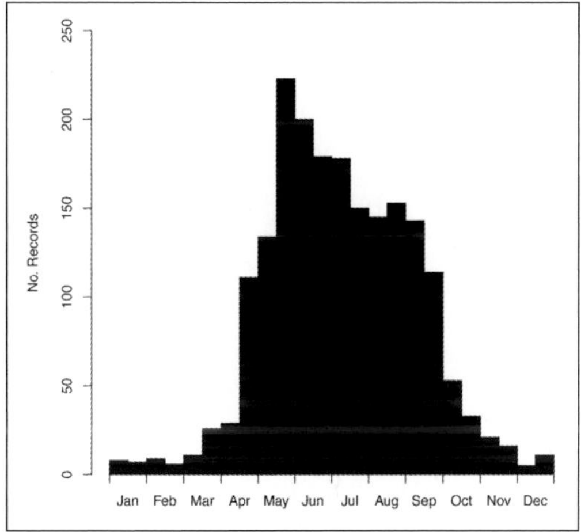

Figure 47. Water ladybird phenogram.

UK distribution status Widespread

UK distribution trend (1990-2010) Decreasing

Tytthaspis sedecimpunctata (Linnaeus, 1761) (16-spot ladybird)

Synonyms *Micraspis sedecimpunctata*
Tytthaspis sexdecimpunctata auctt. (misspelling)

Number of records 2738
Number of 10km squares 528

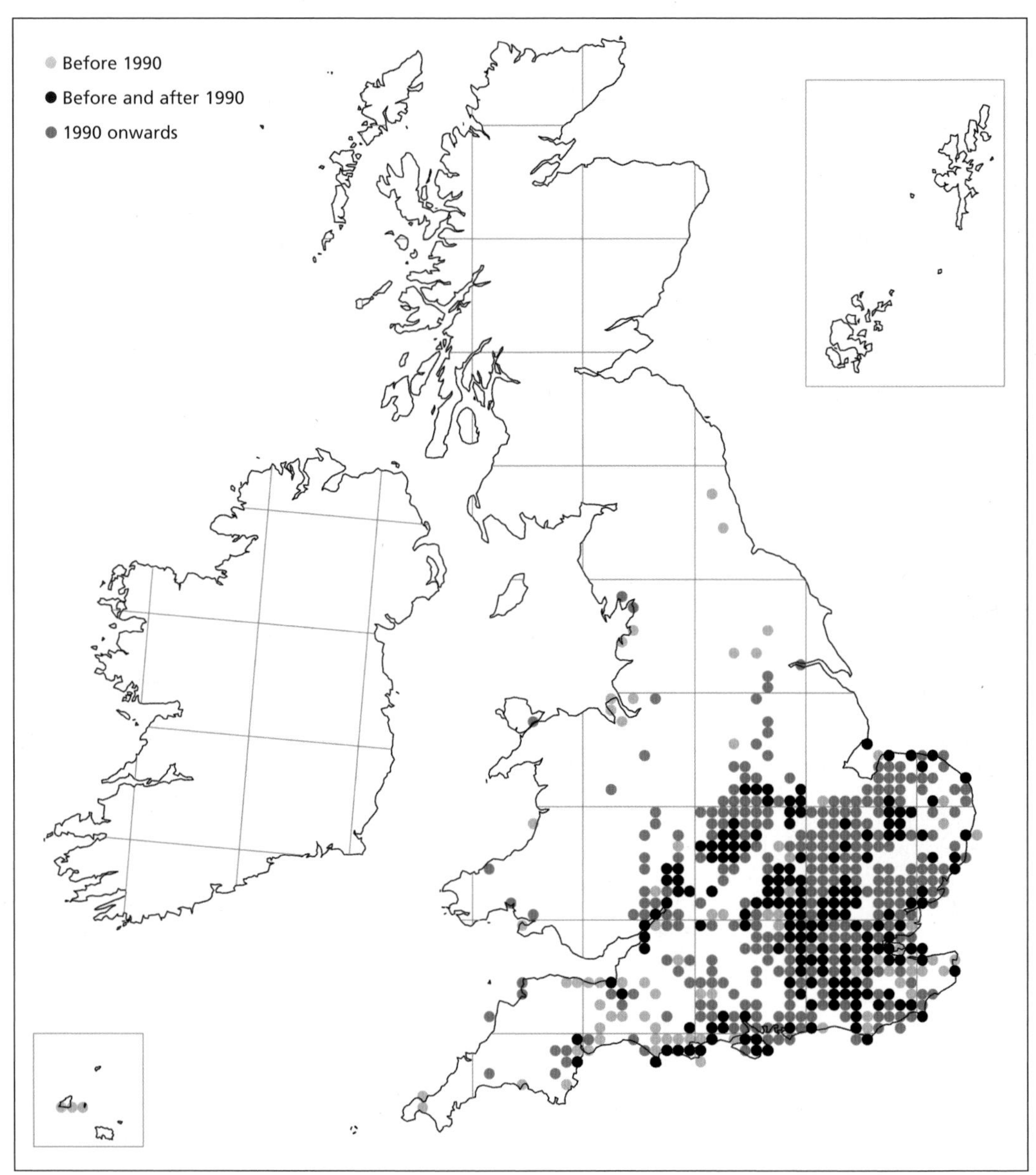

Map 9. Distribution (10km) of 16-spot ladybird.

The 16-spot ladybird is the smallest conspicuous ladybird in Britain (although absent from Scotland and Ireland). A combination of small size, rather camouflaged colouration and a tendency to stay close to the ground make this a species that is very easy to overlook, although it can be very abundant in grassland. Indeed, Hawkins (2000) found it to be *the* most abundant ladybird species over a twenty-year period of Surrey surveys. It is best found using a sweep net in grassland habitats. The 16-spot is a species that tends to aggregate, especially in winter; large numbers may be beaten from gorse and, occasionally, large and obvious overwintering groups (comprising hundreds or thousands of individuals) may be found on fence posts or tree trunks in exposed positions – a spectacular sight. It has been suggested that this may be a result of local flooding causing the ladybirds to move up from grass tufts (Hawkins, 2000). The markings of the 16-spot are rather consistent, with a central black line between the elytra. The 16 spots are arranged in two inner lines of three unfused spots and two outer lines of five spots, three of which are usually fused to form a zigzag mark.

Figure 48. 16-spot ladybird adults.
Photo: Michael Majerus.

Figure 49. 16-spot ladybird adults overwintering on a fence post. Photo: Bruce Martin.

Figure 50. 16-spot ladybird late-instar larva.
Photo: Gilles San Martin.

Figure 51. 16-spot ladybird pupa.
Photo: Peter Brown.

Identification

Length: 3mm. *Background colour*: beige. *Pattern colour*: black spots. *Number of spots*: 13-18 (16). *Spot fusions*: common: the three lateral spots on each elytron are usually fused. *Melanic (black) forms*: rare. *Pronotum*: beige with black spots. *Leg colour*: brown.

Fourth-instar larva: pale brown-grey with conspicuous long black hairs emanating from darker coloured tubercles. *Pupa*: pale yellowish brown with four rows of diffuse darker markings running longitudinally; remains of hairy fourth-instar larval skin visible at base.

Ecology

Habitats: 16-spot ladybirds are commonly found in grassland. There are also records from scrub, saltmarsh and dune systems.

Host plants: most 16-spot ladybird records are from grasses and other low plants, including reeds, nettle, dandelion, knapweed, hogweed, cow parsley and buttercup. This species has also been recorded from shrubs, including gorse, and from Scots pine.

Food: pollen, nectar, fungi.

Overwintering sites: 16-spot ladybirds overwinter in low herbage, on gorse, in plant litter, on logs, fence posts and stone walls, often in extremely large aggregations.

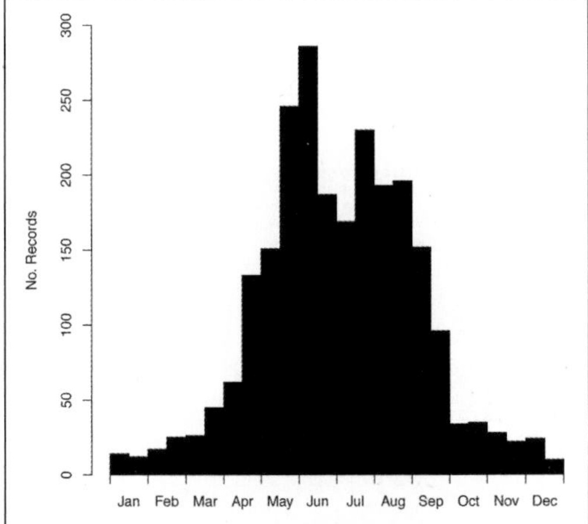

Figure 52. 16-spot ladybird phenogram.

UK distribution status Widespread

UK distribution trend (1990-2010) Stable

Myzia oblongoguttata (Linnaeus, 1758) (Striped ladybird)

Synonyms *Mysia oblongoguttata*
Neomysia oblongoguttata
Paramysia oblongoguttata

Number of records 397
Number of 10km squares 202

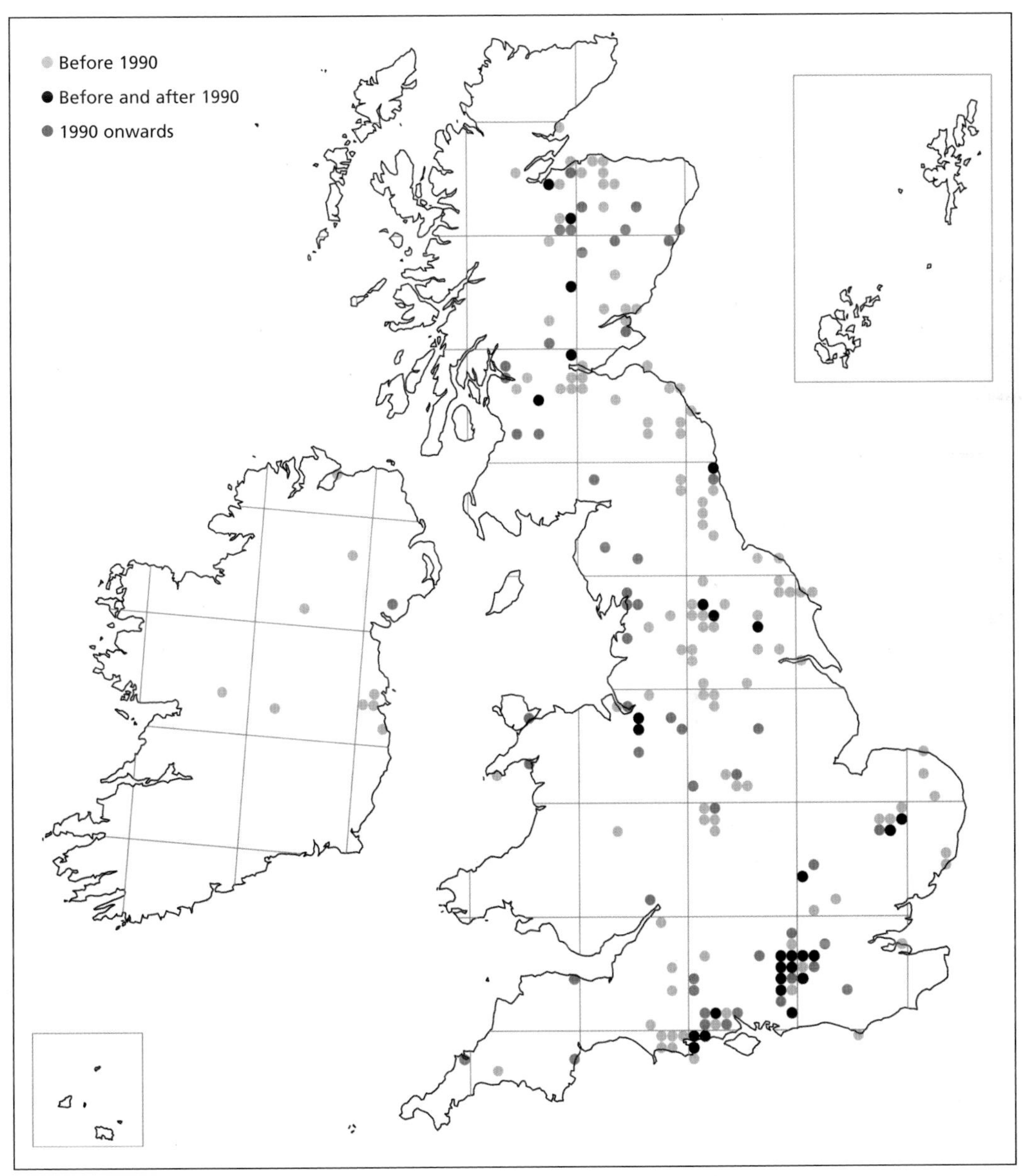

Map 10. Distribution (10km) of striped ladybird.

The striped ladybird is the most specialised of all the aphid-feeding ladybirds in Britain and Ireland and is largely restricted to mature Scots pine trees. It is locally distributed and is generally less common and abundant than most of the other ladybirds found on pines, at least in England. However, unlike several other ladybird species, it is tolerant of cool conditions and is widespread in pine forests across Scotland. It is largely restricted to feeding on the large brown aphids of the genus *Cinara*, which occur on pines and appear to be an essential dietary requirement for successful breeding (Majerus, 1994). The striped ladybird is our second largest ladybird, and is a striking chestnut colour with pale stripy markings, making it very distinctive and difficult to confuse with any other species, although it is rather well camouflaged in its habitat. The pronotum is sometimes a darker brown than the elytra. Like many of our ladybird species, the striped ladybird has a single generation each year in Britain and Ireland (Majerus, 1994).

Figure 53. Striped ladybird adult.
Photo: Michael Majerus.

Figure 54. Striped ladybird adult reflex bleeding.
Photo: Richard Comont.

Figure 55. Striped ladybird adults mating.
Photo: Michael Majerus.

Figure 56. Striped ladybird late-instar larva.
Photo: Remy Poland.

Identification

Length: 6-8mm. *Background colour*: chestnut brown. *Pattern colour*: cream stripes and spots. *Number of spots*: 0-15 (13). *Spot fusions*: common. *Melanic (black) forms*: rare. *Pronotum*: white with chestnut M-mark or trapezium. *Leg colour*: brown.

Fourth-instar larva: large (up to 12mm), with long black legs; body is grey with contrasting dark grey/black tubercles; outer and middle tubercles of first abdominal segment orange; outer tubercles of fourth and sixth segments also orange; tubercles do not bear spines or hairs, and the body has an overall smooth appearance. *Pupa*: cream with four rows of black spots running longitudinally and an additional black spot on the outer edges of the third abdominal segment; third thoracic segment flanked by thick black diagonal markings; rounded projections on each side of middle section, spanning segments two to five.

Ecology

Habitats: striped ladybirds are conifer specialists. However, they have also been reported on scrub and dune systems with conifers in the vicinity.

Host plants: this species is most commonly found on Scots pine but there are a few records from larch.

Food: aphids.

Overwintering sites: in soil or moss below Scots pine trees.

UK distribution status Local

UK distribution trend (1990-2010) Stable

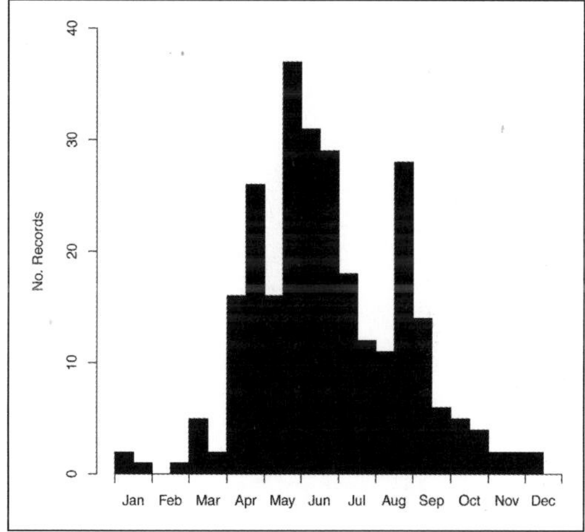

Figure 57. Striped ladybird phenogram.

Myrrha octodecimguttata (Linnaeus, 1758) (18-spot ladybird)

Synonyms *Halyzia octodecimguttata*

Number of records 636
Number of 10km squares 245

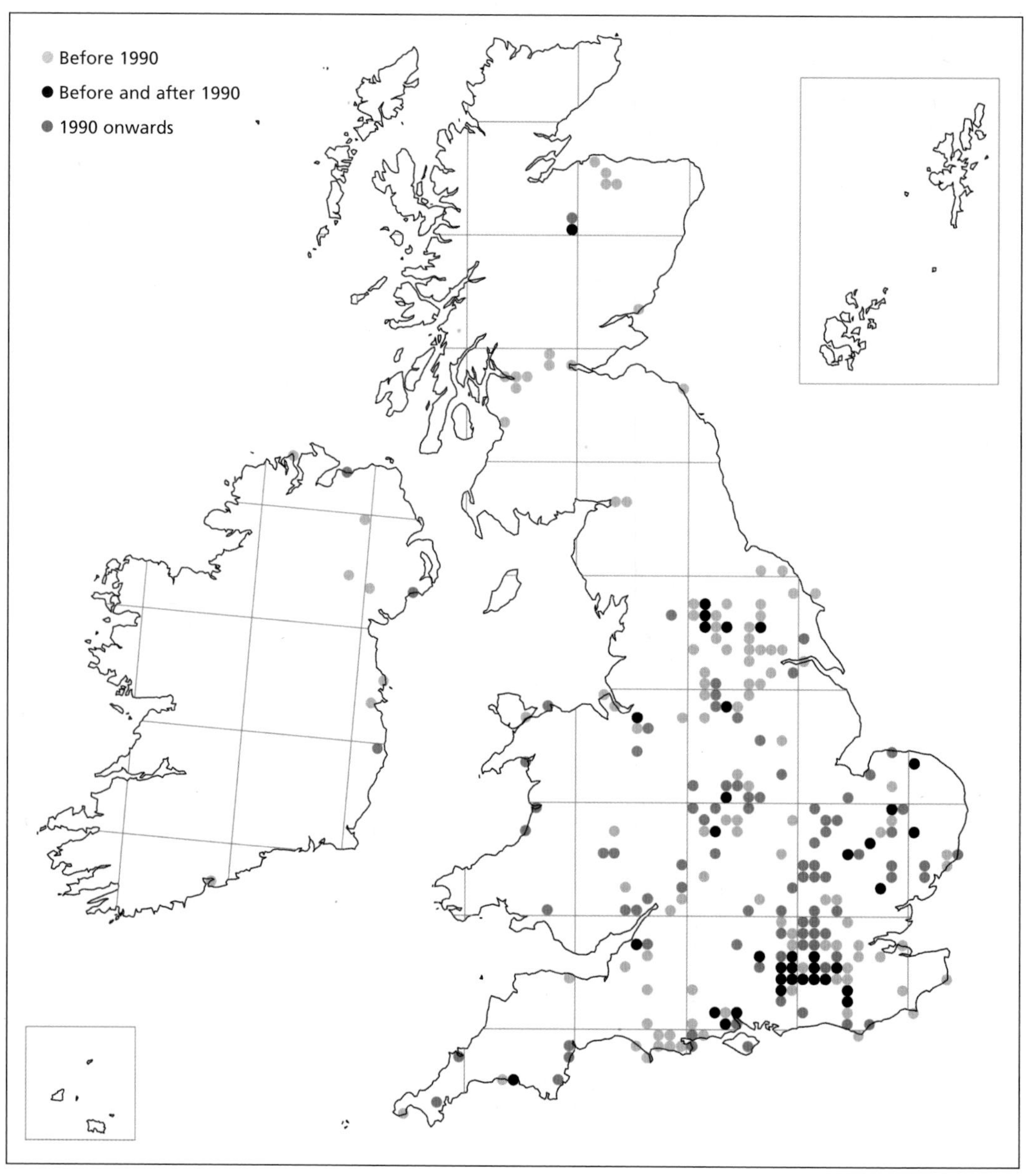

Map 11. Distribution (10km) of 18-spot ladybird.

Figure 58. 18-spot ladybird adult.
Photo: Peter Brown.

Figure 59. 18-spot ladybird adult.
Photo: Michael Majerus.

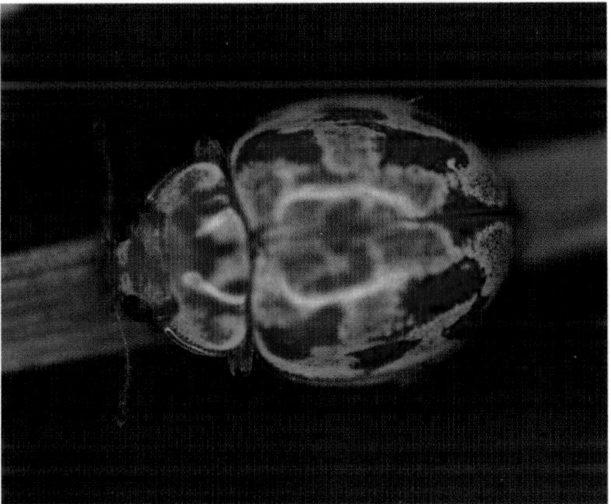

Figure 60. 18-spot ladybird adult (unusual colour form).
Photo: Michael Majerus.

Figure 61. 18-spot ladybird pupa.
Photo: Remy Poland.

The 18-spot is a species usually restricted to Scots pine, with a few records from black pine (Hawkins 2000). Reported by Majerus (1994) to favour the canopies of mature trees, the species may also be dislodged in small numbers from the lower branches of pines. The 18-spot is reported to be repelled by the presence of wood ants, which may partly explain it favouring tree tops, to avoid the ants. Whilst favouring mature trees, the species is sometimes found on young Scots pines (R. Frost, personal observation). In Britain and Ireland the only ladybird with which the 18-spot might be confused is the cream-spot, which is generally not found in the same habitat. The colour of the two species is similar, a maroon-brown with creamy-white spots. However, the pattern of spotting is different, the cream-spot having 14 round spots on the elytra, whilst the spots of the 18-spot vary more in shape and are sometimes fused, and the two spots at the front of the elytra are distinctively 'L' shaped. The patterns on the pronota of the two species are also rather different.

Identification

Length: 4-5mm. *Background colour*: maroon-brown. *Pattern colour*: cream spots and fusions. *Number of spots*: 14-18 (18). *Spot fusions*: common. *Melanic (black) forms*: no. *Pronotum*: creamy-white with rounded M-mark. *Leg colour*: brown.

Fourth-instar larva: very similar to larva of larch ladybird, so rearing through to adulthood is recommended for accurate identification; pale grey with pairs of stippled dark grey patches on thoracic segments; middle and outer tubercles on first abdominal segment pale yellow; all other tubercles dark grey with a few short hairs protruding; legs dark brown/black. Majerus & Kearns (1989) suggest that the larvae of the larch and 18-spot ladybirds are similar, but describe differences in leg colour. We have found the legs of both 18-spot and larch larvae to be uniformly dark, whereas Majerus & Kearns (1989) described the legs of 18-spot larvae as 'pale but dark at the end'. *Pupa*: cream, with two rows of diffuse brown markings flanking the midline; similar markings found laterally along abdominal segments three to eight; yellow lateral markings on first abdominal segment.

Ecology

Habitats: 18-spot ladybirds are conifer specialists and are found in coniferous woodlands or on scrub, heathland, grassland and dune systems where conifers are present.

Host plants: Scots pine is the most commonly recorded plant on which 18-spots have been found. Other conifers are also occupied by this species, including black pine and Monterey cypress. There are occasional records from deciduous trees, including oak and sycamore, but these are unlikely to be favoured for reproduction.

Food: aphids.

Overwintering sites: this species overwinters high in the crown of Scots pine trees, and under the bark.

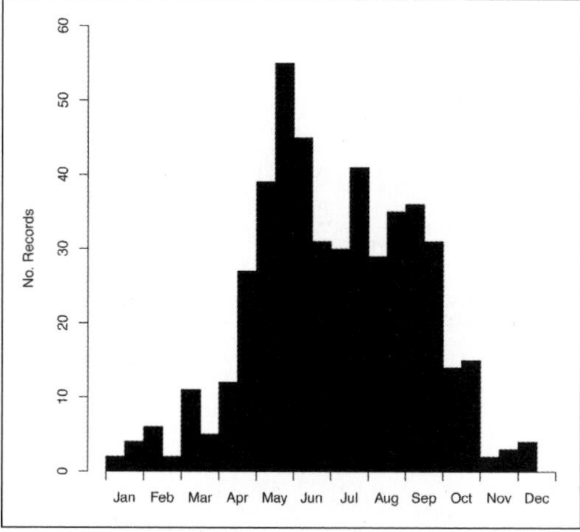

Figure 62. 18-spot ladybird phenogram.

UK distribution status Local

UK distribution trend (1990-2010) Stable

Propylea quattuordecimpunctata (Linnaeus, 1758) (14-spot ladybird)

Synonyms *Propylaea quattuordecimpunctata* auctt. (misspelling)
Halyzia quattuordecimpunctata sensu
Propylea quatuordecimpunctata auctt. (misspelling)
Propylea conglobata sensu auctt. Brit. non (Linnaeus, 1758)

Number of records 10146
Number of 10km squares 1200

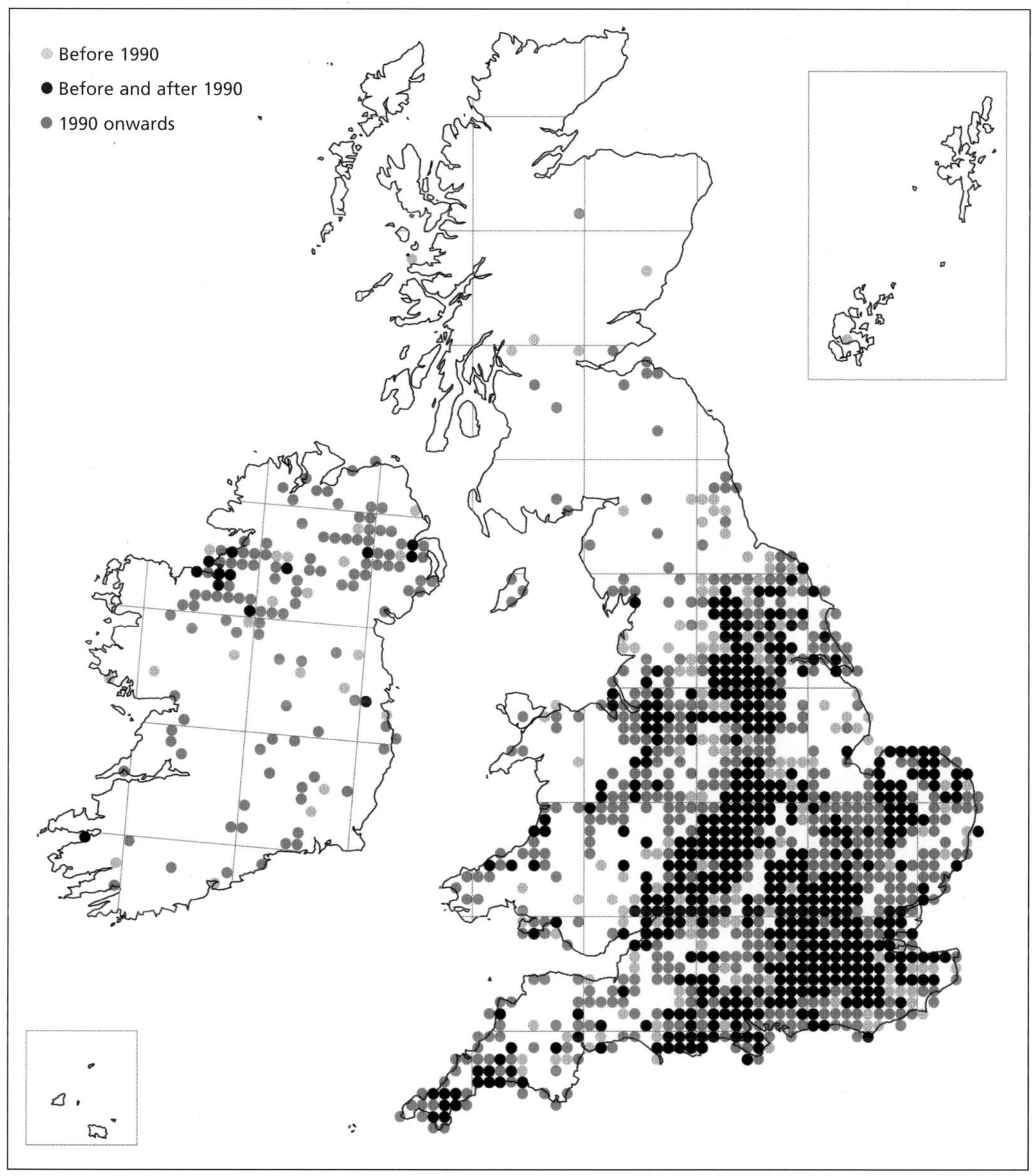

Map 12. Distribution (10km) of 14-spot ladybird.

The 14-spot is one of the most common species of ladybird in England, Wales and Ireland, but there are few Scottish records. It is a medium-sized yellow ladybird with distinctive markings. On its yellow elytra it has rectangular black spots which are often fused and resemble an anchor shape or clown's face. The 14-spot is sometimes referred to as the 'dormouse' ladybird (Hawkins 2000) because it emerges from overwintering later than many of the other conspicuous species. The species occupies many diverse habitats, but is most common on low herbaceous vegetation, particularly nettle. It is considered a major aphid predator in agricultural systems, although it is not as voracious as the larger 7-spot ladybird (a very common species on crops). The larval stage is extremely characteristic, with long legs and distinctive markings.

Figure 63. 14-spot ladybird adult.
Photo: Maris Midgley.

Figure 64. 14-spot ladybird adults mating.
Photo: Remy Poland.

Figure 65. 14-spot ladybird late-instar larva.
Photo: Gilles San Martin.

Figure 66. 14-spot ladybird pupa.
Photo: Richard Comont.

Identification

Length: 3.5-4.5mm. *Background colour*: yellow or rarely black. *Pattern colour*: black or rarely yellow spots. *Number of spots*: 4-14 (14). *Spot fusions*: very common. *Melanic (black) forms*: very rare. *Pronotum*: yellow or cream with black spots or trapezium or crown-shaped mark. *Leg colour*: brown. *Other features*: spots are rather rectangular.

Fourth-instar larva: dark greyish brown with cream patches surrounding tubercles on thoracic segments; all outer tubercles, the middle tubercles of the first abdominal segment and all tubercles of the fourth abdominal segment are cream; and cream markings along the midline. *Pupa*: overall a pale brown, but with slightly darker thoracic segments; third thoracic segment bearing a pair of dark spots flanking the midline; a band of yellow to cream spots across the first thoracic segment; four rows of diffuse dark markings running longitudinally down abdominal segments two to eight.

Ecology

Habitats: 14-spot ladybirds are found in many diverse habitats, commonly on low herbage, such as grasslands, saltmarsh and scrub. However, the species also occurs in mature woodlands (both deciduous and conifer) and orchards. Crops, including cereals, but particularly broad-leaved crops such as field beans, are common habitats for 14-spot ladybirds. There are also a number of records of this species from wetlands. 14-spot ladybirds overlap with a number of other species of ladybird and are commonly found with 2-spot, 7-spot, 10-spot, pine and harlequin ladybirds.

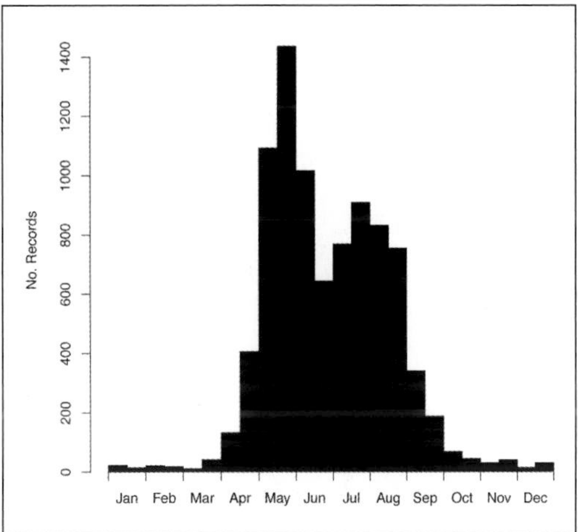

Figure 67. 14-spot ladybird phenogram.

Host plants: most 14-spot ladybird records are associated with low herbage, particularly nettle. However, there are many observations of 14-spot ladybirds on other herbaceous plants such as foxglove, angelica, dock, cow parsley, hogweed, mugwort, tansy, thistles, rosebay willowherb and fat-hen. Cultivated beans, blackcurrants and roses are popular host plants for 14-spot ladybirds in gardens. There are many records of this species from deciduous trees and shrubs including hawthorn, sallow, willow, sycamore, lime, oak and birch.

Food: aphids.

Overwintering sites: this species overwinters in many habitats, commonly on low herbage.

UK distribution status Ubiquitous

UK distribution trend (1990-2010) Decreasing

Calvia quattuordecimguttata (Linnaeus, 1758) (Cream-spot ladybird)

Synonyms *Halyzia quattuordecimguttata*
Calvia quatuordecimguttata auctt. (misspelling)

Number of records 4329
Number of 10km squares 907

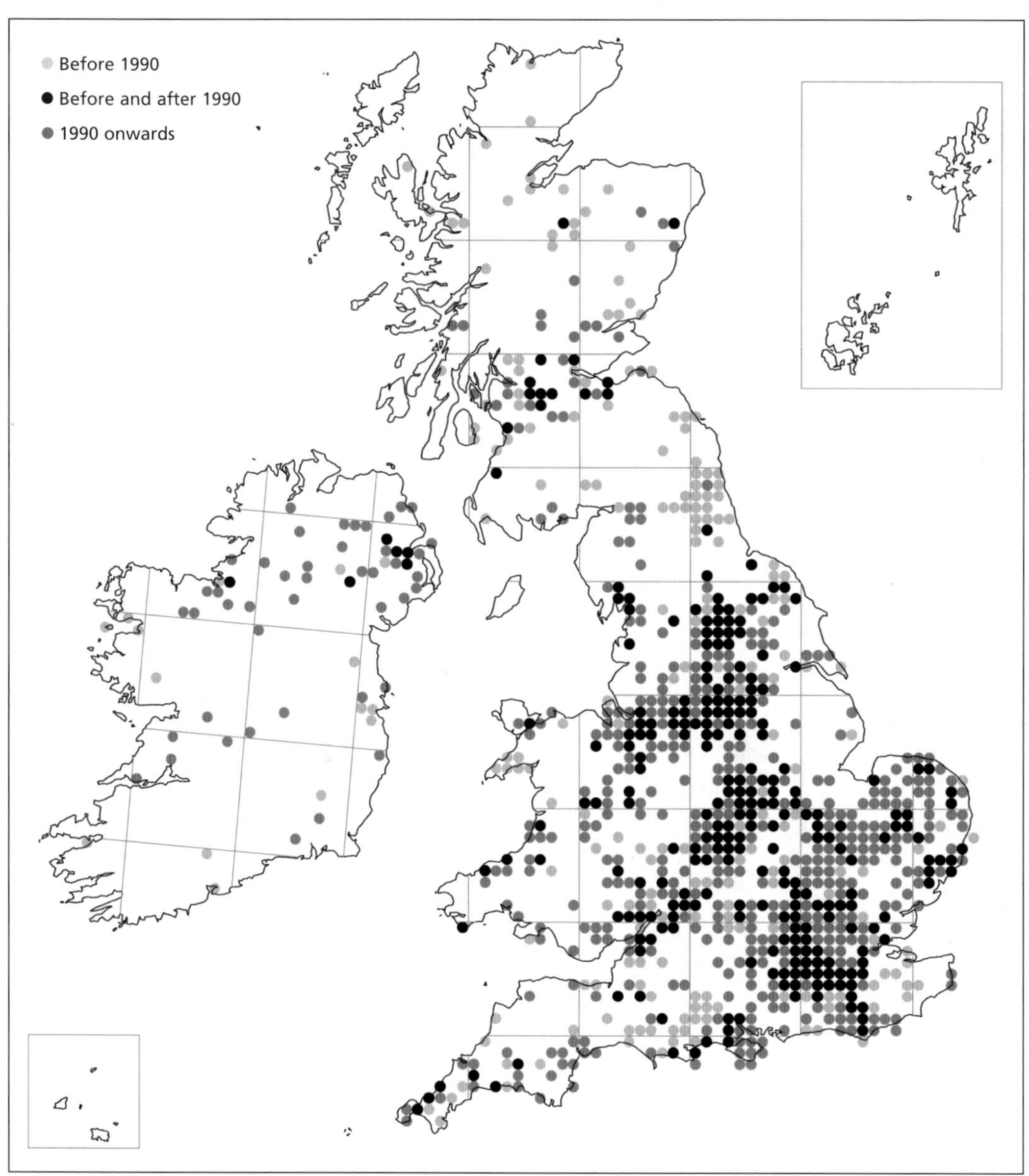

Map 13. Distribution (10km) of cream-spot ladybird.

The cream-spot ladybird is a deciduous tree specialist and lives among the foliage of broad-leaved deciduous trees, hedges and shrubs. It has a particular association with ash and lime (Hawkins, 2000) and feeds on both aphids and psyllids. It overwinters close to the ground in the leaf litter layer and requires a true diapause before becoming reproductively mature. As such, this species is only capable of producing one generation a year, and new generation adults are occupied with the sole purpose of building up fat reserves for the winter. Female cream-spot ladybirds deposit a red waxy substance on the surface of their eggs (visible with a hand lens). This has been shown to be an effective deterrent against predators, such as other ladybird larvae, including those of the harlequin ladybird (Ware *et al.*, 2008).

Figure 68. Cream-spot ladybird adult.
Photo: Maris Midgley.

Figure 69. Cream-spot ladybird adult.
Photo: Remy Poland.

Figure 70. Cream-spot ladybird late-instar larva.
Photo: Gilles San Martin.

Figure 71. Cream-spot ladybird pupa.
Photo: Richard Comont.

Identification

Length: 4-5mm. *Background colour*: maroon-brown. *Pattern colour*: cream spots. *Number of spots*: 14. *Spot fusions*: very rare. *Melanic (black) forms*: very rare. *Pronotum*: maroon with lateral cream marks. *Leg colour*: brown. *Other features*: six of the spots form a line across the elytra.

Fourth-instar larva: dark grey, with two pairs of bold white marks on the middle and outer tubercles of the first and fourth abdominal segments; outer white tubercles of abdominal segments four to six are tall and pointed, giving a saw-toothed appearance to the side of the body. *Pupa*: creamy-yellow with diffuse dark grey/brown markings running longitudinally; three ragged teeth on each side of middle section, spanning segments three to five.

Ecology

Habitats: cream-spot ladybirds have a strong association with deciduous trees and are consequently commonly found in woodlands. However, there are a number of records from grassland, heathland and marshland.

Host plants: cream-spot ladybirds are often found on ash trees. However, they have been reported from many other species of deciduous tree including sycamore, lime, beech and oak. There are also a number of records from hawthorn, hornbeam, sallow and gorse. Records of cream-spots on conifers are scarce, but include some from Scots pine. Some records are from herbaceous plants such as thistles and nettle. Cream-spot ladybirds have also been reported on honeysuckle and broom.

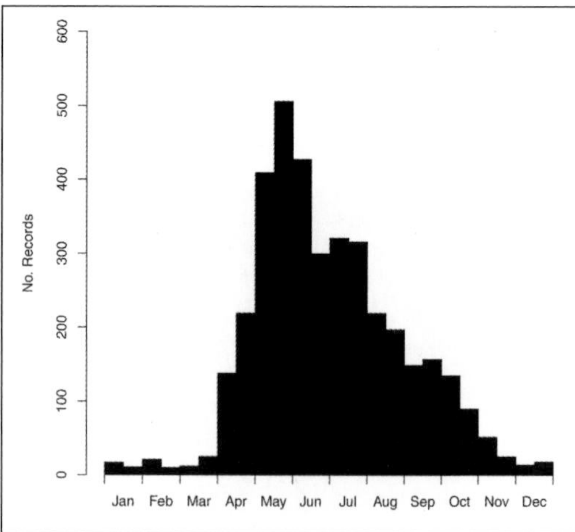

Figure 72. Cream-spot ladybird phenogram.

Food: aphids and psyllids.

Overwintering sites: cream-spot ladybirds overwinter in leaf litter, bark crevices and beech nuts.

UK distribution status Very widespread

UK distribution trend (1990-2010) Decreasing

Halyzia sedecimguttata (Linnaeus, 1758) (Orange ladybird)

Synonyms *Halyzia sexdecimguttata* auctt. (misspelling)

Number of records 4687
Number of 10km squares 797

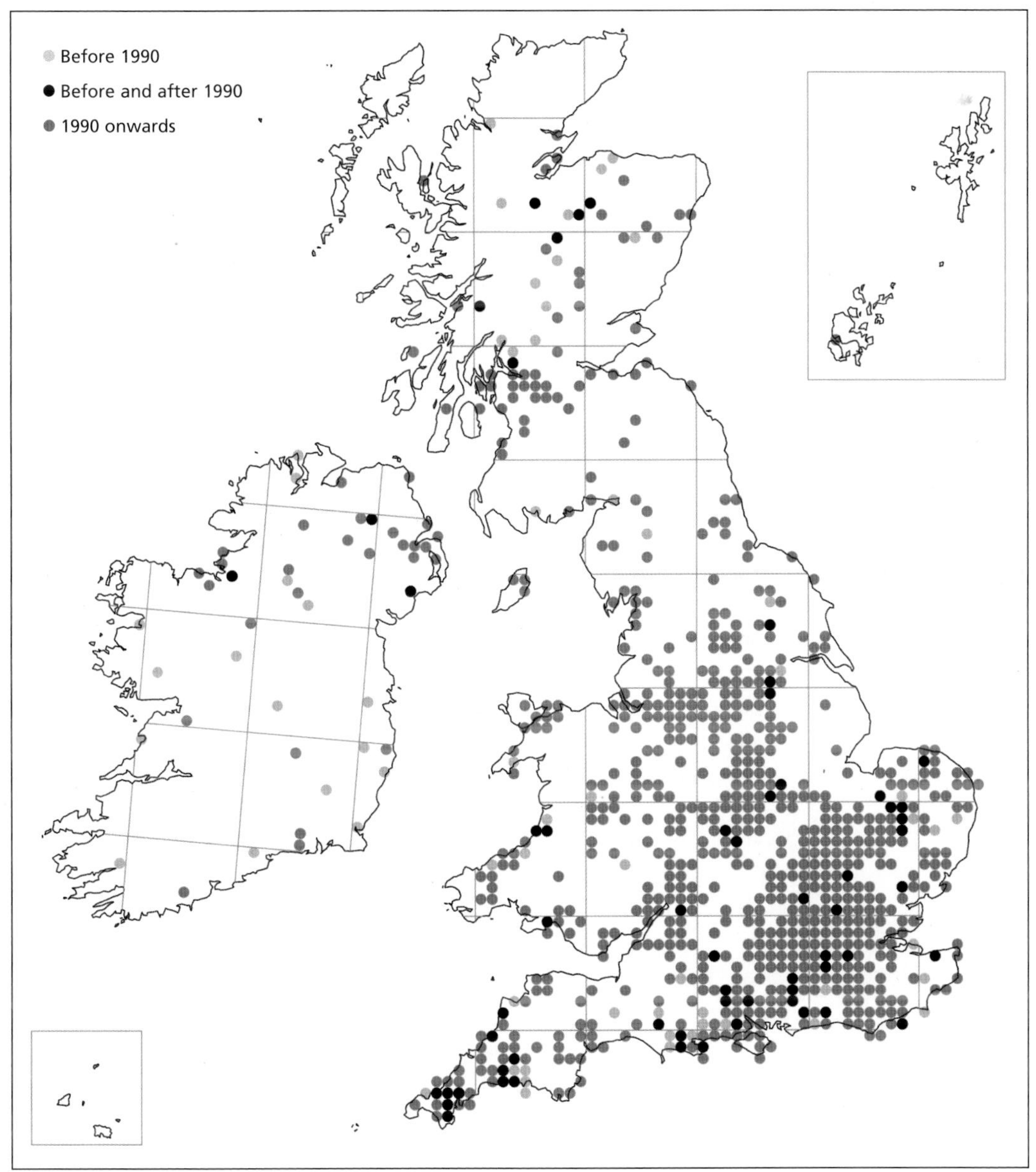

Map 14. Distribution (10km) of orange ladybird.

This attractive species was considered an indicator of ancient woodland until 1987, and an association with oak was even suggested, but later disproved (Hawkins, 2000). However, its recent association with ash and sycamore trees has caused the orange ladybird to increase in abundance and become more widespread across the country. It is a mycophagous species: both the larvae and adults feed on powdery white mildews growing on the leaves of deciduous trees. Orange ladybirds start breeding later in the year than other species, usually around late June-July, as they have to wait until sufficient mildew has grown on the host trees to feed their developing larvae. The larvae also take longer to develop compared to those species which feed on aphids, and the pupae may survive well into the winter if the weather is mild (Majerus & Williams, 1989). Orange ladybirds usually overwinter in sheltered spots on the bark of trees, but in particularly harsh winters have been found occupying the litter layer. Interestingly, Majerus (1994) found that the proportion of orange ladybirds overwintering up in the trees correlated to winter temperature.

Figure 73. Orange ladybird adult.
Photo: Edward Bartoszewicz.

Figure 74. Orange ladybird adults overwintering.
Photo: Toni Watt

Figure 75. Orange ladybird late-instar larva.
Photo: Stephen Plant.

Figure 76. Orange ladybird pupa.
Photo: Michael Majerus.

Identification

Length: 4.5-6mm. *Background colour*: orange. *Pattern colour*: white spots. *Number of spots*: 12-16 (16). *Spot fusions*: none. *Melanic (black) forms*: no. *Pronotum*: orange with translucent edging. *Leg colour*: orange.

Fourth-instar larva: pale cream with bright yellow longitudinal stripes running between inner and middle rows of tubercles; tubercles black; first thoracic segment is bright yellow; head and legs are pale cream; the body has a smooth surface. Distinguished from 22-spot larva by colour, longer legs, pale head, and middle tubercle on each side of first abdominal segment having black tip (yellow in 22-spot). *Pupa*: highly distinctive; black with pairs of bright yellow spots on the lateral edges of abdominal segments one and two, and duller ones on segments five, six and seven.

Ecology

Habitats: the orange ladybird is a woodland species but is increasingly common on urban trees.

Host plants: sycamore and ash are favoured host plants of orange ladybirds; however, in recent years, an increasing number of records have been from hawthorn, both as adults and larvae. Orange ladybirds have been recorded from a number of other deciduous trees and shrubs including dogwood, lime, hazel, sallow and birch, particularly where ivy is present. There are a scattering of records from coniferous trees including Douglas fir and Scots pine. However, feeding has only been observed on sycamore, ash, birch, dogwood and field maple, and all other plant species are yet to be proven as hosts.

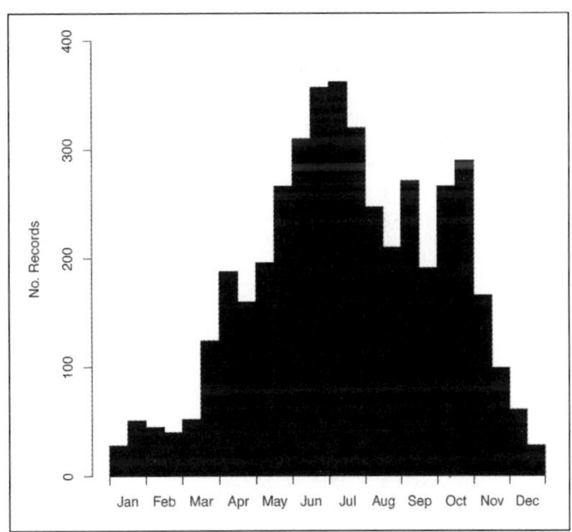

Figure 77. Orange ladybird phenogram.

Food: mildew.

Overwintering sites: orange ladybirds overwinter in leaf litter or in sheltered positions on deciduous and coniferous trees. Overwintering orange ladybirds have also been found on rhododendron and ivy.

UK distribution status Very widespread

UK distribution trend (1990-2010) Increasing

Psyllobora vigintiduopunctata (Linnaeus, 1758) (22-spot ladybird)

Synonyms *Thea vigintiduopunctata*
Halyzia vigintiduopunctata

Number of records 4985
Number of 10km squares 814

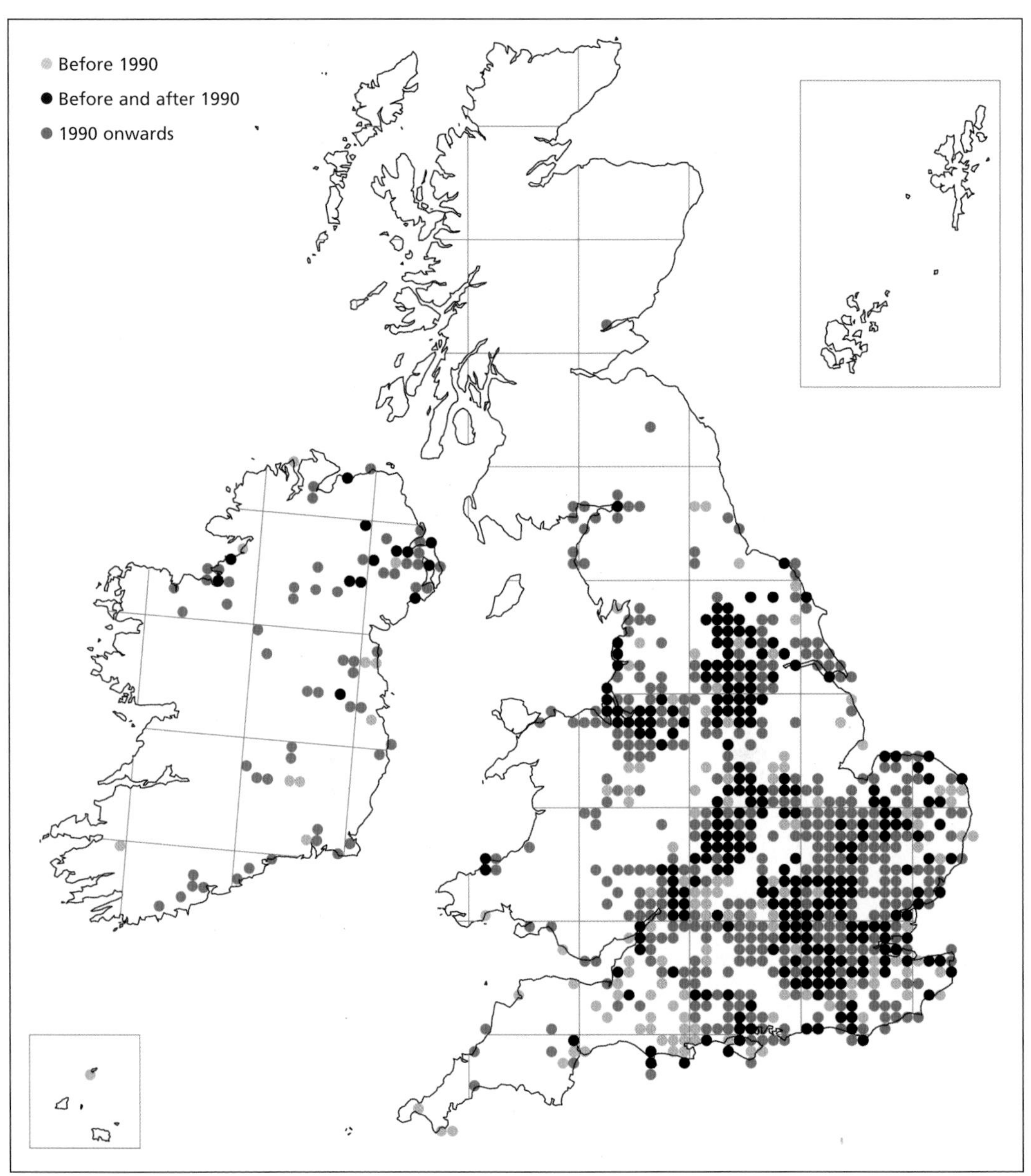

Map 15. Distribution (10km) of 22-spot ladybird.

The 22-spot ladybird is a very common and widespread species in Britain and Ireland, although there are only isolated reports from Scotland. It can be abundant, feeding on the mildew that develops on the upper surfaces of the leaves of hogweed and other umbellifers. Especially towards the end of the season, when hogweed is senescing, 22-spots will feed on the mildews of other herbaceous plants, including creeping thistle, and young trees, especially oak. The 22-spot is the only ladybird species in Britain and Ireland in which the larva, pupa and adult are all of a comparable colour and pattern. The 22-spot is a small and pretty ladybird, with lemon yellow elytra and pronotum. The elytra have 20-22 small black spots (not fused) and the pronotum a further five. 14-spot and 16-spot ladybirds are the only species likely to be confused with the 22-spot. The yellow of the 14-spot is generally less bright and the black spots of that species are larger, usually more rectangular in shape and on most specimens some are fused together. The pronota of the two species are also different. The 16-spot is usually rather smaller than the 22-spot and is duller and usually much paler in colour.

Figure 78. 22-spot ladybird adult.
Photo: Mike Bidwell.

Figure 79. 22-spot ladybird adult.
Photo: Peter Brown.

Figure 80. 22-spot ladybird late-instar larva.
Photo: Robert Frost.

Figure 81. 22-spot ladybird pupa.
Photo: Ken Dolbear.

Identification

Length: 3-4mm. *Background colour*: bright lemon yellow. *Pattern colour*: black spots. *Number of spots*: 20-22 (22). *Spot fusions*: uncommon. *Melanic (black) forms*: no. *Pronotum*: yellow with four discrete black spots in a semi-circle and a black triangle at the mid base. *Leg colour*: brown.

Fourth-instar larva: lemon yellow with black tubercles and black head, distinguished from orange ladybird larva by dark head and middle tubercle on each side of first abdominal segment yellow (black-tipped in orange ladybird). *Pupa*: yellow with black spots.

Ecology

Habitats: 22-spot ladybirds generally favour low vegetation in grassland habitats. This species is often reported from roadside and field-side vegetation, usually on low herbs, although it will visit the lower branches of young trees. It is occasionally found in woodlands and in coastal habitats such as sand dunes.

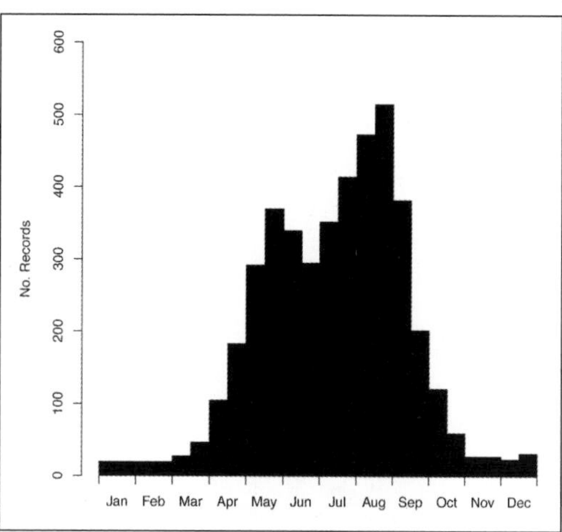

Figure 82. 22-spot ladybird phenogram.

Host plants: in Britain this species is often found on hogweed but in Ireland it is most frequently found on ragwort. In Britain there are also many records associated with other umbellifers, such as cow parsley. 22-spot ladybirds have also been found on teasel, foxglove, mugwort, burdock and wild parsnip. Additionally shrubs and trees are also frequented by 22-spot ladybirds, including ash, willow, sallow, hornbeam, hawthorn and oak.

Food: mildews growing on the upper side of leaves of the host plant.

Overwintering sites: 22-spots overwinter in herbage, including grasses, close to the ground or sometimes in ivy.

UK distribution status Very widespread

UK distribution trend (1990-2010) Decreasing

Anatis ocellata (Linnaeus, 1758) (Eyed ladybird)

Synonyms: None

Number of records: 1425
Number of 10km squares: 481

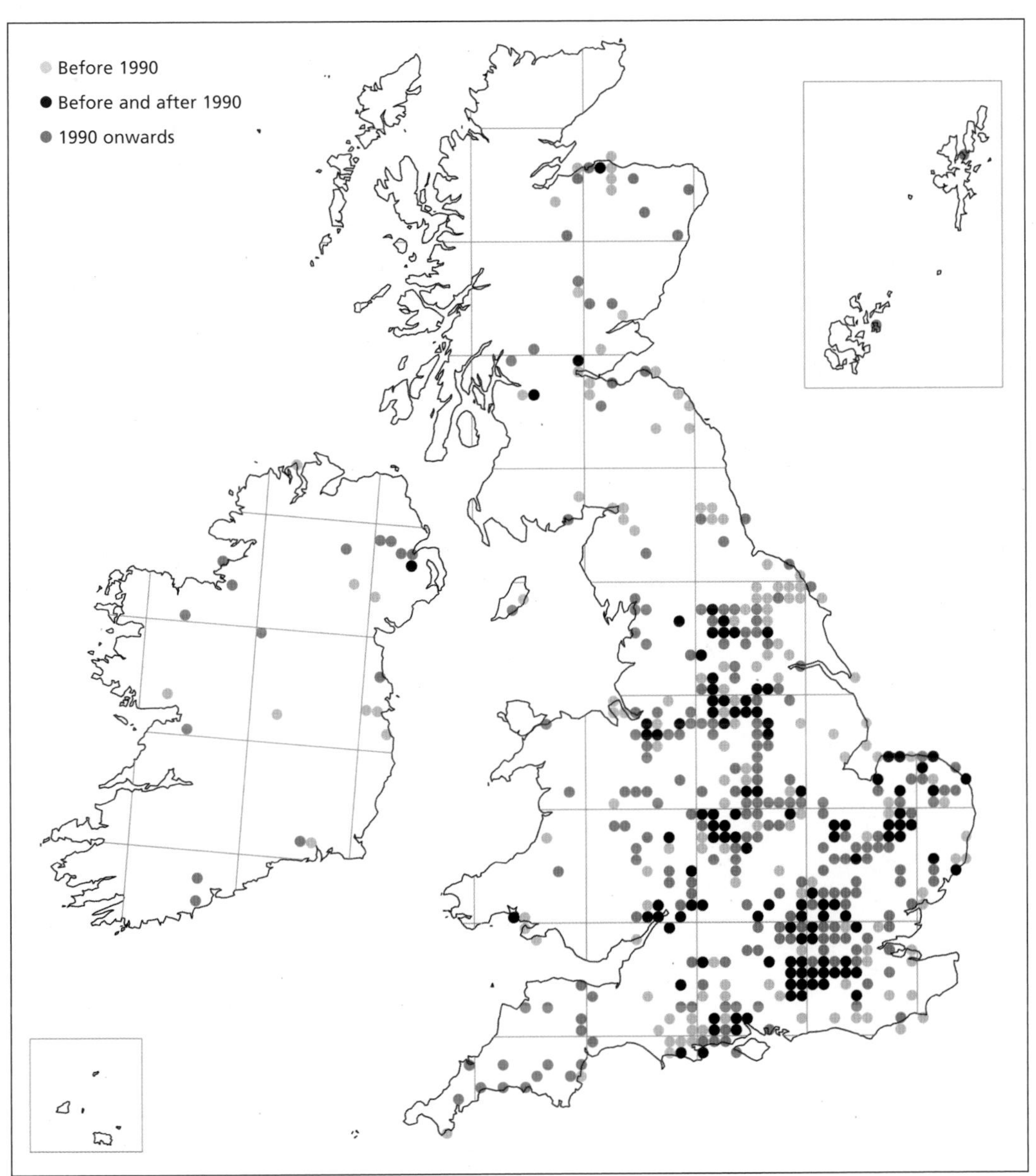

Map 16. Distribution (10km) of eyed ladybird.

Britain and Ireland's largest ladybird, the eyed ladybird gets its name from the pale rings around the black spots on its elytra (although some specimens lack the rings; even more rarely, the black centres are absent). The eyed ladybird is a pine specialist and is most easily found by beating mature Scots pines in mid-summer. Towards the end of the summer, eyed ladybirds will often disperse to deciduous trees in search of supplementary food to build up their winter fat-reserves. Eyed ladybirds overwinter in or just under the ground, and may be seen in early April, crawling up onto low-growing plants in the vicinity of pine woodlands, where they spend some time cleaning off any soil particles they have picked up during their winter underground. The larvae of eyed ladybirds are as large and impressive as the adults. Indeed, the eyed ladybird is one of the few British species whose larvae are able to overcome and consume harlequin ladybird larvae (Ware & Majerus, 2008). The eyed ladybird is a very widespread species in Britain and Ireland and, rarely for a ladybird, has been recorded as far north as the Shetland Islands.

Figure 83. Eyed ladybird adult. Photo: Maris Midgley.

Figure 84. Eyed ladybird adult. Photo: Remy Poland.

Figure 85. Eyed ladybird late-instar larva. Photo: Gilles San Martin.

Figure 86. Eyed ladybird pupa. Photo: Remy Poland.

Identification

Length: 7-8.5mm. *Background colour*: russet or burgundy. *Pattern colour*: black spots, with or without cream rings around them (sometimes spots absent). *Number of spots*: 0-23 (15). *Spot fusions*: rare. *Melanic (black) forms*: very rare. *Pronotum*: distinctively patterned with white markings and black M-mark. *Leg colour*: black. *Other features*: largest ladybird in Britain and Ireland.

Fourth-instar larva: large (can exceed 12mm), with thick black spines projecting from tubercles; two large orange spots on the outer tubercles of the first two abdominal segments; pairs of small white or yellowish spots along the bottom edges of abdominal segments five to eight. *Pupa*: cream with four rows of black spots running longitudinally and an additional pair of black spots on the sides of abdominal segments two and three; three ragged teeth on each side of middle section, spanning segments three to five.

Ecology

Habitats: eyed ladybirds are conifer specialists and are most often found in coniferous and mixed woodlands.

Host plants: in Britain the vast majority of eyed ladybird records are associated with conifers – particularly Scots pine, but also Douglas fir and larch. In late summer they may be found on deciduous trees such as lime and oak. There are occasional records of this species from nettle and other herbaceous plants, but usually in the vicinity of conifers. In Ireland this species has been most commonly recorded on sycamore followed by Sitka spruce, lime and larch.

Food: aphids.

Overwintering sites: eyed ladybirds overwinter in the soil or leaf litter in coniferous or mixed woodlands.

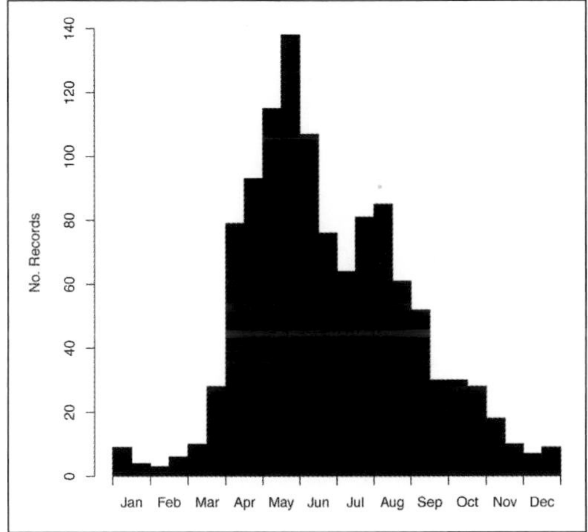

Figure 87. Eyed ladybird phenogram.

UK distribution status Widespread

UK distribution trend (1990-2010) Stable

Aphidecta obliterata (Linnaeus, 1758) (Larch ladybird)

Synonyms *Aphideita obliterata*
Adalia obliterata

Number of records 1281
Number of 10km squares 519

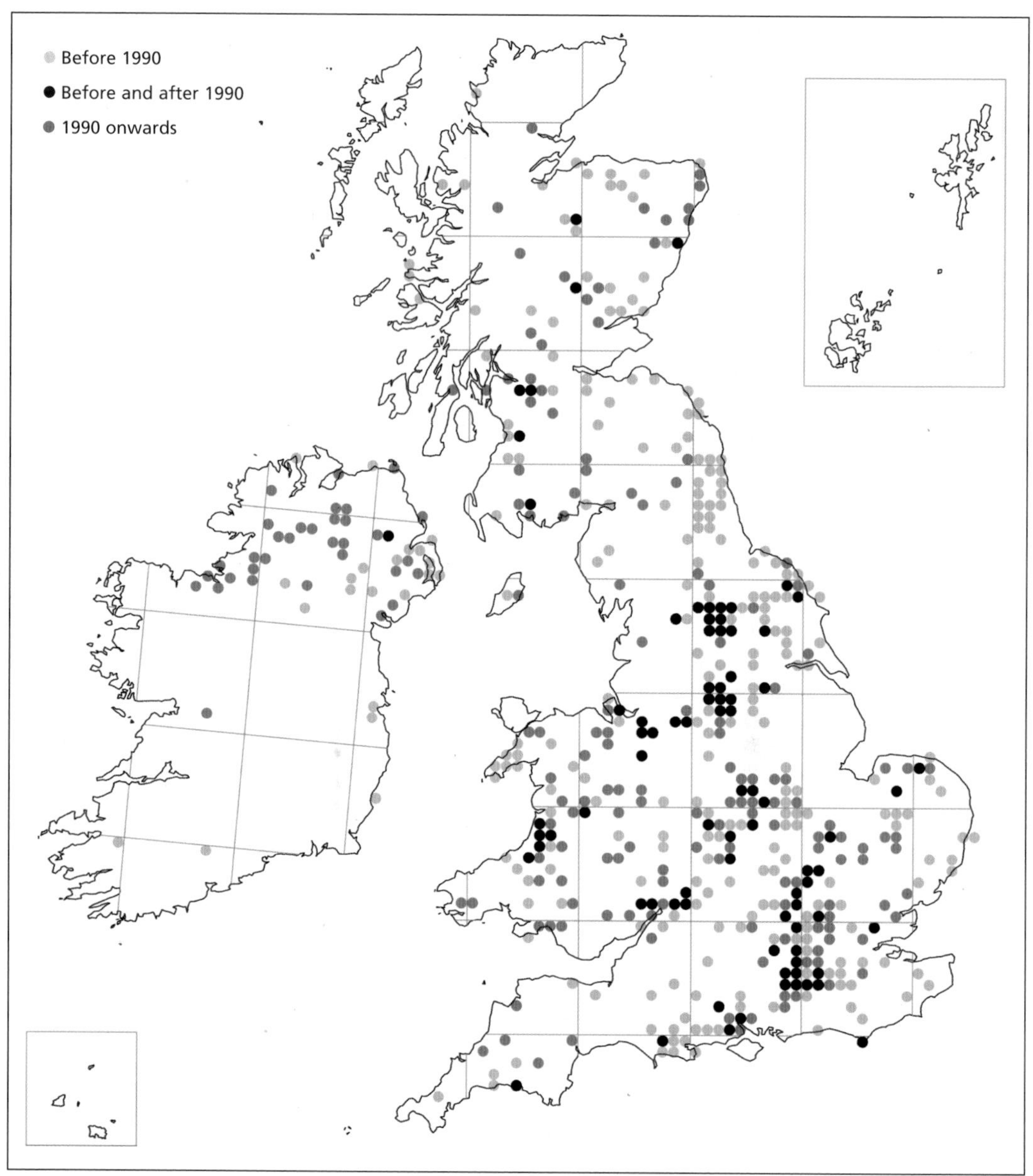

Map 17. Distribution (10km) of larch ladybird.

The larch ladybird is not instantly recognised as a ladybird by some, having a somewhat dull appearance compared to other members of the group. Its elytra are light brown, usually with a diffuse dark line running down the midsection, and sometimes speckled with tiny reddish brown spots. It has a black M-shaped mark on its pale pronotum. The larch ladybird probably relies on camouflage for defence against birds, but can also reflex bleed. As its name suggests, this ladybird lives and breeds on larch, but can be found on other conifers, such as Scots pine and Douglas fir. It feeds primarily on adelgids (woolly aphids) but will also accept aphids and coccids (Majerus, 1994).

Figure 88. Larch ladybird adult.
Photo: Richard Comont.

Figure 89. Larch ladybird adult.
Photo: Gilles San Martin.

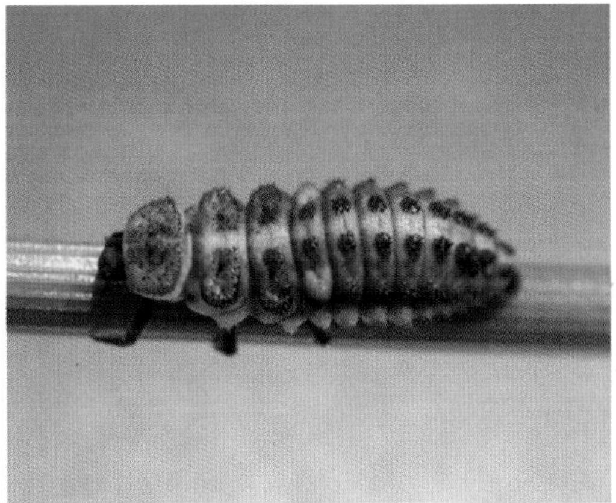

Figure 90. Larch ladybird late-instar larva.
Photo: Gilles San Martin.

Figure 91. Larch ladybird pupa.
Photo: Richard Comont.

Identification

Length: 4-5mm. *Background colour*: light brown, sometimes speckled with tiny brown spots. *Pattern colour*: none, or dark oblique line posteriorly. *Number of spots*: 0-10 (0). *Spot fusions*: rare. *Melanic (black) forms*: rare in Britain and Ireland. *Pronotum*: pale with black M-mark or spots. *Leg colour*: brown. *Other features*: can appear well-camouflaged.

Fourth-instar larva: very similar to larva of 18-spot ladybird, so rearing through to adulthood is recommended for accurate identification; light grey; thoracic region with darker speckled patches; a pair of yellow spots on middle and outer tubercles of first abdominal segment, remaining tubercles dark grey with short stubby hairs protruding; legs uniformly black. *Pupa*: pale grey with four rows of dark grey squarish patches running longitudinally; anterior section with dark zigzag markings; yellow patches on sides of first abdominal segment.

Ecology

Habitats: a conifer specialist, the larch ladybird is commonly found in coniferous or mixed woodlands.

Host plants: in Britain most records of the larch ladybird are indeed from larch (also Norway spruce, Douglas fir and occasionally Scots pine) but in Ireland records are almost entirely from Sitka or Norway spruce.

Food: adelgids, coccids.

Overwintering sites: larch ladybirds overwinter primarily in bark crevices on larch, Norway spruce and Douglas fir; it is not uncommon for this species to be beaten from ivy growing on or near these trees.

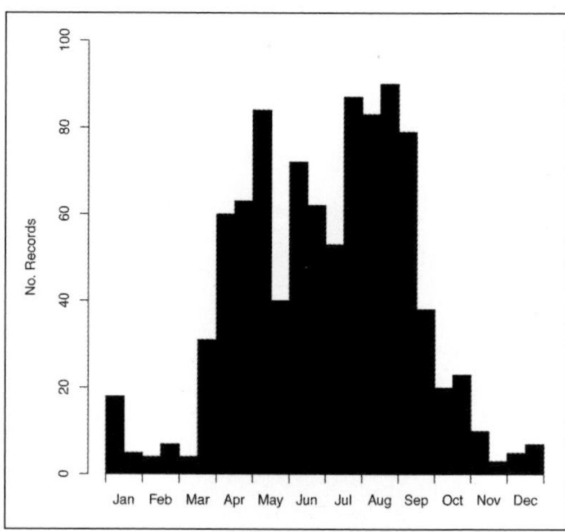

Figure 92. Larch ladybird phenogram.

UK distribution status Widespread

UK distribution trend (1990-2010) Stable

Hippodamia tredecimpunctata (Linnaeus, 1758) (13-spot ladybird)

Synonyms None

Number of records 87
Number of 10km squares 39

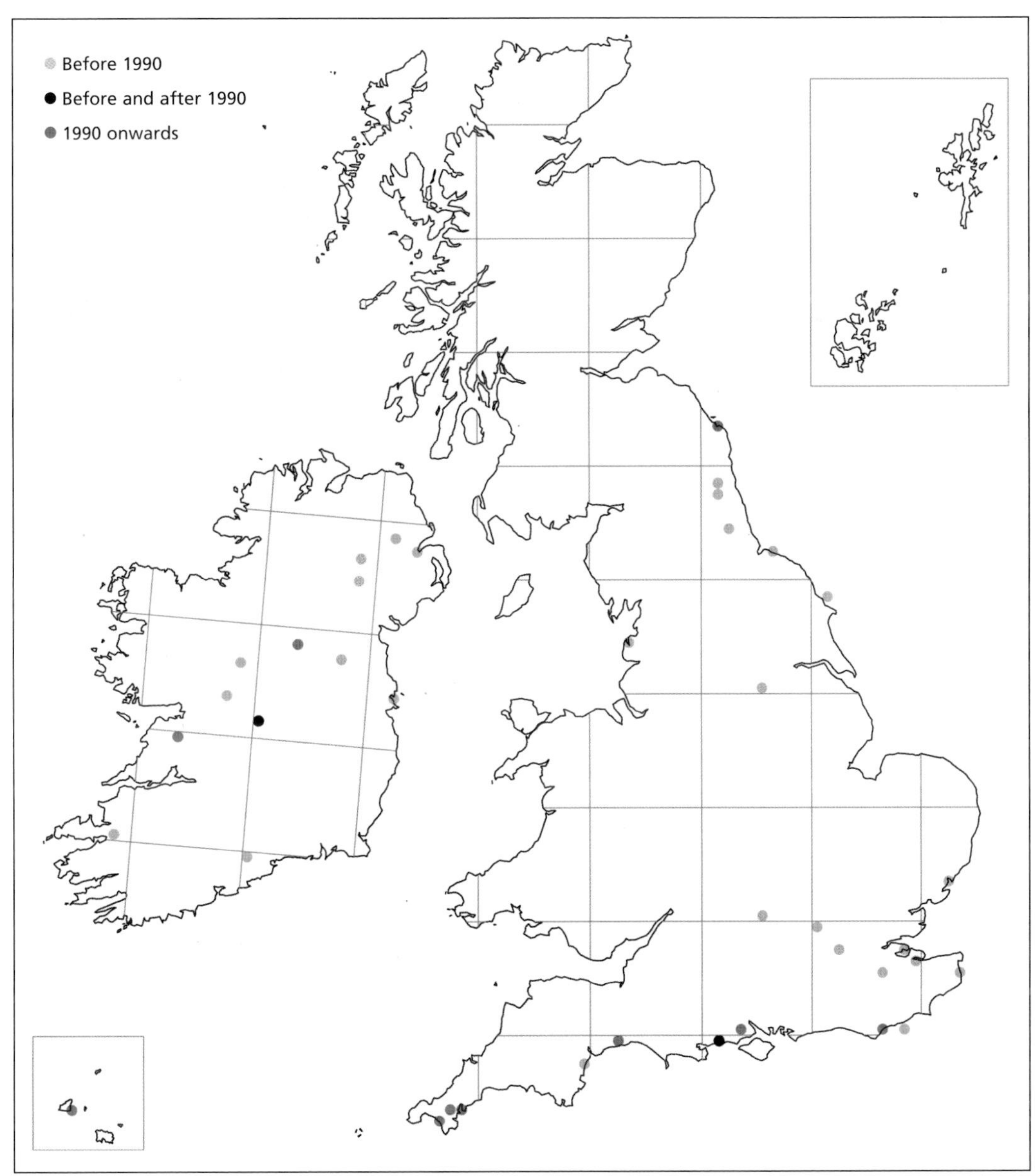

Map 18. Distribution (10km) of 13-spot ladybird.

The 13-spot ladybird is an intriguing, if elusive, species in Britain but quite a different perspective is given from Ireland. In Britain it is a very rare and noteworthy ladybird that dies out, then re-colonises from Europe. In central Ireland (All Saints Bog, Co. Offaly) the 13-spot is resident (Speight, 1990). In contrast, until recently, there had not been any British records since 1952, but, over the last few years, a number of sightings from the south of England suggest that the 13-spot is re-colonising. However, it is likely that this species is now a migrant to Britain; there is no recent evidence that there are established populations. It is a species that is associated with damp habitats, such as marshes, and is common across continental Europe. Indeed, many studies on agricultural systems in the Palaearctic region list the 13-spot as one of the three most abundant species of ladybird, particularly favouring dense and humid stands (Hodek & Honěk, 1996). The status of the 13-spot in Britain is puzzling, but is possibly linked to habitat degradation through agricultural intensification.

Figure 93. 13-spot ladybird adult.
Photo: Gilles San Martin.

Figure 94. 13-spot ladybird adult.
Photo: Peter Brown.

Figure 95. 13-spot ladybird late-instar larva.
Photo: Gilles San Martin.

Identification

Length: 5-7mm. *Background colour*: orange-red. *Pattern colour*: black. *Number of spots*: 7-15 (13). *Spot fusions*: rare. *Melanic (black) forms*: rare. *Pronotum*: white with distinctive black pattern of solid black disc and pair of lateral black spots. *Leg colour*: black. *Other features*: distinctly elongate and slightly flattened.

Fourth-instar larva: dark grey with 6 rows of tubercles bearing short stubby hairs; tubercles are inky black except for those on abdominal segment four, which are all pale grey, as are the middle and outer tubercles on the first abdominal segment. *Pupa*: dark grey with two rows of small black spots running longitudinally (formed from inner tubercles); pale lateral patches on first abdominal segment.

Ecology

Habitats: in Ireland the 13-spot has been recorded from transition mires, wooded bogs and limestone lakeshores. Whereas the vast majority of 13-spot ladybird records in Britain are from marshy lowland habitats such as fens, marshes, riverbanks and dune systems.

Host plants: the records in Britain are from reeds and grasses. In continental Europe it is mainly found on plants in marshy habitats but is also commonly found on crops.

Food: aphids.

Overwintering sites: the overwintering sites of this species are unknown in Britain, but in continental Europe it favours litter or upper soil layers in damp habitats.

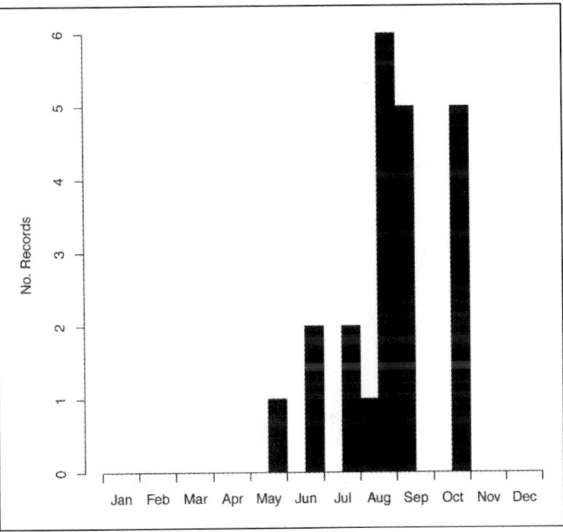

Figure 96. 13-spot ladybird phenogram.

UK conservation designation IUCN (pre-1994) – insufficiently known

UK distribution status Very local

UK distribution trend (1990-2010) Stable (based on 100 records or less)

Hippodamia variegata (Goeze, 1777) (Adonis' ladybird)

Synonyms *Adonia variegata*

Number of records 918
Number of 10km squares 295

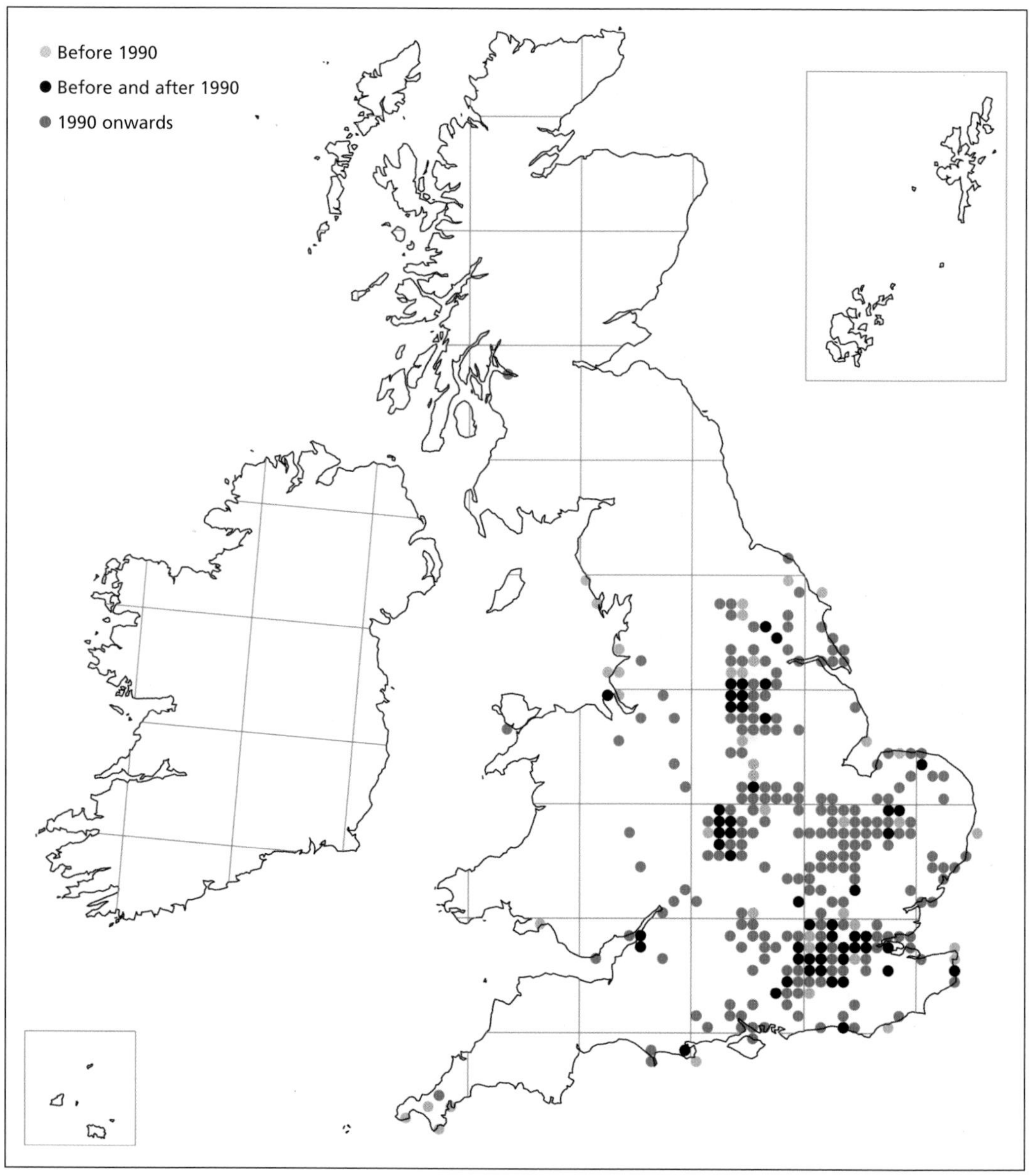

Map 19. Distribution (10km) of Adonis' ladybird.

Records of the Adonis' ladybird are concentrated in southern, eastern and central England as far north as Yorkshire, with few records from Wales and none from Ireland. The one record from Scotland is of the species being found indoors on grapes, and is thus regarded as incidental. The Adonis' is a fairly small ladybird with a rather elongate body. Whilst seven spots are most common, the number varies and a distinctive feature is that usually the spots are positioned in the posterior half of the elytra. Those spots nearer the front, if present, are usually small. The Adonis' may sometimes be confused with the 11-spot, which may occur in the same dry habitats, but the pronotum pattern of the former is distinctive. Populations of the Adonis' are usually transient, and like the 11-spot, the species can be elusive. The Adonis' may be found in a suitable habitat one year, but when searched for at the same site the following year, it may well be absent (Hawkins 2000). Normally, when sweeping an area for this species, one expects to find one or rarely two in the net. However, in good years (e.g. 2001 and 2010) up to 65 have been found in a small area (A. Frost, R. Frost and J. Milne, personal observations). This species is one of the most abundant ladybirds in Mediterranean Europe and there it can be very common in fields, especially where there is bare ground and weedy vegetation. In Britain the Adonis' is at the north-western edge of its range, but in recent years the species has been increasing here, possibly aided by climate warming.

Figure 97. Adonis' ladybird adult.
Photo: Michael Majerus.

Figure 98. Adonis' ladybird pupa.
Photo: Gilles San Martin.

Identification

Length: 4-5mm. *Background colour*: red. *Pattern colour*: black spots. *Number of spots*: 3-15 (7). *Spot fusions*: common. *Melanic (black) forms*: no. *Pronotum*: white with distinctive black pattern. *Leg colour*: black.

Fourth-instar larva: greyish-brown with a pale orange transverse band at the back of the head in front of the first thoracic segment and a thicker, orange transverse band between the first and second thoracic segment; outer and middle tubercles on first abdominal segment are orange; all other tubercles dark grey/black. *Pupa*: Pale brown with darker background; dark rectangular markings running longitudinally; remains of shed larval skin, with fine hairs, visible at the base.

Ecology

Habitats: often a coastal species, inhabiting dune systems, but increasingly also found in many inland areas. It favours habitats where the vegetation surrounds, or is adjacent to, areas of dry soil, shingle or shale. Found on waste ground and at gravel pits, often walking across bare ground. This species has also been recorded from grassland and scrub.

Host plants: Adonis' ladybirds have been reported on a number of herbaceous plants including nettle, wild parsnip, thistles, cow parsley, hogweed and tansy.

Food: aphids.

Overwintering sites: Adonis' ladybirds have been recorded overwintering in leaf litter and on low plants.

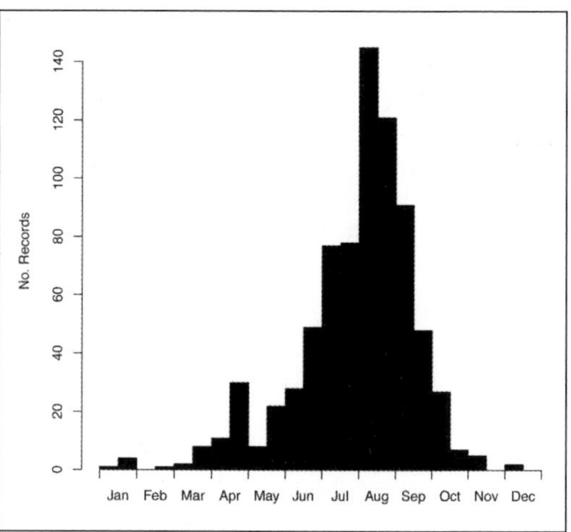

Figure 99. Adonis' ladybird phenogram.

UK distribution status Local

UK distribution trend (1990-2010) Stable

Coccinella hieroglyphica Linnaeus, 1758 (Hieroglyphic ladybird)

Synonyms None

Number of records 527
Number of 10km squares 241

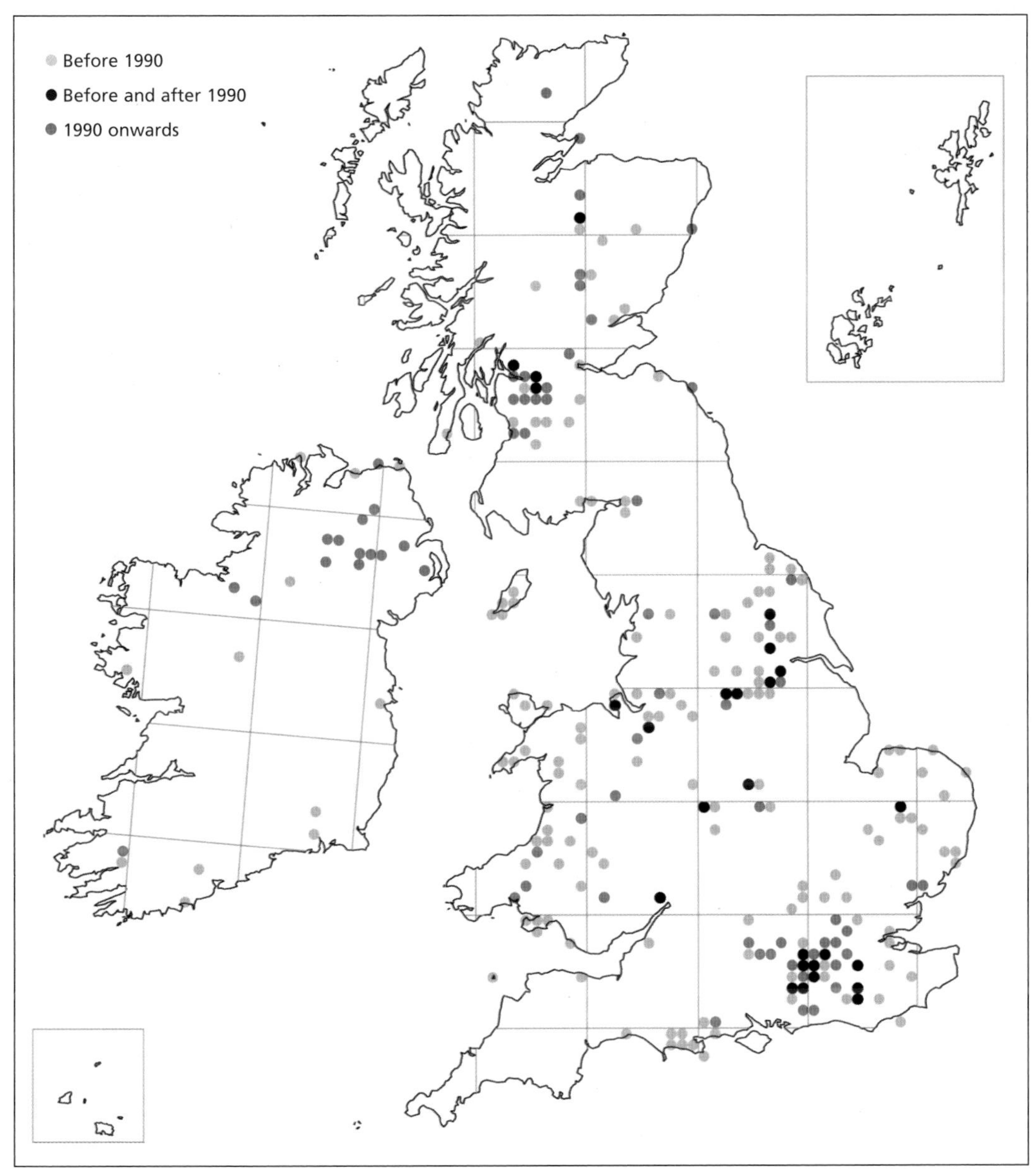

Map 20. Distribution (10km) of hieroglyphic ladybird.

The hieroglyphic ladybird is a somewhat elusive species, due to its specific habitat and unusual diet. It lives on heather and the larvae prey on the larvae of the heather leaf beetle, *Lochmaea suturalis* (Smith *et al.*, 1985), although adults are also known to consume the heather aphid, *Aphis callunae* (Hawkins, 2000). The species varies greatly in abundance from year to year due to prey availability. Overwintering individuals may be found by beating pine trees or gorse bushes growing in the vicinity of heather heathland. The hieroglyphic ladybird is a variable species, coloured anything from bronzy-brown with a squiggly black mark resembling an Egyptian hieroglyph, to completely black (Majerus, 1994).

Figure 100. Hieroglyphic ladybird adult.
Photo: Gilles San Martin.

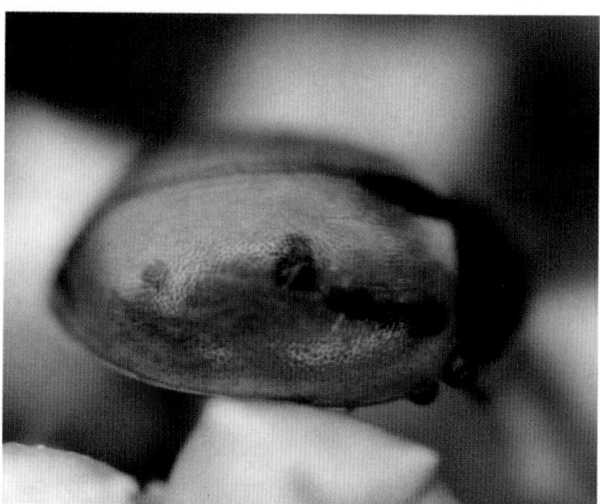

Figure 101. Hieroglyphic ladybird adult (f. *typica*).
Photo: Michael Majerus.

Figure 102. Hieroglyphic ladybird adult (f. *areata*).
Photo: Michael Majerus.

Figure 103. Hieroglyphic ladybird late-instar larva.
Photo: Gilles San Martin.

Identification

Length: 4-5mm. *Background colour*: brown or black. *Pattern colour*: black stripes, spots and patches, sometimes resembling an Egyptian hieroglyph. *Number of spots*: 0-7 (5). *Spot fusions*: common. *Melanic (black) forms*: common. *Pronotum*: black with anterior-lateral white marks. *Leg colour*: black.

Fourth-instar larva: dark grey/black; with black tubercles producing fine hairs; pale yellow patches in the centre of second and third thoracic segments; middle and outer tubercles on abdominal segments one and four are pale yellow/whitish. *Pupa*: unknown.

Ecology

Habitats: hieroglyphic ladybirds are found on heathland, often on old heather plants, or where the heathland has been invaded by scrub. This species is also found on acid grassland and heathland mosaics.

Host plants: hieroglyphic ladybirds are strongly associated with heathers.

Food: heather aphid, *Aphis callunae;* eggs/larvae of the heather leaf beetle, *Lochmaea suturalis*; chrysomelids within the genera *Altica* and *Galerucella*.

Overwintering sites: hieroglyphic ladybirds overwinter in litter under heather, pine trees and gorse bushes.

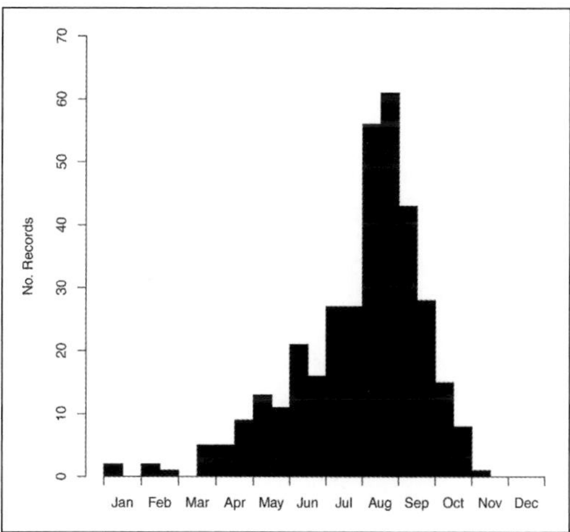

Figure 104. Hieroglyphic ladybird phenogram.

UK distribution status Local

UK distribution trend (1990-2010) Decreasing

Coccinella magnifica Redtenbacher, 1843 (Scarce 7-spot ladybird)

Synonyms *Coccinella divaricata* sensu auctt. non Olivier, 1808
Coccinella distincta Faldermann, 1837 non Thunberg, 1781

Number of records 177
Number of 10km squares 55

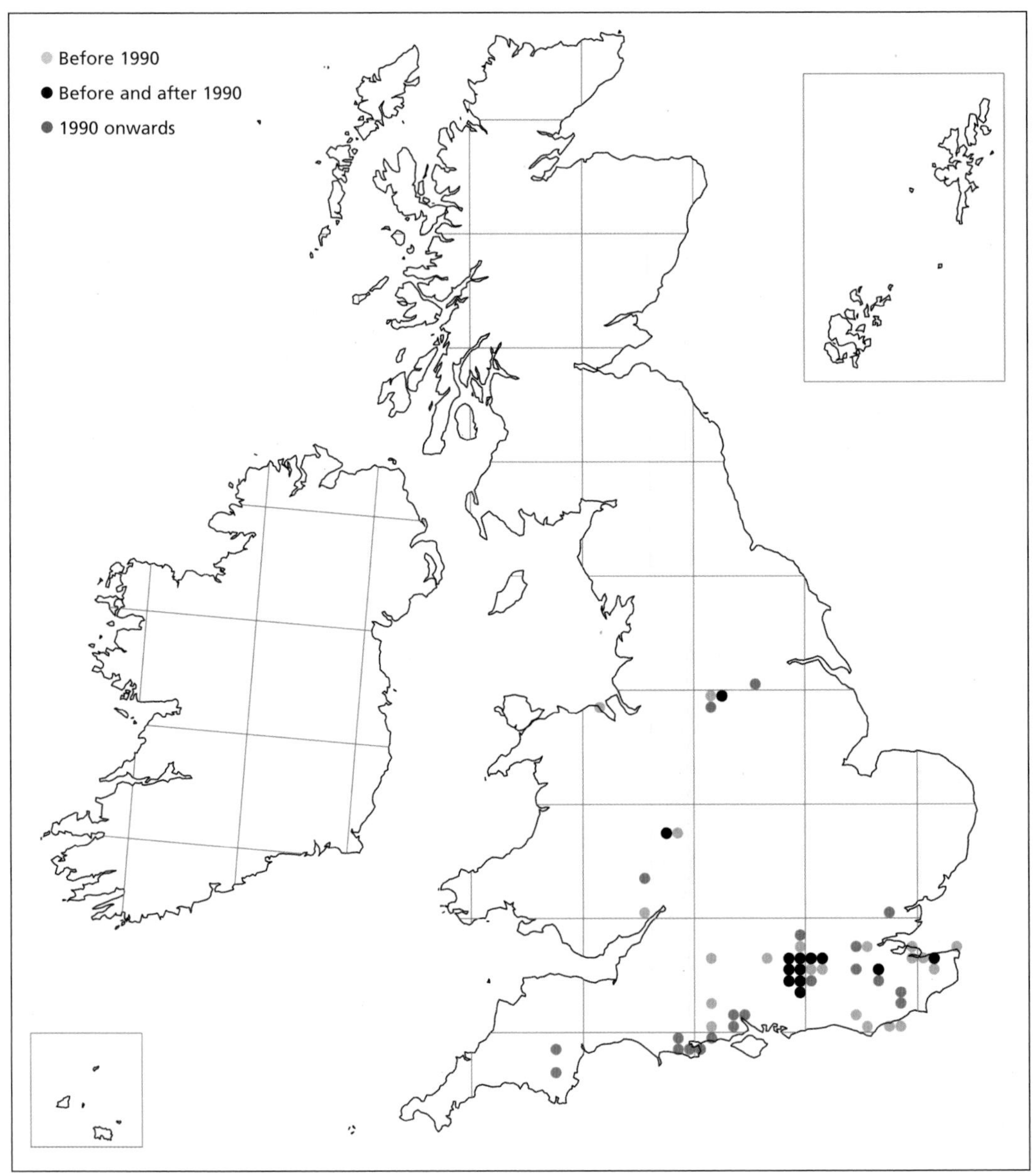

Map 21. Distribution (10km) of scarce 7-spot ladybird.

The scarce 7-spot ladybird has a very unusual lifestyle: it is myrmecophilous (ant-loving). In Britain, scarce 7-spots are only found living close to the nests of wood ants of the genus *Formica*, most commonly *Formica rufa*. This ant builds large mound nests of pine needles and other debris, and the scarce 7-spot is found in bushes or trees near these nests, feeding on ant-tended aphid colonies. The wood ants deter most aphid predators and parasites, and, in return, the ants get honeydew from the aphids (Sloggett & Majerus, 2000). Most ladybird species are not tolerated by this ant, but the scarce 7-spot appears to have special chemical and behavioural adaptations that allow it to resist ant-attack and feed on the aphids (Sloggett & Majerus, 2003). The scarce 7-spot ladybird looks very similar to the common 7-spot, but usually has a more domed shape and larger spots. The clearest way to distinguish the two species is to look at the white markings below the legs on their undersides; the scarce 7-spot has four white markings whereas the 7-spot only has two. Scarce 7-spots are possibly under-recorded due to misidentifications.

Figure 105. Scarce 7-spot ladybird adult.
Photo: Ken Dolbear.

Figure 106. Scarce 7-spot ladybird adult with ant.
Photo: Ken Dolbear.

Figure 107. Scarce 7-spot ladybird adult.
Photo: Helen Roy.

Identification

Length: 6-8mm. *Background colour*: red. *Pattern colour*: black spots, central spots comparatively large and foremost spots comparatively small. *Number of spots*: 5-11 (7). *Spot fusions*: rare. *Melanic (black) forms*: no. *Pronotum*: black with anterior-lateral white marks. *Leg colour*: black. *Other features*: can be distinguished from the 7-spot by more domed shape and presence of small white triangular marks on the underside, below both the middle and hind legs (the 7-spot has such marks only below the middle legs).

Fourth-instar larva: dark grey/black; with black tubercles producing fine hairs; pale yellow lateral patches on first thoracic segment; sides of second and third thoracic segments pale grey; middle and outer tubercles on abdominal segments one and four yellow. *Pupa*: unknown.

Ecology

Habitats: scarce 7-spot ladybirds are found in habitats close to wood ant nests, usually in woodland but also in heathland. Indeed, this species is always within a few metres of wood ant nests, although never in the nests.

Host plants: scarce 7-spots have been recorded from various plants including gorse, thistles and heather, but are most commonly found on Scots pine.

Food: aphids.

Overwintering sites: scarce 7-spots overwinter in various locations but always within a few metres of wood ant nests.

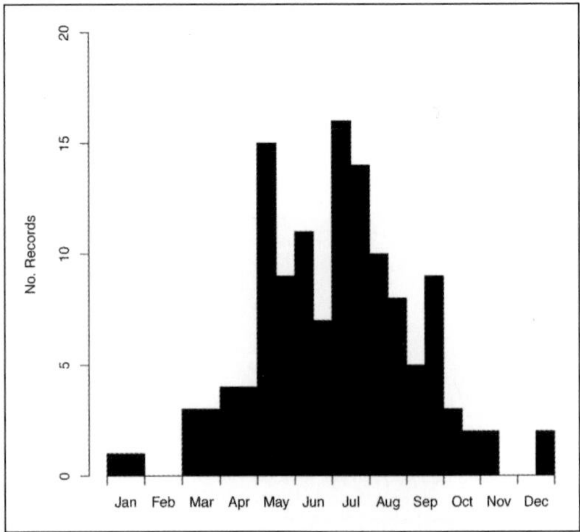

Figure 108. Scarce 7-spot ladybird phenogram.

UK conservation designation Nationally notable B

UK distribution status Very local

UK distribution trend (1990-2010) Stable

Coccinella quinquepunctata Linnaeus, 1758 (5-spot ladybird)

Synonyms None

Number of records 151
Number of 10km squares 39

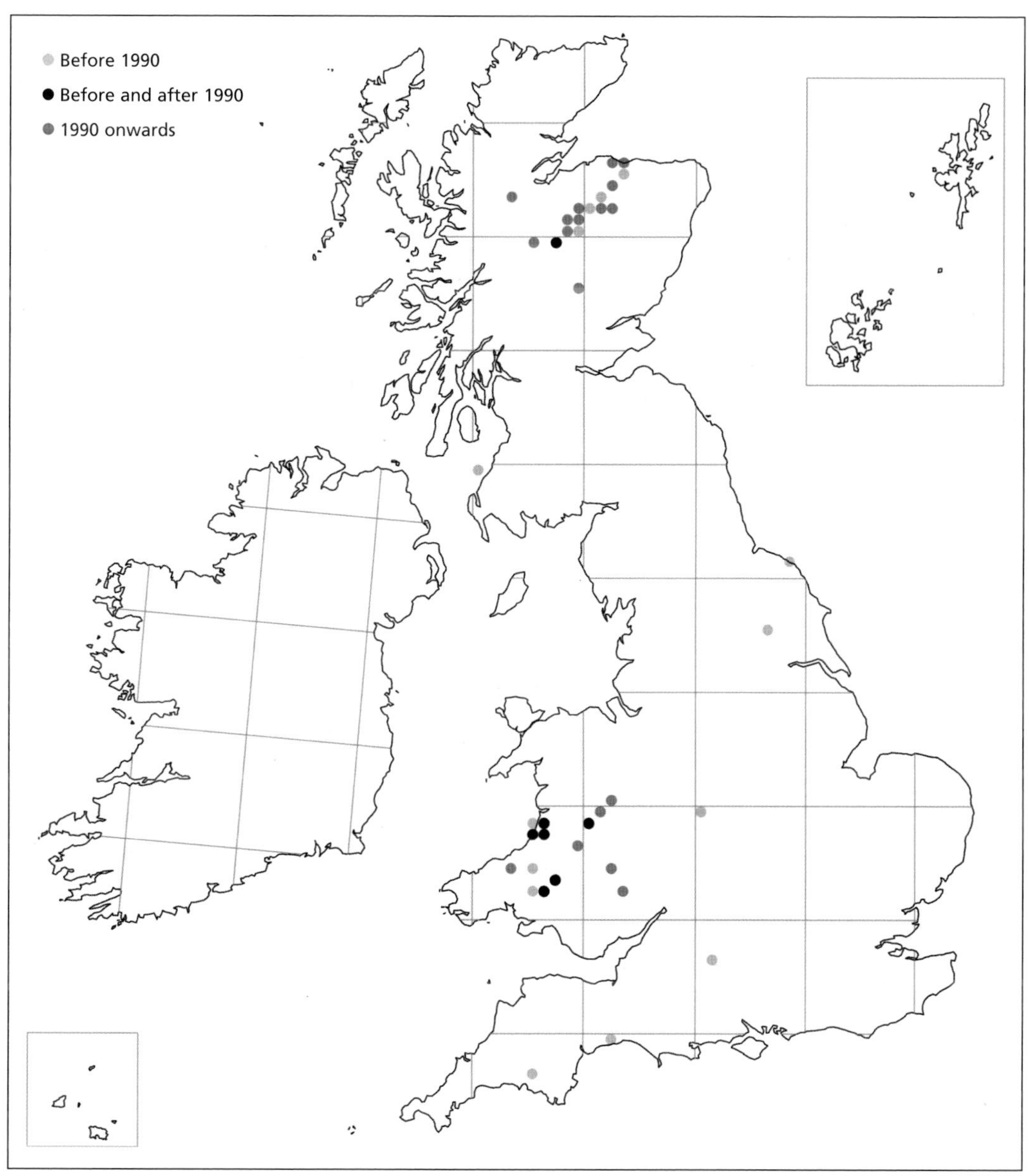

Map 22. Distribution (10km) of 5-spot ladybird.

The 5-spot ladybird is a rare (Red List) species in Britain and does not occur in Ireland. It is rarely found more than a few metres from its preferred habitat of unstable river shingle, yet it is common in many habitats elsewhere in Europe (Majerus, 1994). The reasons for its high degree of habitat specialisation in Britain (at the edge of its range) are not fully understood. The 5-spot feeds on aphids on low-growing vegetation, such as gorse, nettle and thistles, along shingled river banks. As the distribution map shows, there are relatively few records of this species overall, but particular hotspots are the Afon Ystwyth, Afon Rheidol and River Severn in Wales, and the River Spey in Scotland. Continued monitoring of the distribution and abundance of 5-spot ladybirds is essential if we are to fully understand the status of this rare species in Britain.

Figure 109. 5-spot ladybird adult. Photo: Remy Poland.

Figure 110. 5-spot ladybird adult. Photo: Peter Brown.

Figure 111. 5-spot ladybird late-instar larva. Photo: Gilles San Martin.

Figure 112. 5-spot ladybird adult consuming aphid on disturbed river bank. Photo: Helen Roy.

Identification

Length: 4-5mm. *Background colour*: red. *Pattern colour*: black spots. *Number of spots*: 5-9 (5). *Spot fusions*: very rare. *Melanic (black) forms*: no. *Pronotum*: black with anterior-lateral white marks. *Leg colour*: black. *Other features*: quite rounded and domed in shape

Fourth-instar larva: dark grey, with black tubercles producing fine hairs; bright orange lateral patches on first thoracic segment; middle and outer tubercles on abdominal segments one and four bright orange; middle tubercle on segments six and seven also orange. *Pupa*: unknown.

Ecology

Habitats: 5-spot ladybirds in Britain are found only on unstable river shingle. In continental Europe they occur in more varied habitats.

Host plants: 5-spot ladybirds can be observed scurrying between low-lying herbaceous plants in amongst river shingle. Specifically, they have been reported on nettle, thistles, bitter-cress and angelica. There are a few records of this species on broom. 5-spot ladybirds can also be found in flood debris.

Food: aphids.

Overwintering sites: 5-spot ladybirds overwinter on gorse, under shingle stones and in leaf litter.

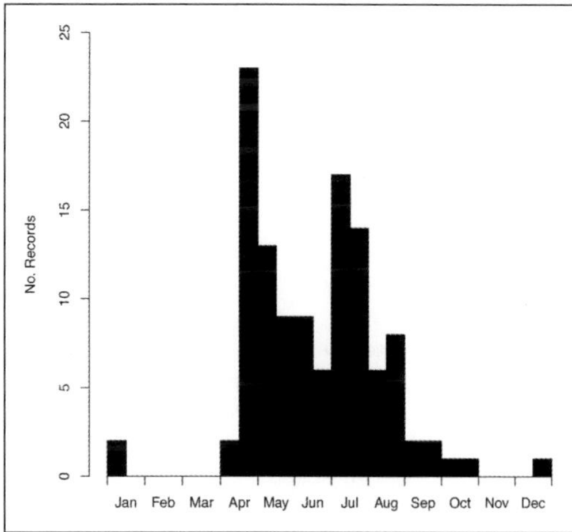

Figure 113. 5-spot ladybird phenogram.

UK conservation designation Rare

UK distribution status Very local

UK distribution trend (1990-2010) Stable

Coccinella septempunctata Linnaeus, 1758 (7-spot ladybird)

Synonyms None

Number of records 27166
Number of 10km squares 1786

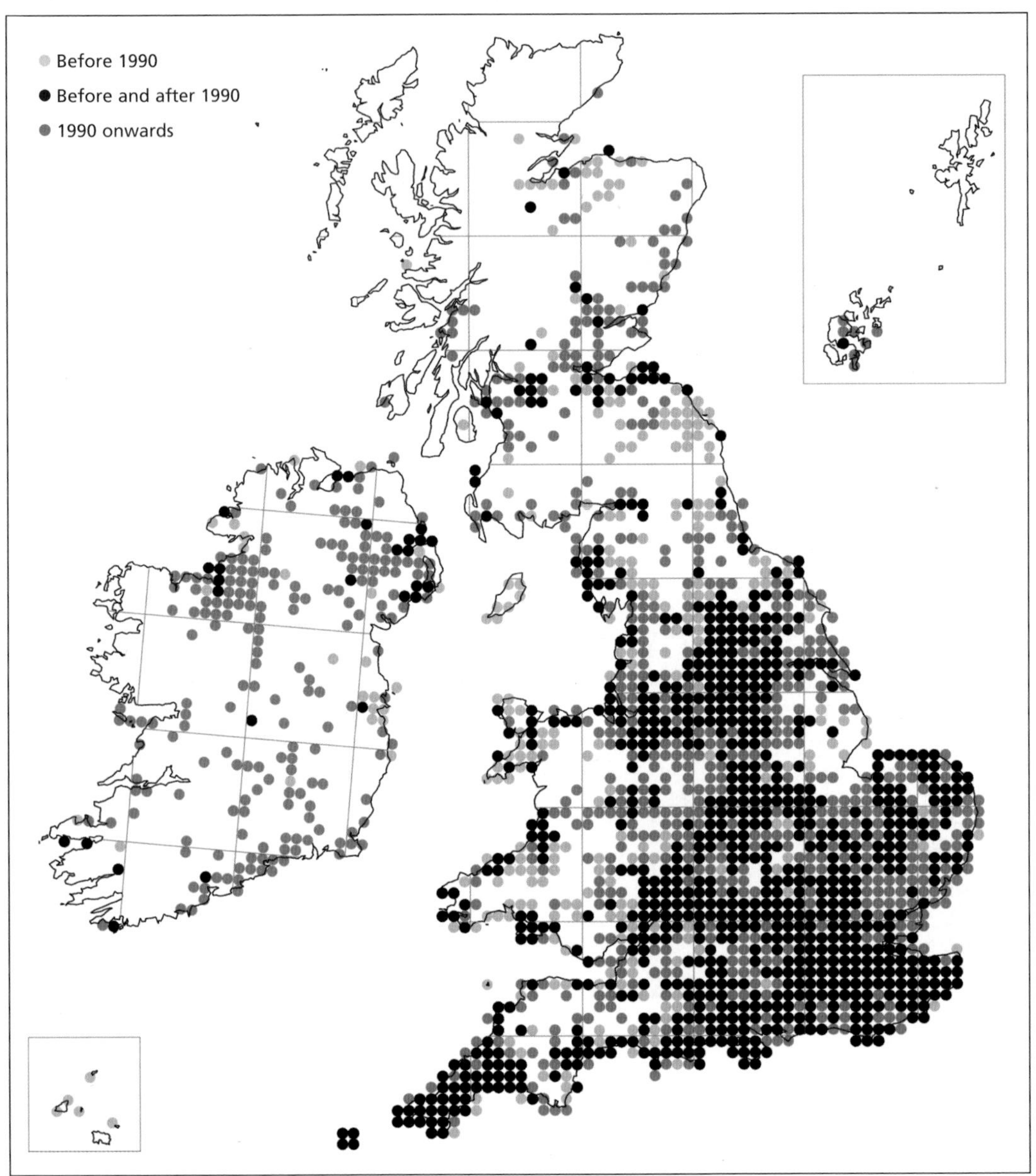

Map 23. Distribution (10km) of 7-spot ladybird.

The 7-spot ladybird is an iconic species. It is thought that the word 'ladybird' originates from the red colour of this species symbolising the red cloak of the Virgin Mary ('Our Lady'), with its seven black spots representing Mary's seven joys and seven sorrows (Majerus, 1994). The 7-spot is a common inhabitant of most gardens, where it enjoys a broad diet of aphids on herbaceous vegetation. It is also particularly common in nettle patches, and along roadside verges. It can easily be spotted by eye, but is also found in large numbers by sweeping grassy habitats. In the autumn, 7-spot ladybirds form tight overwintering clusters, often close to the ground and in protected spots such as within gorse bushes, or amongst the needles of pine trees. New generation adults must feed up and undergo an overwintering diapause before being able to reproduce, although observations of mating 7-spots are not uncommon in late summer.

Figure 114. 7-spot ladybird adult.
Photo: Michael Kilner.

Figure 115. 7-spot ladybird adults mating.
Photo: Anne Riley.

Figure 116. 7-spot ladybird late-instar larva.
Photo: Robert Frost.

Figure 117. 7-spot ladybird pupa.
Photo: Gilles San Martin.

Identification

Length: 5-8mm. *Background colour*: red. *Pattern colour*: black spots. *Number of spots*: 0-9 (7). *Spot fusions*: very rare. *Melanic (black) forms*: very rare. *Pronotum*: black with anterior-lateral white marks. *Leg colour*: black. *Other features*: can be distinguished from the scarce 7-spot by presence of small white triangular marks on the underside, below only the middle pair of legs (the scarce 7-spot has an additional pair of white marks under the hind legs).

Fourth-instar larva: dark grey/black with bluish tinge; with black tubercles producing fine hairs; dark orange lateral patches on first thoracic segment; sides of second and third thoracic segments dark grey/black; middle and outer tubercles on abdominal segments one and four dark orange. *Pupa*: often pale orange with two rows of dark triangular markings running down the middle; four small dark spots on anterior section. However, (as with other ladybirds) the amount of melanin (black pigment) decreases with developmental temperature, so some 7-spot pupae are darker than others.

Ecology

Habitats: 7-spot ladybirds are found in many habitats (including dunes, grassland, heathland, scrub, coniferous, deciduous and mixed woodland) but usually on low herbage. This species is very common in agro-ecosystems and can be found on both cereals and broad-leaved crops such as field beans.

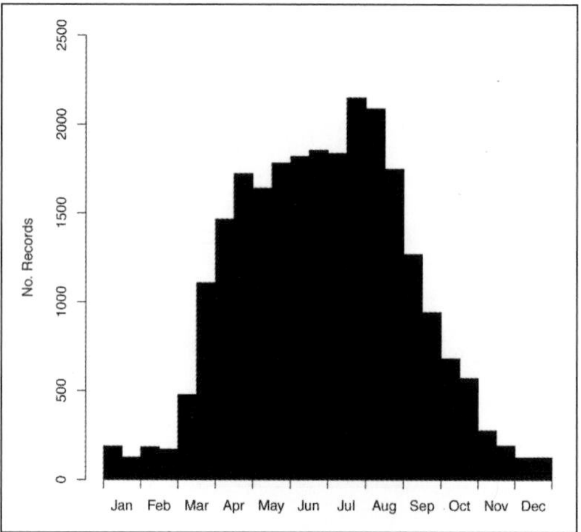

Figure 118. 7-spot ladybird phenogram.

Host plants: 7-spot ladybirds are found associated with an extensive range of host plants, which reflects the variety of aphids that they consume. The species is often found on low herbage including nettle (very commonly associated with this plant in spring), rosebay willowherb, thistles, cow parsley, wild carrot, yarrow, ragwort, heathers, angelica, hogweed, fat-hen, reeds, dead-nettle and mugwort. 7-spot ladybirds are found on numerous garden plants including roses, lavender, buddleja, wallflowers, peonies and camellias. It is a species commonly associated with crop plants and vegetables, particularly field beans. 7-spot ladybirds are often found in hawthorn hedgerows and occasionally on trees (including oak, limes, sycamore, Douglas fir and Scots pine) and can often be seen on ivy growing around the trunks.

Food: aphids.

Overwintering sites: 7-spot ladybirds overwinter in a variety of places including low herbage, gorse, conifer foliage and in leaf litter, often in curled dead leaves. In the autumn it is very common to see this species sheltering in senescing seed heads, such as those forming on rosebay willowherb, teasel and cow parsley.

UK distribution status Ubiquitous

UK distribution trend (1990-2010) Stable

Coccinella undecimpunctata Linnaeus, 1758 (11-spot ladybird)

Synonyms None

Number of records 2664
Number of 10km squares 854

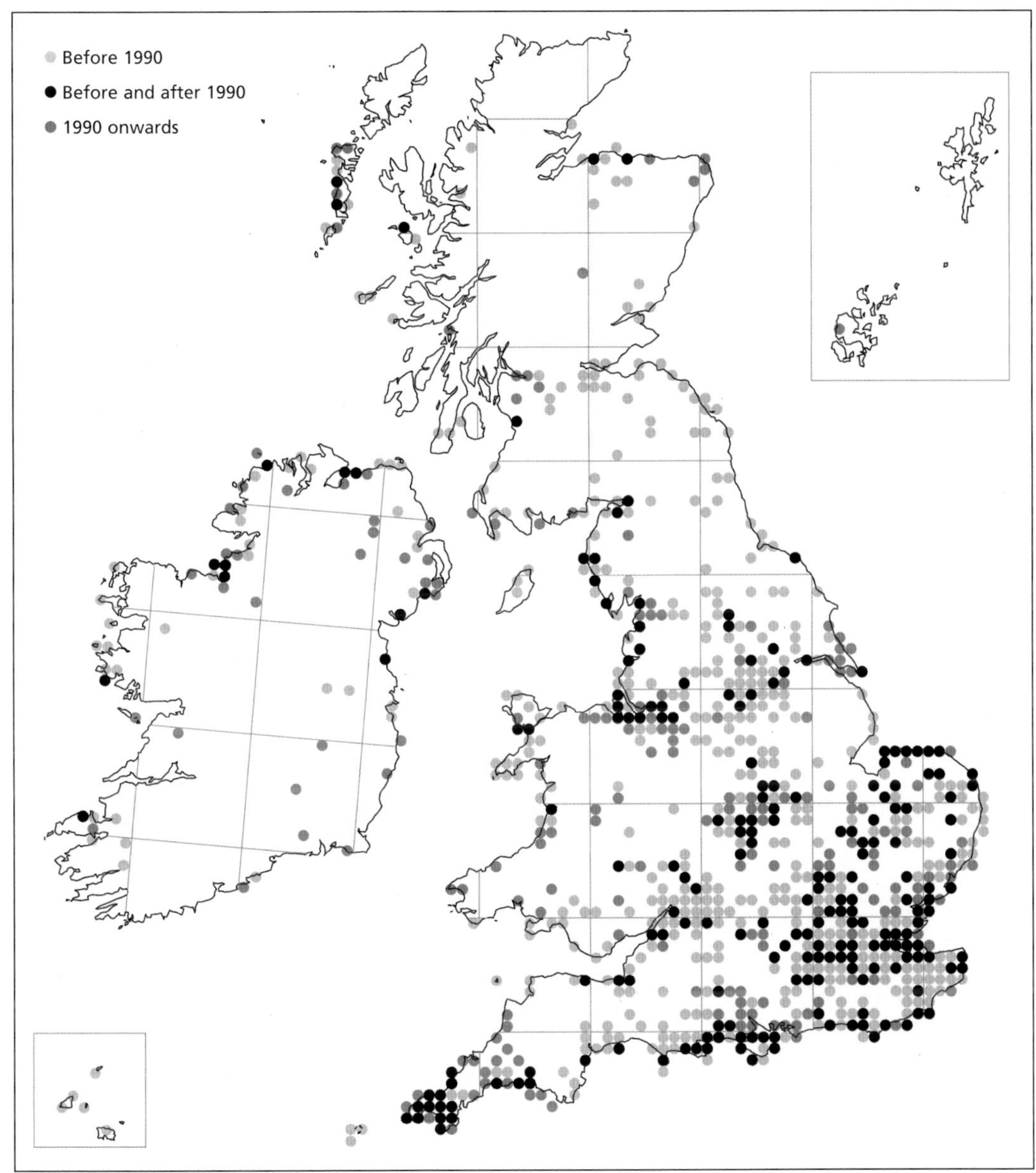

Map 24. Distribution (10km) of 11-spot ladybird.

In the autumn and winter months, 11-spot ladybirds may become most obvious because the species enters homes and buildings to overwinter, sometimes amongst groups of 2-spot and harlequin ladybirds. This species has some similarities with the congeneric 7-spot ladybird, such as the orange-red colour of the elytra in young adults, which tends to deepen as the ladybirds age. However, it is a smaller species with a narrower body shape, and some specimens bear diffuse yellow rings around their eleven black spots (in a similar way to the eyed ladybird). The 11-spot is most often found in herbaceous vegetation, particularly in coastal habitats, or in inland regions with sandy soils. The distribution of the 11-spot is notably coastal in northern and western parts of Britain and Ireland, with more inland records occurring in southern and central England. In the 'great ladybird year of 1976' 7-spot and 11-spot ladybirds were found in very high abundance, but, since then, 11-spot ladybird populations are thought to have plummeted (Majerus, 1994). The UK Ladybird Survey has received low numbers of records for this species in recent years.

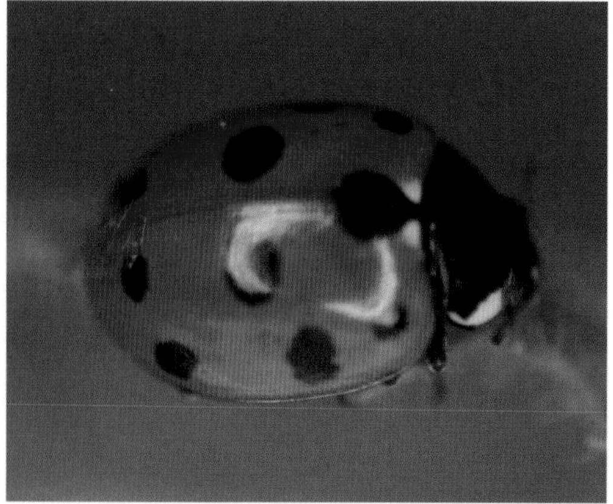

Figure 119. 11-spot ladybird adult.
Photo: Michael Majerus.

Figure 120. 11-spot ladybird adult.
Photo: Michael Majerus.

Figure 121. 11-spot ladybird all life stages: eggs, first, second, third and fourth instar larvae, pupa, adult.
Photo: António Soares.

Identification

Length: 4-5mm. *Background colour*: red. *Pattern colour*: black spots. *Number of spots*: 7-11 (11). *Spot fusions*: uncommon. *Melanic (black) forms*: no. *Pronotum*: black with anterior-lateral white marks; broadest at base. *Leg colour*: black. *Other features*: black spots occasionally surrounded by a thin yellow ring.

Fourth-instar larva: closely resembles 7-spot ladybird, but smaller and without the conspicuous orange lateral patches on first thoracic segment; abdomen has orange spots in pairs on a grey-black background. *Pupa*: black front section but otherwise cream with inner tubercles on abdominal segments forming two dark bands running longitudinally; orange lateral patches on first abdominal segment; inner and outer tubercles on fourth abdominal segment also orange.

Ecology

Habitats: the 11-spot ladybird is an elusive species that occupies a variety of habitats but particularly dune systems. The coastal nature of this species is further highlighted by the number of strandline records.

Host plants: 11-spot ladybirds are commonly associated with sea radish, nettle, gorse, rosebay willowherb and thistles. There are a scattering of records from deciduous trees including ash, beech, sycamore and oak.

Food: aphids.

Overwintering sites: 11-spot ladybirds overwinter in leaf litter and buildings.

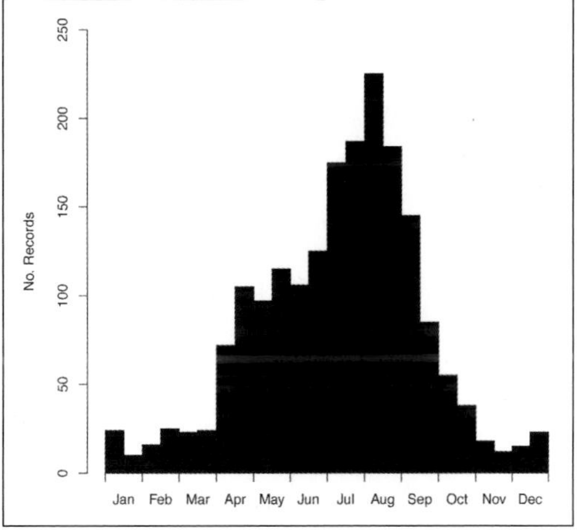

Figure 122. 11-spot ladybird phenogram.

UK distribution status Very widespread

UK distribution trend (1990-2010) Decreasing

Adalia bipunctata (Linnaeus, 1758) (2-spot ladybird)

Synonyms None

Number of records 16535
Number of 10km squares 1192

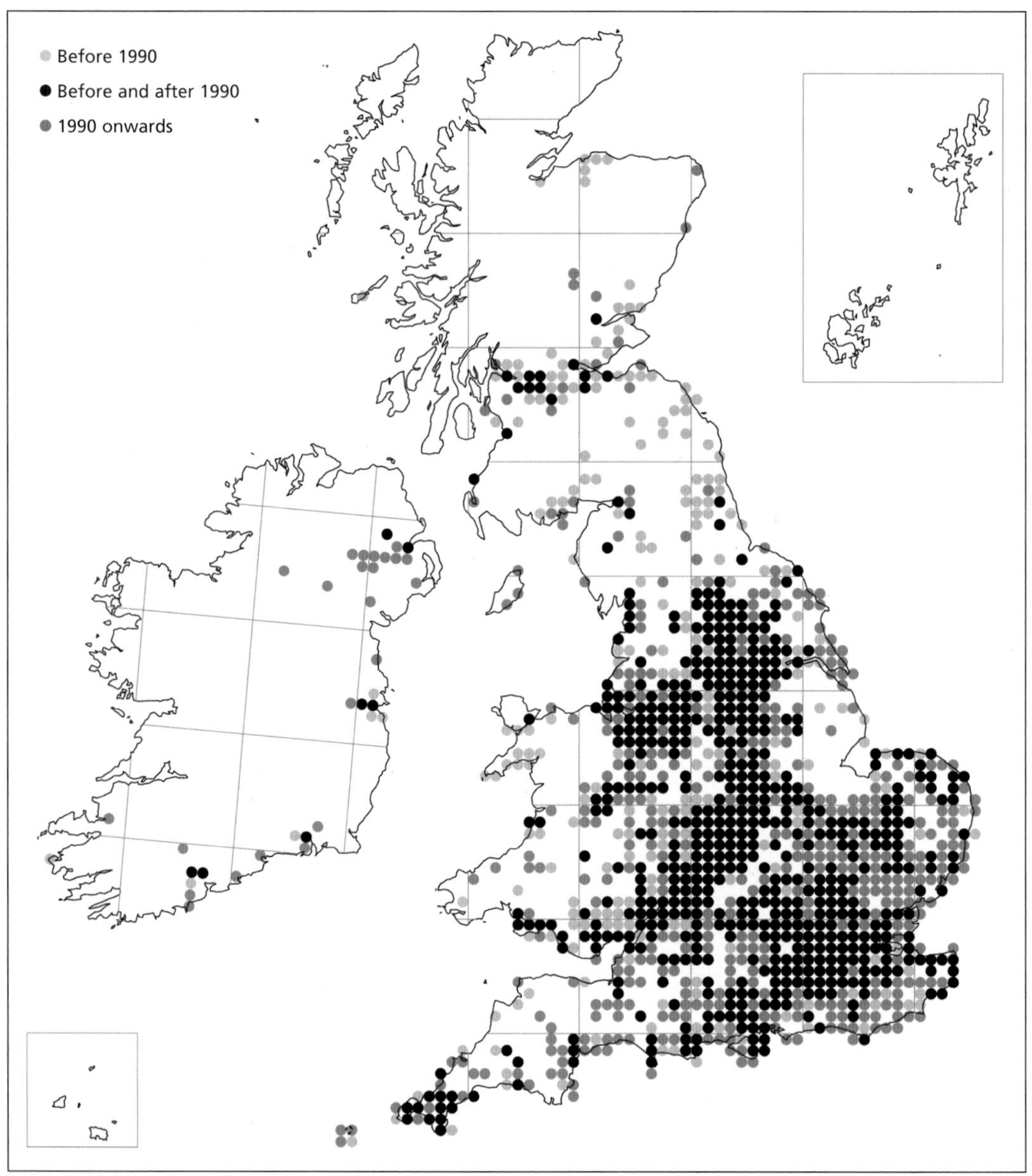

Map 25. Distribution (10km) of 2-spot ladybird.

The 2-spot ladybird is notable for its variety of colour patterns (polymorphism). Although the typical form (red background colour with a single black spot on each elytron) is by far the most common, there are many permutations, some with a black background colour to the elytra (Majerus & Kearns, 1989). The inheritance of these colour patterns has fascinated geneticists for

Figure 123. 2-spot ladybird adult (f. *typica*).
Photo: Richard Comont.

Figure 124. 2-spot ladybird adult (f. *quadrimaculata*).
Photo: Michael Majerus.

Figure 125. 2-spot ladybird adult (f. *sexpustulata*).
Photo: Steven Pascoe.

Figure 126. 2-spot ladybird late-instar larva.
Photo: Gilles San Martin.

Figure 127. 2-spot ladybird pupa.
Photo: Remy Poland.

decades, and the evolutionary conundrum of why an insect displaying warning colours is polymorphic remains unanswered. The 2-spot ladybird is often referred to as the 'gardener's friend', due to its predilection for aphids infesting roses and other garden plants. It is also found in large numbers on nettle, thistles and cow parsley, and on deciduous trees in urban environments. In autumn, 2-spot ladybirds frequently enter homes and buildings to overwinter, sometimes forming aggregations of several hundred individuals. The 2-spot ladybird was historically restricted to southern counties in Ireland (although the species was reported from Belfast in the 1980s) but is widespread and common in Britain. Sadly, recent evidence from Britain (Brown *et al.*, 2011), Belgium and Switzerland suggests a decline in 2-spot populations following the arrival of the harlequin ladybird. This can be attributed to the overlap of its habitat with that of the harlequin, and the fact that harlequin ladybirds will both compete with 2-spots and consume their eggs and larvae (Ware & Majerus, 2008).

Identification

Length: 4-5mm. *Background colour*: (1) 'typical' form (*typica*) and (2) 'spotty' form: red or orange; (3) 'four-spot melanic' (*quadrimaculata*) and (4) 'six-spot melanic' (*sexpustulata*): black. *Pattern colour*: (1) with two black spots; (2) with up to 16 black spots; (3) with four red spots; (4) with six red spots. *Number of spots*: 0-16 (2). *Spot fusions*: sometimes. *Melanic (black) forms*: many and common. *Pronotum*: white with black spots, a black M-mark or mainly black. *Leg colour*: black (a good feature for distinguishing from 10-spot ladybird, which has brown legs). *Other features*: very variable in colour pattern.

Fourth-instar larva: closely resembles larva of 10-spot ladybird; 2-spot larva is dark grey (10-spot larva is pale grey) with a triangle of orange spots across the first and fourth abdominal segments; outer tubercles on abdominal segments five to eight are dark (pale in 10-spot); fine hairs projecting from tubercles. *Pupa*: closely resembles pupa of 10-spot ladybird; 2-spot pupa has a black front section but otherwise cream with six rows of dark spots running longitudinally (10-spot pupa similar but with a paler overall appearance, two orange spots on edges of first abdominal segment and an orange patch in the middle of segments four to six).

Ecology

Habitats: 2-spot ladybirds are noted for occupying very varied habitats in Britain whereas in Ireland this species is mainly restricted to wetlands and urban gardens. In Britain many 2-spot records are also from urban areas where deciduous trees are abundant. This species can be readily found on mature lime or sycamore trees, for example in parks or churchyards. However, in Britain 2-spot ladybirds also occupy mature woodlands (both deciduous and coniferous), scrub and grasslands. Orchards and crops, including cereals but particularly broad-leaved crops such as field beans, are common habitats for 2-spot ladybirds. There are a number of records of this species from wetlands and coastal habitats, particularly dune systems. 2-spot ladybirds overlap with a number of other species of ladybird and are commonly found with 7-spot, 10-spot, 14-spot, pine and harlequin ladybirds.

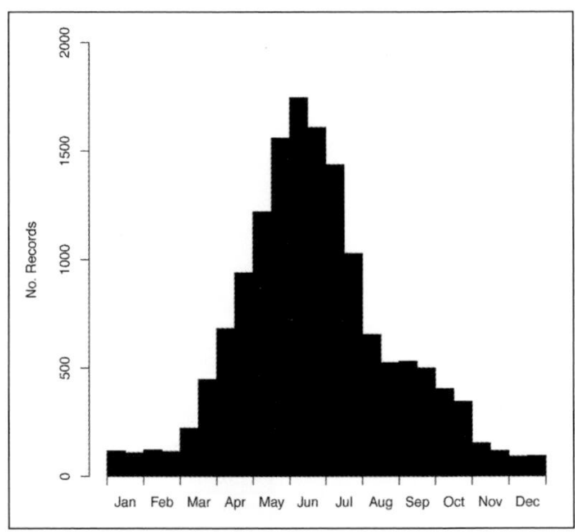

Figure 128. 2-spot ladybird phenogram.

Host plants: in Britain most 2-spot ladybird records are associated with deciduous trees, such as lime and sycamore, particularly in urban localities. However, there are many observations of 2-spot ladybirds on herbaceous plants such as nettle, thistles, rosebay willowherb and fat-hen. Beans are a popular host plant for 2-spot ladybirds in gardens, where they can also be found on ornamental plants such as roses, buddleja, lavender and hebe. In Ireland 2-spot ladybirds have primarily been recorded breeding on willows and birch.

Food: aphids.

Overwintering sites: 2-spot ladybirds overwinter in locations at slightly elevated positions, such as in the attics and upstairs window-frames of houses, or on tree trunks and under bark.

UK distribution status Ubiquitous

UK distribution trend (1990-2010) Stable but decreasing following the arrival of the harlequin ladybird

Adalia decempunctata (Linnaeus, 1758) (10-spot ladybird)

Synonyms *Adalia bothnica* sensu Fowler, 1889 non (Paykull, 1799)
Adalia biabilis Marriner, 1926

Number of records 7191
Number of 10km squares 1272

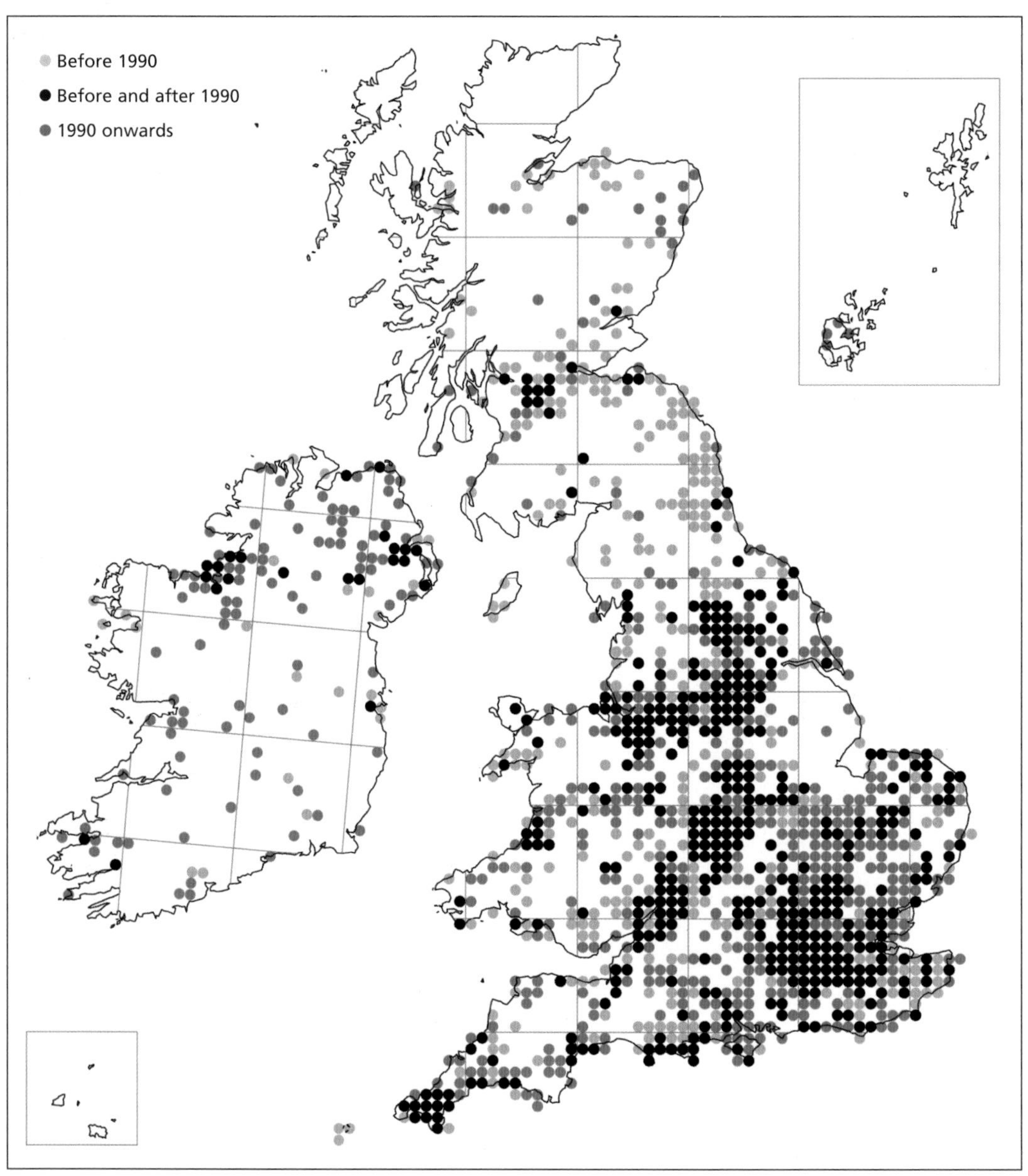

Map 26. Distribution (10km) of 10-spot ladybird.

The 10-spot ladybird is the most variable of the British and Irish ladybirds in terms of colour pattern (Majerus, 1994). In addition, the hues of the colour patterns vary greatly with age, generally getting darker as the ladybird gets older (a trait also observed in other ladybird species). This ladybird is commonly found on the foliage of broad-leaved deciduous trees and shrubs, especially oak, lime, sycamore, hawthorn and birch, but can occasionally be found on conifers. The species is considered to be an aphid specialist (Sloggett & Majerus, 2000) and is known to produce a second generation in a year, if sufficient aphids are available (Hawkins, 2000). The

Figure 129. 10-spot ladybird adult (f. *decempunctata*).
Photo: Michael Majerus.

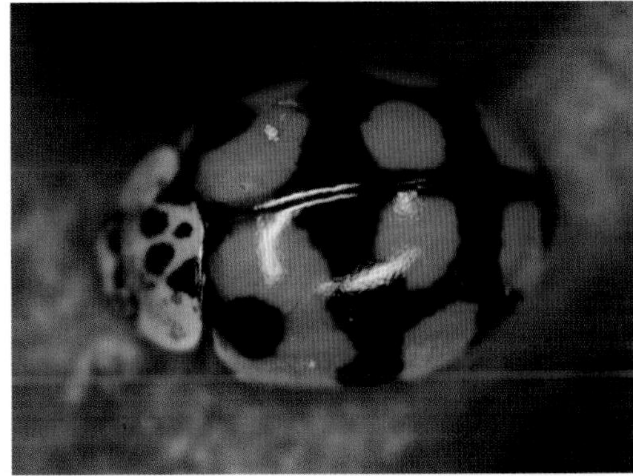

Figure 130. 10-spot ladybird adult (f. *decempustulatus*).
Photo: Michael Majerus.

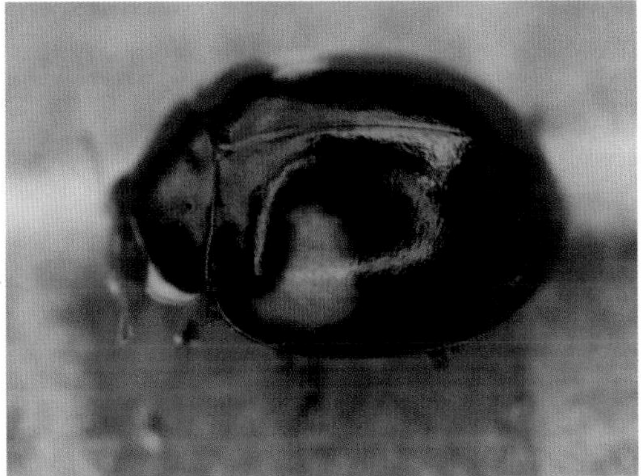

Figure 131. 10-spot ladybird adult (f. *bimaculata*).
Photo: Michael Majerus.

Figure 132. 10-spot ladybird late-instar larva.
Photo: Remy Poland.

Figure 133. 10-spot ladybird pupa.
Photo: Remy Poland.

10-spot ladybird is frequently found with harlequin ladybirds on deciduous trees, so it is another species which is likely to come under threat from competition and predation by the harlequin.

Identification

Length: 3.5-4.5mm. *Background colour*: (1) 'typical' form (*decempunctata*): yellow, orange or red; (2) 'chequered' form (*decempustulatus*): buff, beige, light brown; (3) 'melanic' form (*bimaculata*): purple, dark brown or black. *Pattern colour*: (1) with 0-15 maroon, dark brown or black spots; (2) with grid-like markings giving a chequered pattern; (3) with two yellow, orange or red shoulder flashes. *Number of spots*: 0-15 (10). *Spot fusions*: common. *Melanic (black) forms*: various and common. *Pronotum*: white with 5 dark spots, which may be fused, or dark trapezium mark. *Leg colour*: brown (a good feature for distinguishing from 2-spot ladybird, which has black legs). *Other features*: extremely variable in colour and pattern.

Fourth-instar larva: closely resembles larva of 2-spot ladybird; 10-spot larva is pale grey (2-spot larva is dark grey), with a triangle of yellow spots across the first and fourth abdominal segments; outer tubercles on abdominal segments five to eight are pale (dark in 2-spot); fine hairs projecting from tubercles. *Pupa*: closely resembles pupa of 2-spot ladybird; 10-spot pupa has a black front section but otherwise cream with six rows of dark spots running longitudinally; two orange spots on edges of first abdominal segment and an orange patch in the middle of abdominal segments four to six (2-spot pupa similar but with a darker overall appearance and lacking the orange markings).

Ecology

Habitats: 10-spot ladybirds are more habitat specific than 2-spot ladybirds but still occupy a variety of habitats. Generally, 10-spot ladybirds are found on deciduous trees and hedgerows. Many 10-spot records are from urban areas where deciduous trees are abundant. Like 2-spot ladybirds, this species can be readily found on mature lime or sycamore trees, for example in parks or churchyards. A number of 10-spot ladybird records are from deciduous and conifer woodlands, scrub and grasslands. There are some records of this species from wetlands and coastal habitats, particularly dune systems. 10-spot ladybirds overlap with a number of other species of ladybird and are commonly found with 2-spot, 7-spot, 14-spot, pine and harlequin ladybirds.

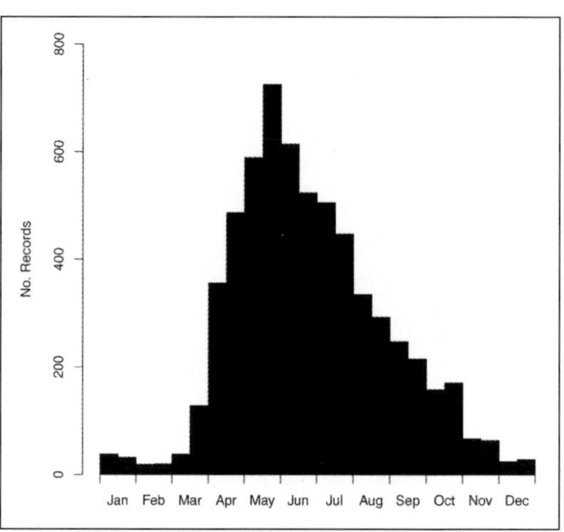

Figure 134. 10-spot ladybird phenogram.

Host plants: most 10-spot ladybird records are associated with deciduous trees, such as oak, lime, willow, and sycamore. There are records of this species from conifers, including larch and Scots pine. Hawthorn and blackthorn are also common plants on which 10-spot ladybirds are found. However, there are also many observations of 10-spot ladybirds on herbaceous plants such as nettle, hogweed, thistles, rosebay willowherb and fat-hen. 10-spot ladybirds are associated with garden plants, such as roses and buddleja, fruit trees and shrubs, such as blackcurrant and cherry, but less commonly than 2-spots.

Food: aphids.

Overwintering sites: 10-spot ladybirds are found overwintering in leaf litter, plant debris and beech nuts.

UK distribution status Ubiquitous

UK distribution trend (1990-2010) Decreasing

Harmonia axyridis (Pallas, 1773) (Harlequin ladybird)

Synonyms None

Number of records 25676
Number of 10km squares 1099

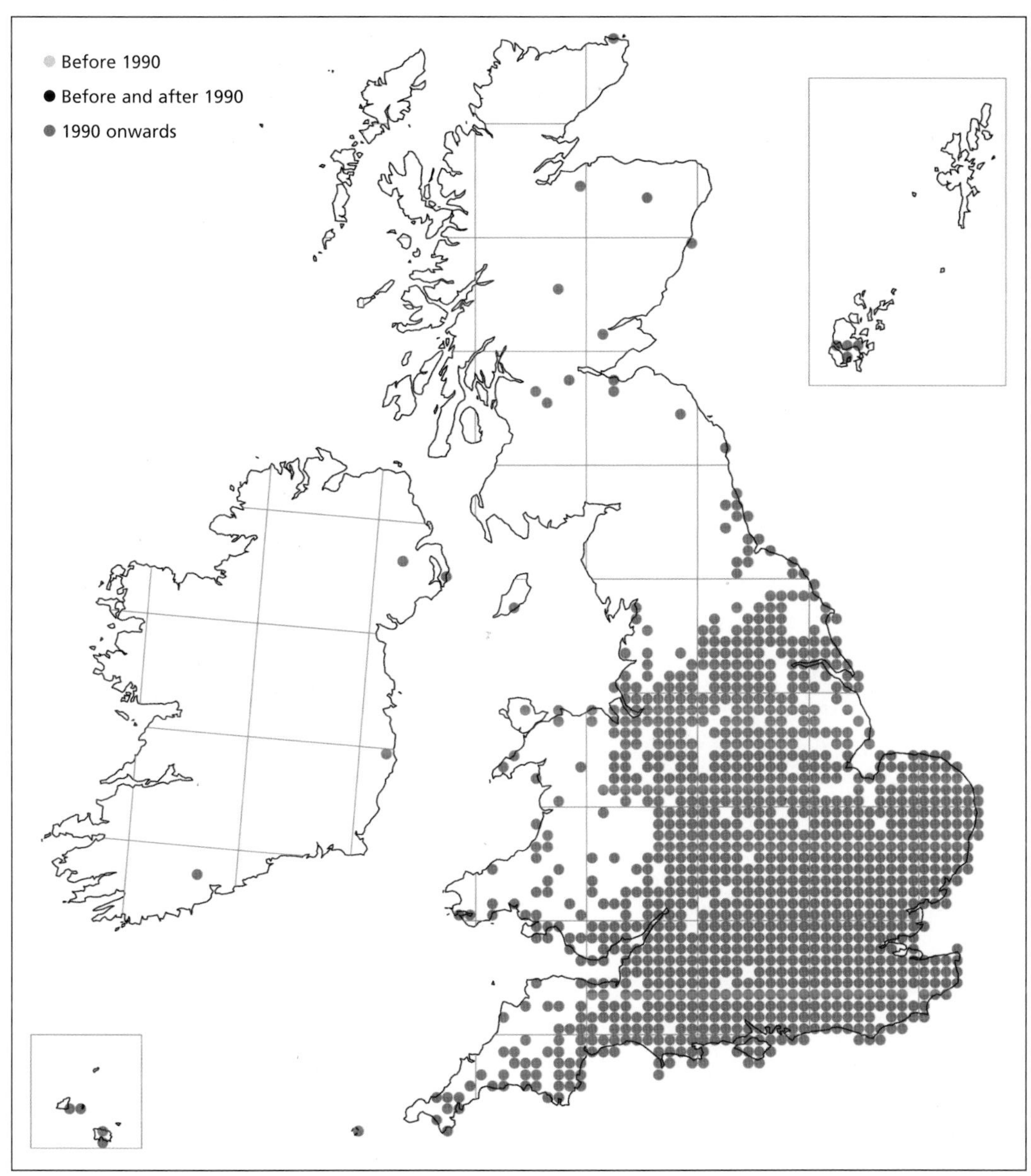

Map 27. Distribution (10km) of harlequin ladybird.

The harlequin ladybird has recently been described as the fastest-spreading invasive insect in Europe (Roy & Migeon, 2010). The name 'harlequin' stems from the nominate *axyridis* colour form of the species (a form not so far recorded in Britain and Ireland) which resembles a

Figure 135. Harlequin ladybird adult (f. *spectabilis*). Photo: Ken Dolbear.

Figure 136. Harlequin ladybird adults (f. *succinea*) mating. Photo: Michael Majerus.

Figure 137. Harlequin ladybird adult (f. *conspicua*). Photo: Ken Dolbear.

Figure 138. Harlequin ladybird adults overwintering. Photo: Nick Greatorex-Davies.

Figure 139. Harlequin ladybird late-instar larva. Photo: Michael Majerus.

Figure 140. Harlequin ladybird pupa. Photo: Richard Comont.

characteristic harlequin chequered pattern. The species is native to central and eastern Asia and is sometimes also known as the 'multicoloured Asian ladybird'. The harlequin arrived in England in 2003, after intentional introductions into North America and continental Europe for the biological control of aphids and coccids. The first records in Britain came from south-east England, but it has since spread at a remarkable rate (Brown *et al.*, 2008b) and is now found as far north as Orkney and as far west as the Pembrokeshire coast and western Cornwall. Recently it has also been recorded in Ireland (Murchie *et al.*, 2008), the Isles of Scilly and the Isle of Man, but there is no evidence of establishment there yet. The harlequin ladybird has a wide dietary and habitat range, and threatens many native ladybirds and other insects through competition for aphids and predation of their eggs and larvae. It is also increasingly becoming a human nuisance, due to its habit of sucking the juice of ripe fruits in late summer and its preference to overwinter inside buildings in very large numbers (sometimes over 1000 individuals). Since the arrival of the harlequin in Britain, the Harlequin Ladybird Survey has received over 38 000 on-line records (not all verified), submitted by members of the public, and this dataset has been invaluable in monitoring the spread and impact of this important invasive alien species.

Identification

Length: 5-8mm. *Background colour*: (1) '*succinea*': yellow/orange/red; (2) '*spectabilis*' and (3) '*conspicua*': black. *Pattern colour*: (1) with 0-21 black spots; (2) with four red/orange spots/patches; (3) with two red/orange spots/patches. *Number of spots*: 0-21 (16). *Spot fusions*: common in '*succinea*' form. *Melanic (black) forms*: common ('*spectabilis*' and '*conspicua*'). *Pronotum*: white or cream with up to 5 spots, or fused lateral spots forming 2 curved lines, M-shaped mark or solid trapezoid. *Leg colour*: brown. *Other features*: many specimens have a slight keel along the posterior margin of the dorsal surface; extremely variable in colour and pattern.

Fourth-instar larva: black, with thick dorsal spines coming from each tubercle, each branching at the top into two to four prongs; bright orange upside-down L-shaped marking on each side, made from middle tubercles of abdominal segments one to five and inner tubercles of abdominal segment one; two pairs of orange dots on dorsal surface, made from inner tubercles of abdominal segments four and five. *Pupa*: orange, with pairs of black squarish markings running down the second thoracic segment and abdominal segments two to six; black and white remains of shed spiky larval skin visible at base of pupa.

Ecology

Habitats: harlequin ladybirds are noted for being habitat generalists. Like the 2-spot ladybird, the species is considered to be arboreal, and many records are from urban areas where deciduous trees are abundant. This species can be readily found on mature lime or sycamore trees, for example in churchyards and parks. However, harlequin ladybirds also occupy mature woodlands (both deciduous and coniferous), scrub, grassland, marshland and reed beds. Crops and orchards are common habitats for harlequin ladybirds. Harlequin ladybirds overlap with a number of other species of ladybird including 2-spot, 7-spot, 10-spot, 14-spot and pine ladybirds.

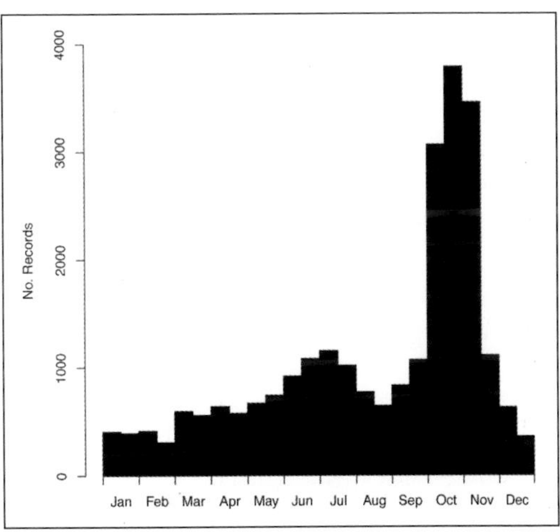

Figure 141. Harlequin ladybird phenogram.

Host plants: the host plant list for the harlequin is diverse and extensive; however, it undoubtedly has a preference for lime and sycamore trees. It is also commonly associated with herbaceous plants such as nettle, thistles, cow parsley, rosebay willowherb and fat-hen. Harlequin ladybirds are common in gardens where they can be found on many ornamental plants.

Food: primarily aphids, but also coccids, coccinellids and others.

Overwintering site: harlequin ladybirds are found in exceptionally large numbers in buildings during winter. Churches appear to be favoured, as well as domestic dwellings. Sheds, compost bins and, indeed, all sheltered locations in urban areas are suitable for overwintering harlequin ladybirds.

UK distribution status Ubiquitous

UK distribution trend (1990-2010) Increasing

Harmonia quadripunctata (Pontoppidan, 1763) (Cream-streaked ladybird)

Synonyms None

Number of records 1009
Number of 10km squares 269

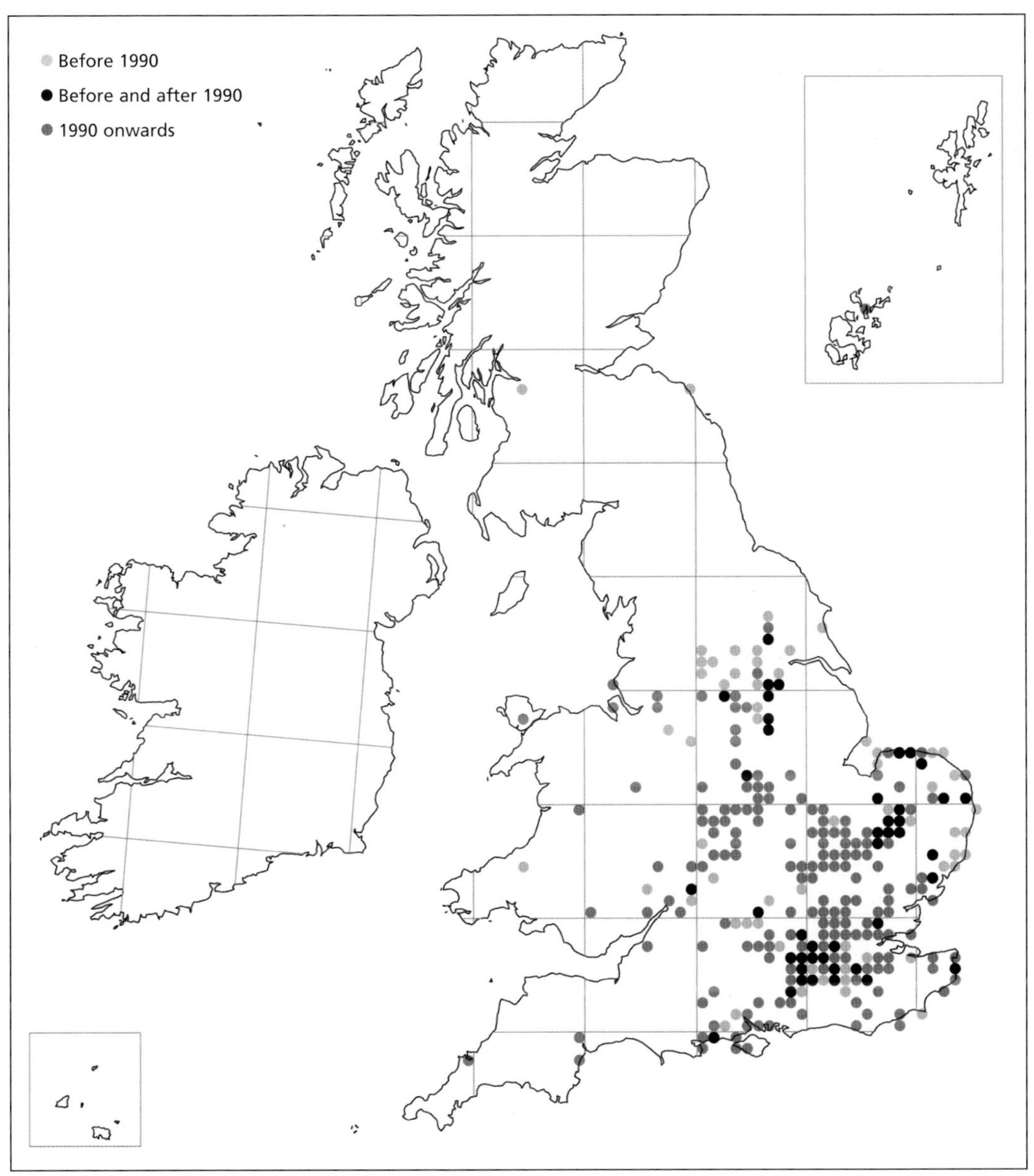

Map 28. Distribution (10km) of cream-streaked ladybird.

The cream-streaked ladybird is a relatively new species to Britain, first recorded in 1937 in West Suffolk (Morley, 1941; Hawkins, 2000). The pathway by which this species arrived in Britain is unknown, but is generally assumed to be natural spread from continental Europe, although human-mediated introduction is also plausible. The spread of the species westwards and northwards across England is clear but gradual; it took 50 years to reach as far west as Devon (Majerus & Kearns, 1989). It was first recorded in Scotland in 1982 (Berwickshire), with subsequent records from two other Scottish sites. The three sites are in very different regions, and it is doubtful whether the cream-streaked reproduces successfully in northern Britain. However, in Wales and England as far north as Yorkshire, the species has successfully found a niche on Scots pine, a range of exotic pine species and sometimes other needled conifers. It has not yet reached Ireland. The cream-streaked is a rather flat ladybird, with cream-streaked markings and two main forms, generally either having four (as reflected in its scientific name) or 16 spots, and only rarely any other number of spots. In East Anglia, the 16-spotted form tends to be more common (P. Brown, unpublished data), though both forms may occur on the same trees. As indicated by its genus, the cream-streaked is the closest relative of the harlequin ladybird in Britain.

Figure 142. Cream-streaked ladybird adult (16-spotted form). Photo: Michael Majerus.

Figure 143. Cream-streaked ladybird adult (4-spotted form). Photo: Michael Majerus.

Figure 144. Cream-streaked ladybird late-instar larva. Photo: Gilles San Martin.

Figure 145. Cream-streaked ladybird pupa. Photo: Gilles San Martin.

Identification

Length: 5-6mm. *Background colour*: pink, salmon, yellow. *Pattern colour*: black spots and cream streaking in two forms: (1) '16-spotted': 16 black spots in a 1-3-3-1 pattern on each elytron (most common) and (2) '4-spotted': 4 black spots on outer sides of elytra. *Number of spots*: 4-20 (16). *Spot fusions*: uncommon. *Melanic (black) forms*: rare. *Pronotum*: white with 5-9 black spots in a distinctive pattern. *Leg colour*: brown. *Other features*: often rests head-down on pine buds, where it is very well camouflaged.

Fourth-instar larva: black, with thick dorsal spines coming from each tubercle, each branching from base; bright orange line on each side, made from orange spots on the middle tubercles of abdominal segments one to four; one pair of orange dots on dorsal surface, made from inner tubercles of abdominal segment four. *Pupa*: light greyish brown, sometimes with a pink tinge, with six longitudinal rows of black spots; black lateral transverse markings on anterior end; remains of shed spiky larval skin visible at the base of pupa.

Ecology

Habitats: the cream-streaked ladybird is a conifer specialist but records have been received from heathlands, scrub, grassland and dune systems.

Host plants: this species is one of the most common large ladybirds found on conifers, usually Scots pine. There are records from exotic pines, Douglas fir and Norway spruce. Cream-streaked ladybirds are occasionally found on herbaceous plants and shrubs such as nettle and gorse, but these are usually situated close to conifers.

Food: aphids.

Overwintering sites: cream-streaked ladybirds overwinter on various conifers, usually needled-conifers but occasionally scale-leaved conifers such as Leyland cypress.

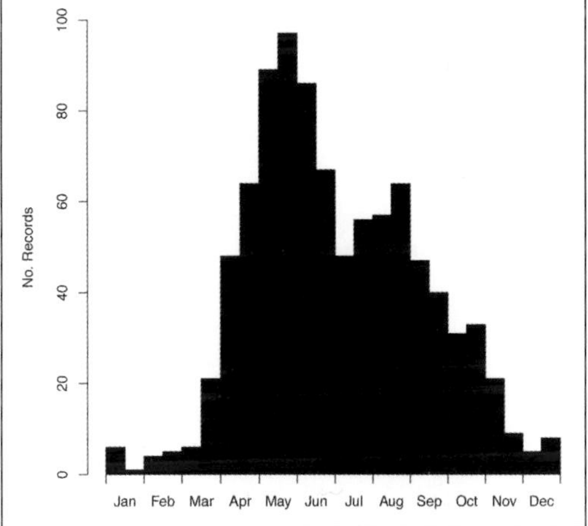

Figure 146. Cream-streaked ladybird phenogram.

UK distribution status Local

UK distribution trend (1990-2010) Stable

Subfamily Epilachninae Mulsant, 1846

Henosepilachna argus (Geoffroy in Fourcroy, 1762) (Bryony ladybird)

Synonyms *Epilachna argus*

Number of records 146
Number of 10km squares 14

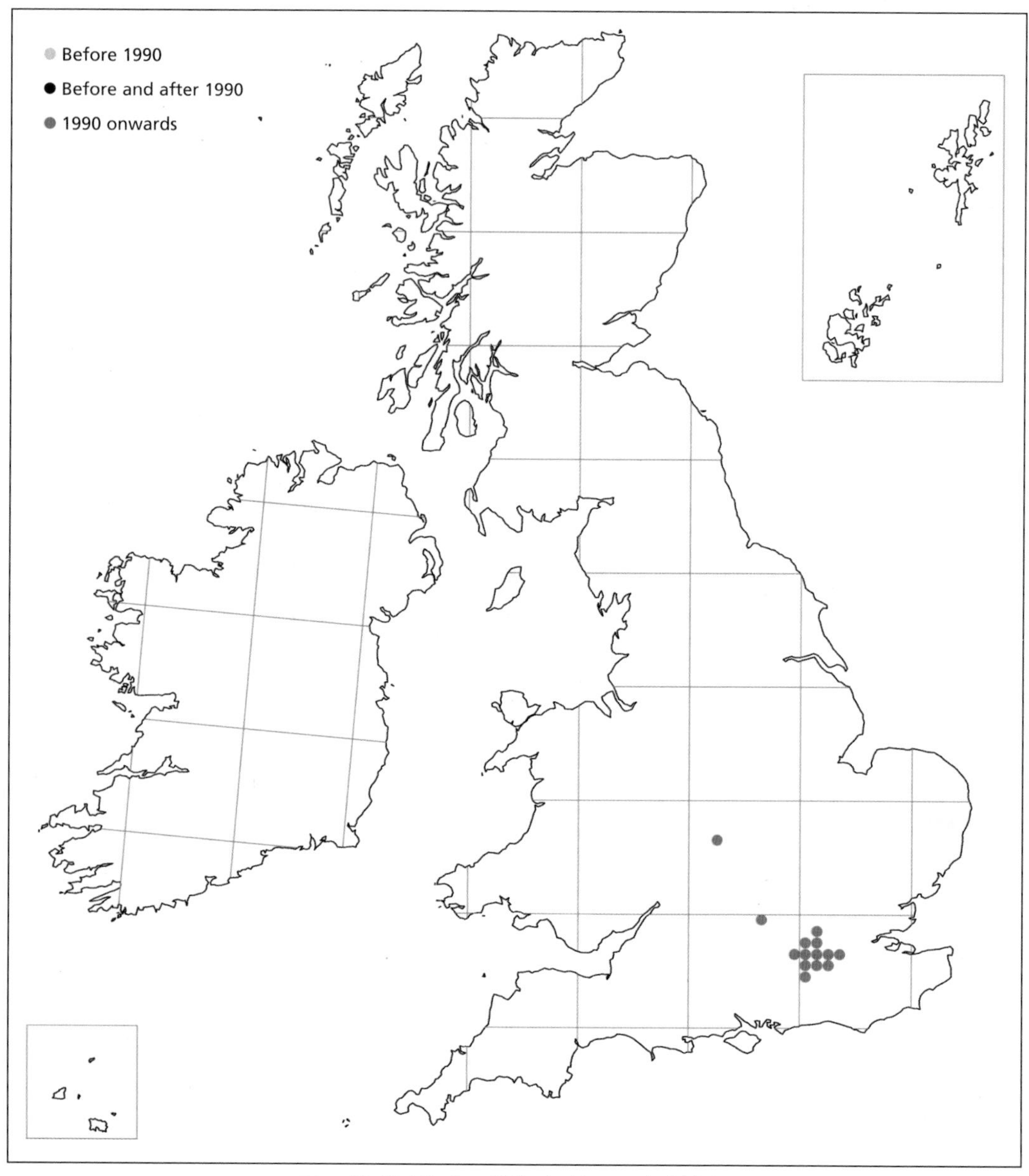

Map 29. Distribution (10km) of bryony ladybird.

The bryony ladybird is a large and distinctive species and a member of the epilachnine subfamily of ladybirds. It is a recent colonist of Britain, having established in south-west London in the 1990s (Menzies & Spooner, 2000), and has spread slowly since then. Most records of the species are from around the London area, but in 2010 it was reported in Oxfordshire for the first time. It is common around the Mediterranean, feeding on the leaves of plants of the cucurbit (cucumber) family, and white bryony in particular, giving rise to its common name. Adults and larvae strip away the leaf tissue with their scraping mandibles, leaving nothing but a framework of veins. A warmth-loving species, the northward spread of *H. argus* in Europe has been linked to recent changes in climate.

Figure 147. Bryony ladybird adult.
Photo: Richard Comont.

Figure 148. Bryony ladybird adults mating.
Photo: Michael Majerus.

Figure 149. Bryony ladybird late-instar larva.
Photo: Gilles San Martin.

Figure 150. Bryony ladybird pupa.
Photo: Richard Comont.

Identification

Length: 5-7mm. *Background colour*: orange. *Pattern colour*: black spots. *Number of spots*: 11. *Spot fusions*: rare. *Melanic (black) forms*: no. *Pronotum*: orange. *Leg colour*: orange. *Other features*: elytra covered in short downy hairs.

Fourth-instar larva: pale yellow with dark tubercles, bearing tall black branching spines. *Pupa*: pale yellow with small black spots; partially covered by shed larval skin at base.

Ecology

Habitats: in Britain the bryony ladybird is found in urban habitats, commonly gardens. However, in Surrey there are recent sightings from more natural habitats on chalk and sand.

Host plants: in Britain it feeds solely on white bryony but in other parts of Europe it has been noted feeding on melons.

Food: leaves of white bryony and other cucurbits.

Overwintering sites: bryony ladybirds overwinter in low herbage.

UK distribution status Very local

UK distribution trend (1990-2010) Stable

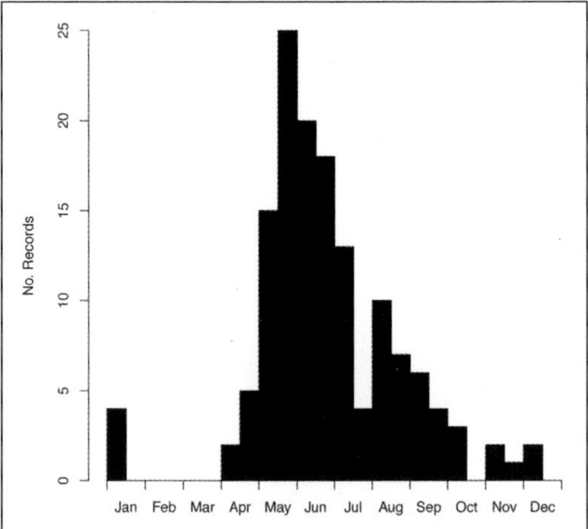

Figure 151. Bryony ladybird phenogram.

Subcoccinella vigintiquattuorpunctata (Linnaeus, 1758) (24-spot ladybird)

Synonyms *Subcoccinella vigintiquatuorpunctata* auctt. (misspelling)

Number of records 3098
Number of 10km squares 578

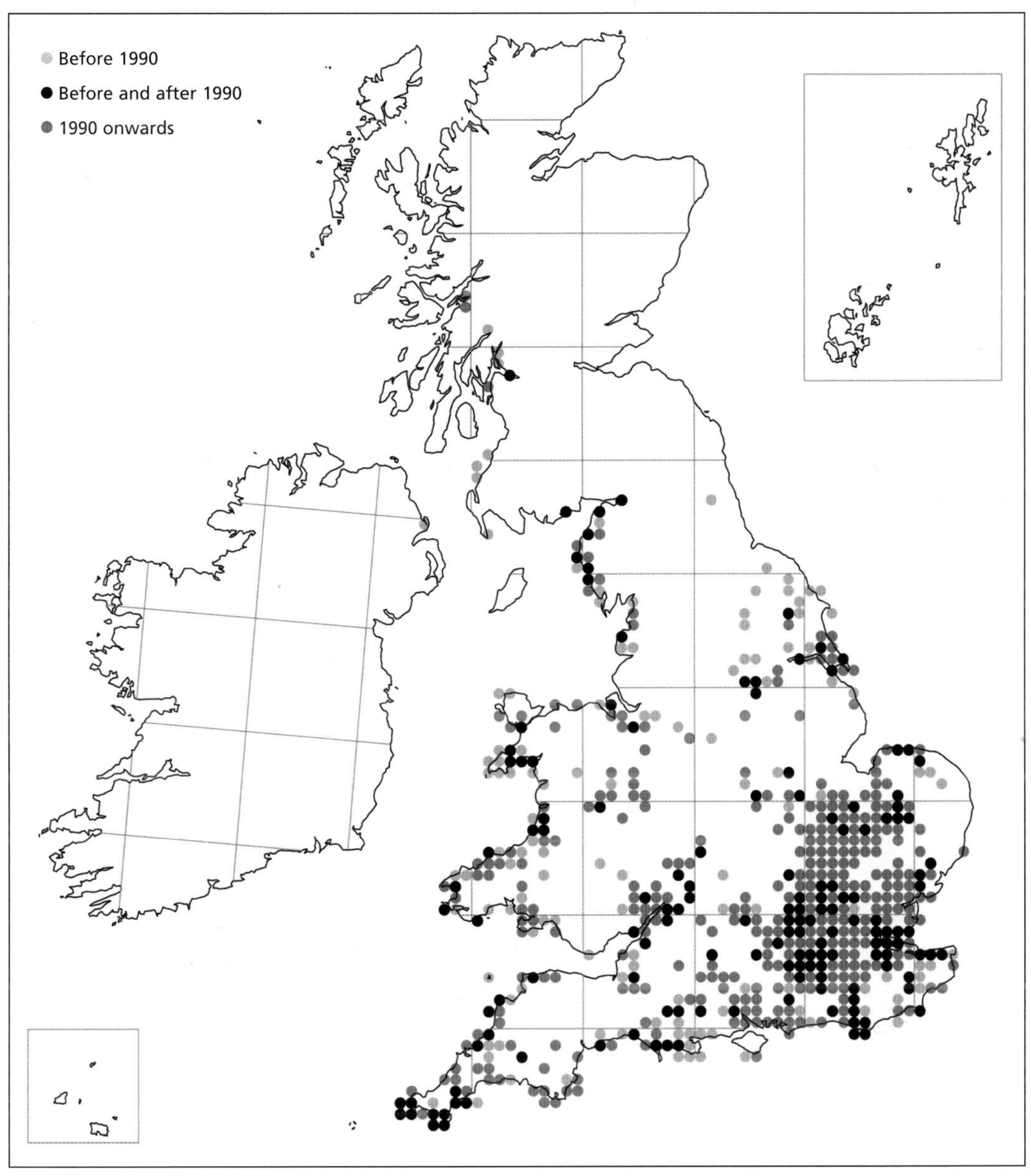

Map 30. Distribution (10km) of 24-spot ladybird.

This small and hairy species is often missed when searching for ladybirds by eye, but in southern Britain it can be abundant in sweep-net surveys of meadows or roadside verges. Like the related bryony ladybird, the 24-spot is a phytophagous species, feeding on the leaves of various plants, using its toothed mandibles to cut and grind up leaf tissue. Its feeding behaviour leaves characteristic grazing marks on leaves, which are sometimes used to infer the presence of the ladybird. It was traditionally found feeding on red campion in England, and on lucerne in south-eastern Europe, but Roger Hawkins' survey of the ladybirds of Surrey (Hawkins, 2000) revealed extensive populations feeding on false oat-grass, apparently a relatively new host plant and one unknown elsewhere in Europe.

Figure 152. 24-spot ladybird adult.
Photo: Peter Brown.

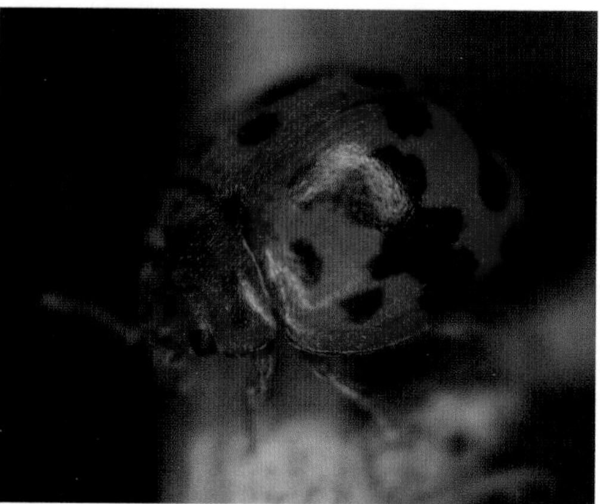

Figure 153. 24-spot ladybird adult.
Photo: Michael Majerus.

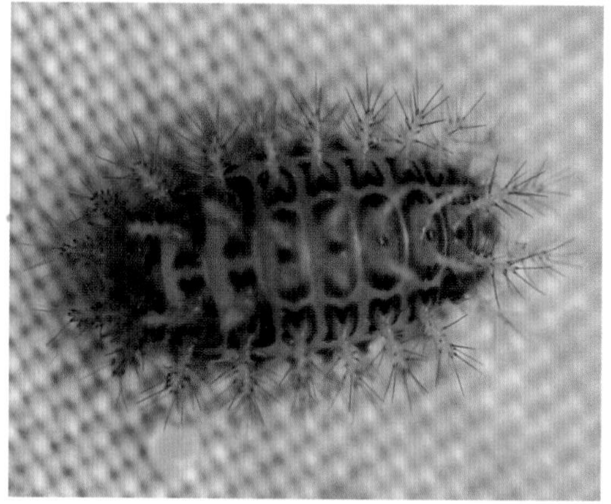

Figure 154. 24-spot ladybird late-instar larva.
Photo: Robert Frost.

Figure 155. 24-spot ladybird pupa.
Photo: Richard Comont.

Identification

Length: 3-4mm. *Background colour*: russet. *Pattern colour*: black spots. *Number of spots*: 0-24 (20). *Spot fusions*: common. *Melanic (black) forms*: rare. *Pronotum*: russet with black spots. *Leg colour*: russet. *Other features*: elytra covered in fine hairs (visible with hand lens), giving the ladybird a matt appearance.

Fourth-instar larva: cream-yellow or greenish in colour; short and stubby in shape; tubercles dark, bearing thick yellow spiny bristles with extensive side-branching. *Pupa*: pale yellow with small black spots, partially covered by shed larval skin at base.

Ecology

Habitats: the 24-spot ladybird is very much a grassland species and its habitat is often described as 'rough grass'; however records have also been received from marshy habitats and scrub.

Host plants: this species is most commonly found on grasses but also on other low growing plants such as thistle, nettle, mugwort, salad burnet, knapweed, spurrey and tansy.

Food: red campion, false oat-grass.

Overwintering sites: 24-spot ladybirds overwinter in low herbage, grass tussocks and gorse bushes.

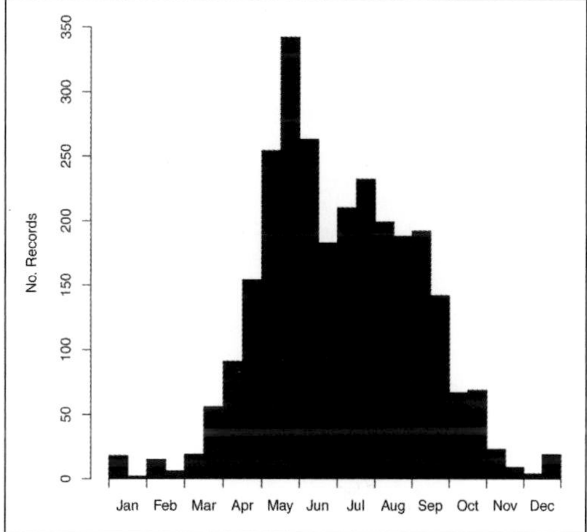

Figure 156. 24-spot ladybird phenogram.

UK distribution status Widespread

UK distribution trend (1990-2010) Increasing

Subfamily Coccidulinae Mulsant, 1846

Coccidula rufa (Herbst, 1783)

Synonyms None

Number of records 3371
Number of 10km squares 845

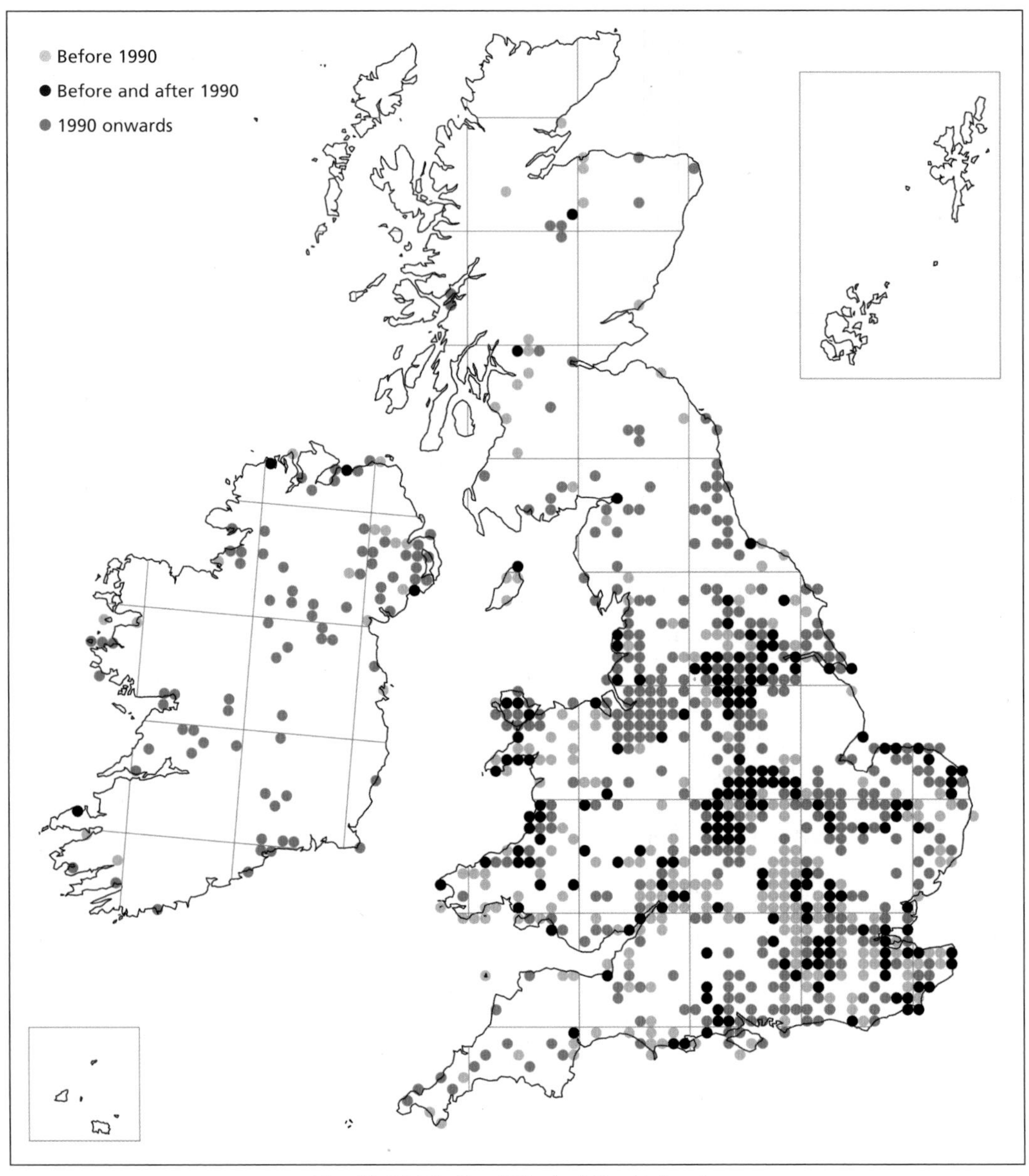

Map 31. Distribution (10km) of *Coccidula rufa*.

This widespread and common species of wet habitats is rather unlike most ladybirds, being distinctly elongate in shape and having long antennae. Like most of the inconspicuous ladybirds, *Coccidula rufa* is covered in short downy hairs, which are clearly visible using a hand lens. It is easiest to find when it is overwintering in the leaf sheaths of reeds or reedmace. *Coccidula rufa* is similar to *Coccidula scutellata*, but is clearly distinguished by having no spots on the brownish-red elytra.

Figure 157. *Coccidula rufa* adult.
Photo: Gilles San Martin.

Identification

Length: 2.5-3mm. *Background colour*: brownish-red. *Pattern*: none. *Pronotum*: brownish-red. *Head colour*: brownish-red. *Leg colour*: brownish-red. *Other features*: hairy; elongate (oblong with parallel sides) and dorsoventrally flattened; long antennae.

Ecology

Habitats: marshes, riversides, pondsides.

Host plants: reeds, rushes, reedmace, wetland grasses.

Food: aphids.

Overwintering sites: leaf sheaths of reeds, rushes and reedmace; tufts of grasses.

UK distribution status Very widespread

UK distribution trend (1990-2010)
Decreasing

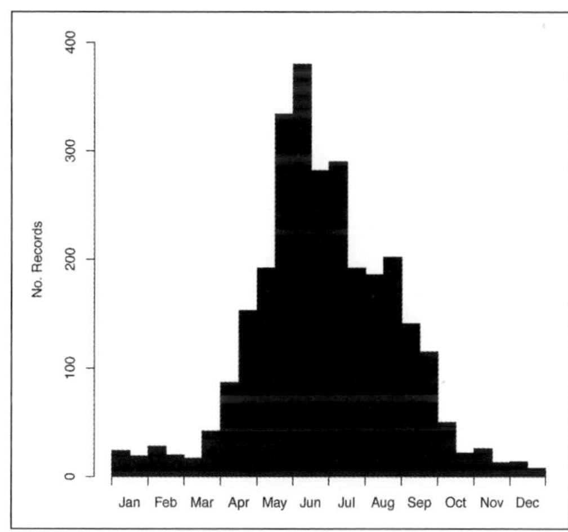

Figure 158. Phenogram for *Coccidula rufa*.

Coccidula scutellata (Herbst, 1783)

Synonyms None

Number of records 332
Number of 10km squares 144

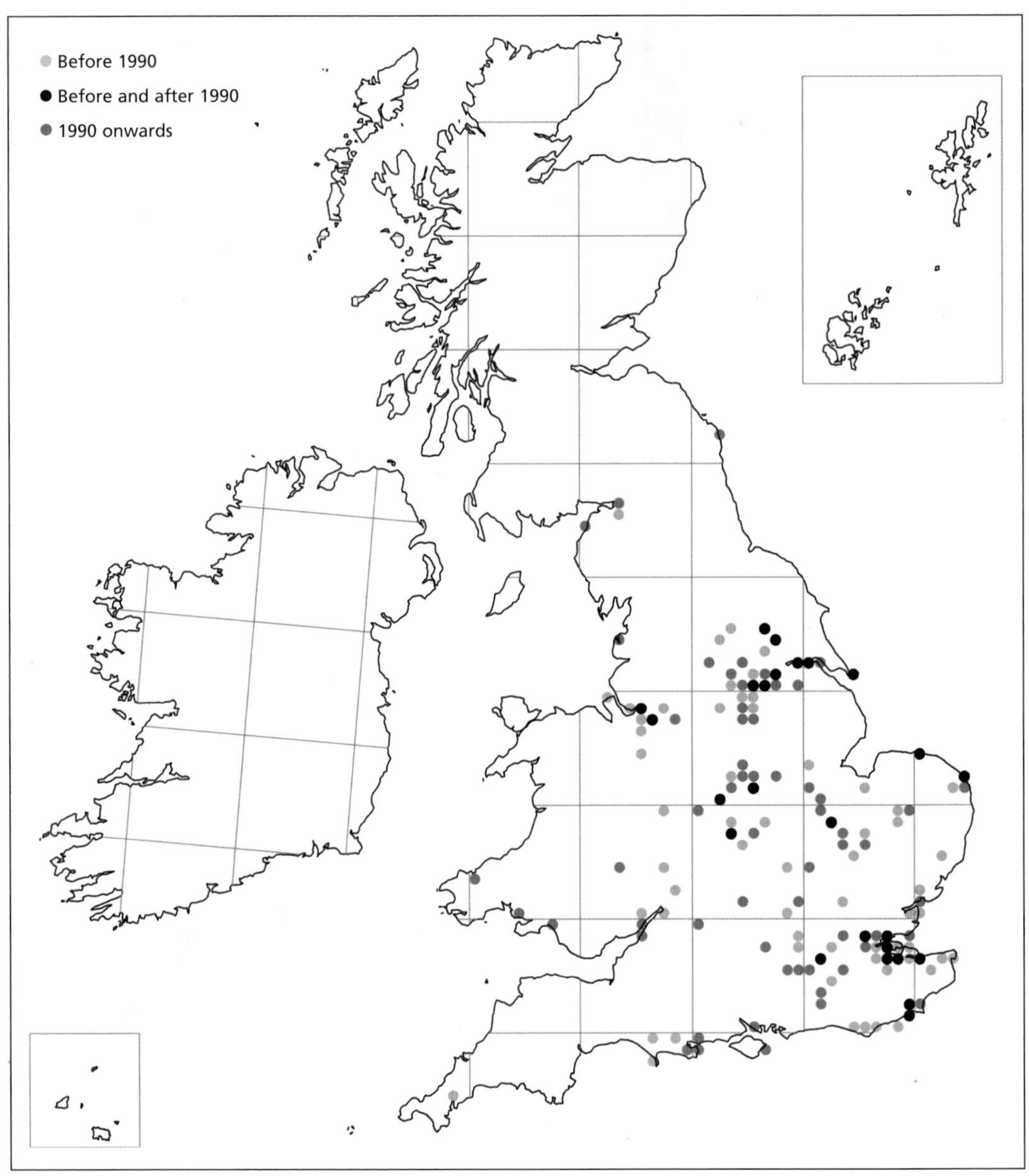

Map 32. Distribution (10km) of *Coccidula scutellata.*

Coccidula scutellata is similar in appearance and size to the much commoner *C. rufa*, and occurs in the same habitats – close to fresh water. However, *C. scutellata* is clearly distinguished by the presence of five black spots on the elytra. It also has a much more restricted distribution than *C. rufa*; although widespread in England, there are no records of *C. scutellata* in Scotland or Ireland.

Figure 159. *Coccidula scutellata* adult.
Photo: Gilles San Martin.

Identification

Length: 2.5-3mm. *Background colour*: reddish-brown. *Pattern*: five black spots. *Pronotum*: reddish-brown, narrower than elytra. *Head colour*: reddish-brown. *Leg colour*: reddish-brown. *Other features*: hairy; elongate (oblong with parallel sides) and dorsoventrally flattened; long antennae.

Ecology

Habitats: marshes, riversides, pondsides.

Host plants: reedmace, reeds, rushes.

Food: aphids.

Overwintering sites: leaf sheaths of reedmace and reeds.

UK distribution status Very local

UK distribution trend (1990-2010) Stable

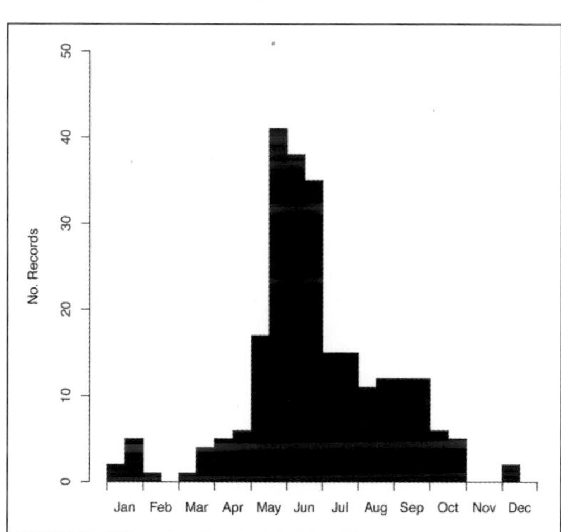

Figure 160. Phenogram for *Coccidula scutellata*.

Rhyzobius chrysomeloides (Herbst, 1792)

Synonyms *Rhizobius chrysomeloides*
Rhizobiellus chrysomeloides

Number of records 108
Number of 10km squares 42

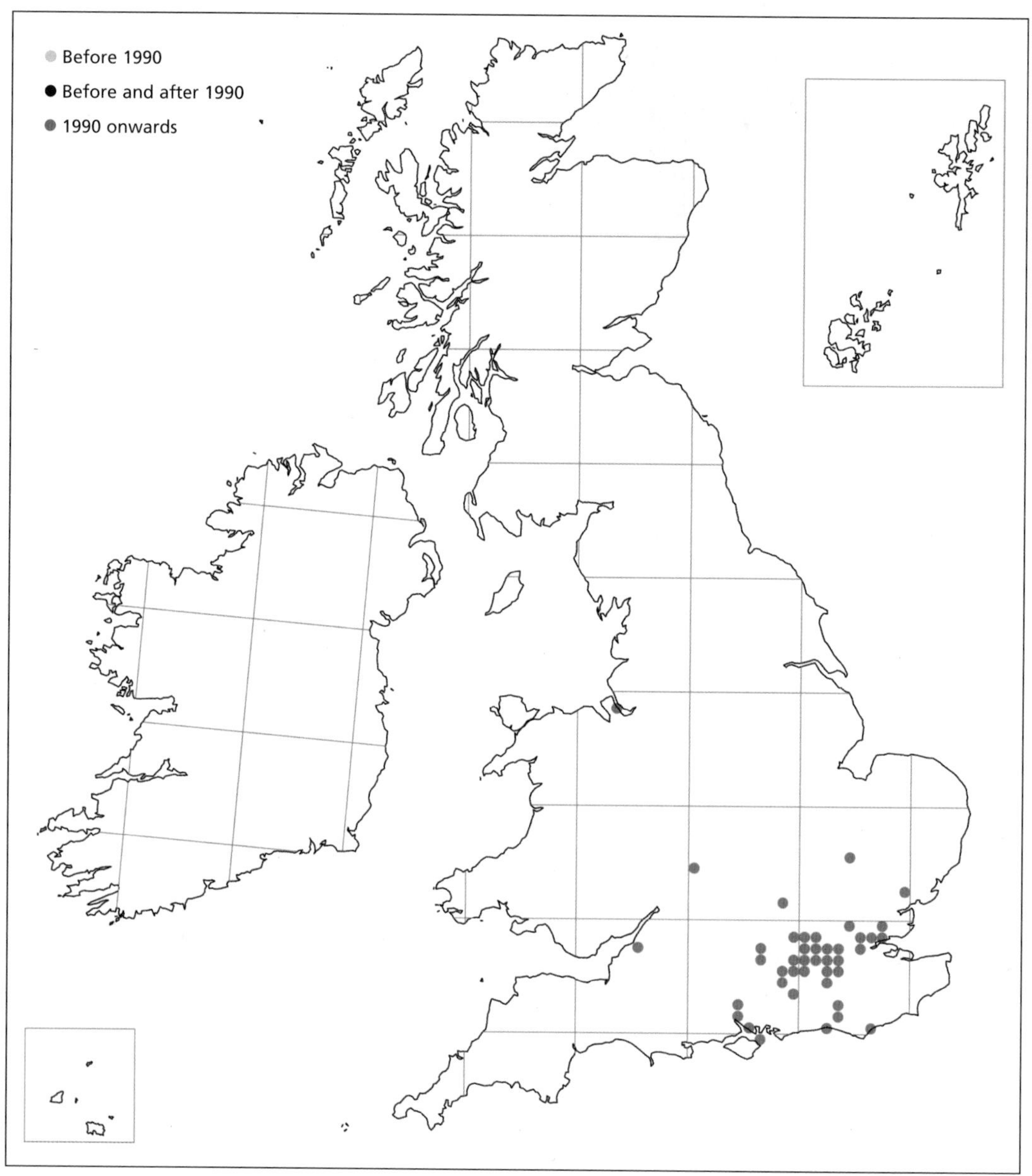

Map 33. Distribution (10km) of *Rhyzobius chrysomeloides.*

Rhyzobius chrysomeloides was first found in Britain on a pine tree on a Surrey motorway bank in 1996 (Hawkins, 2000). It was well established in parts of Surrey by the late 1990s, and seems to have spread across south-east England. It has been recorded as far north as Liverpool, and has also been found in Worcestershire and Cambridgeshire. Some records are from urban habitats. *R. chrysomeloides* is very similar to *R. litura*, requiring dissection to distinguish with certainty, but is often paler, with more extensive black markings on the elytra and a slight difference in the pattern of hair growth on the elytra. Also, *R. chrysomeloides* tends to be found on trees, whereas *R. litura* generally inhabits grasses and thistles.

Figure 161. *Rhyzobius chrysomeloides* adult.
Photo: Gilles San Martin.

Identification

Length: 2.5-3.5mm. *Background colour*: pale to dark brown. *Pattern*: variable, but often with dark U-shaped mark towards end of elytra. *Pronotum*: pale to dark brown. *Head colour*: pale to dark brown. *Leg colour*: pale to dark brown. *Other features*: hairy; long antennae.

Ecology

Habitats: trees.

Host plants: pine trees, deciduous trees, ivy.

Food: aphids.

Overwintering sites: unknown.

UK distribution status Very local

UK distribution trend (1990-2010) Increasing

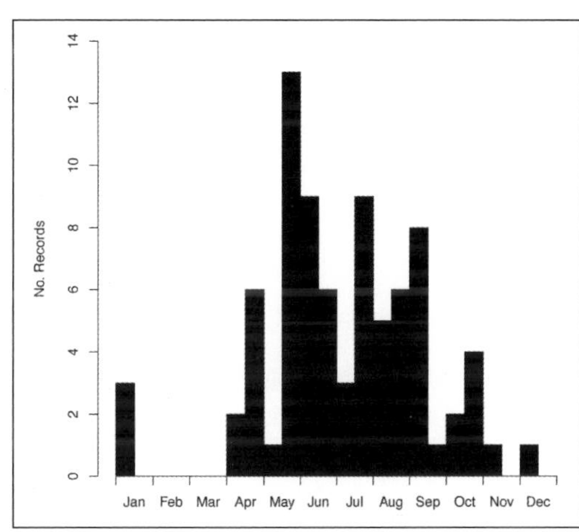

Figure 162. Phenogram for *Rhyzobius chrysomeloides.*

Rhyzobius litura (Fabricius, 1787)

Synonyms *Rhizobius litura*
Rhizobiellus litura

Number of records 2571
Number of 10km squares 715

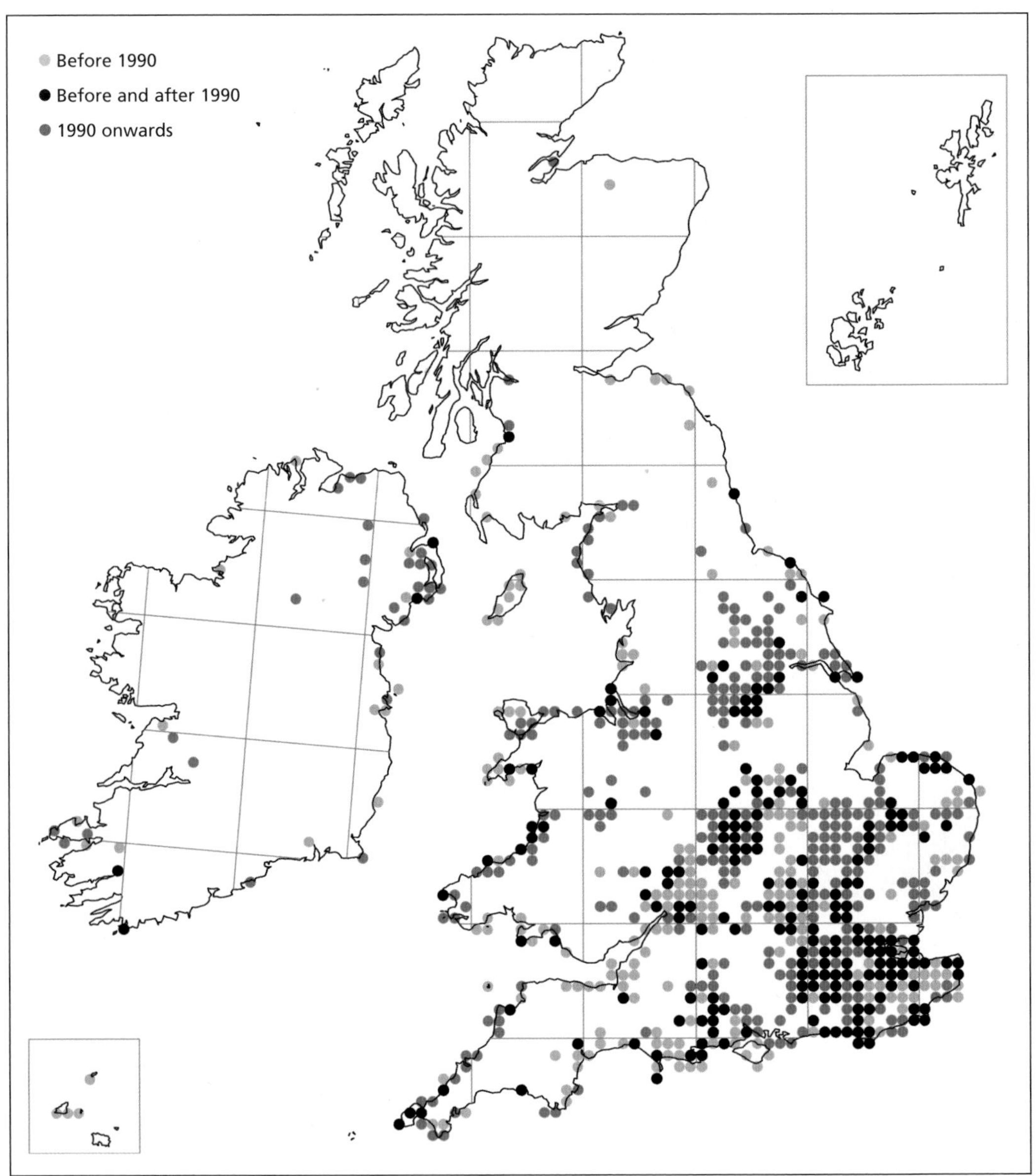

Map 34. Distribution (10km) of *Rhyzobius litura.*

This small ladybird's cryptic colouration makes it difficult to spot, so it tends to be under-recorded and is often overlooked, even by ladybird enthusiasts. However, it can easily be found when sweep-netting in meadows or grass verges. It is one of the more common ladybird species, at least in England and Wales. Most of the records of *R. litura* in Scotland and Ireland are coastal. This small ladybird has a dorsal covering of short downy hairs and varies in colour from pale yellow to dark brown, often with a dark squarish U-shaped mark on the elytra. Its larvae and pupae are lemon yellow and covered in long fine hairs.

Figure 163. *Rhyzobius litura* adult.
Photo: Michael Majerus.

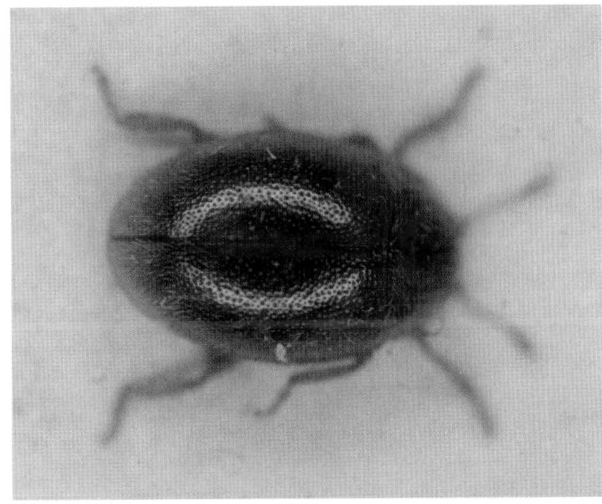

Figure 164. *Rhyzobius litura* adult.
Photo: Remy Poland.

Figure 165. *Rhyzobius litura* late-instar larva.
Photo: Remy Poland.

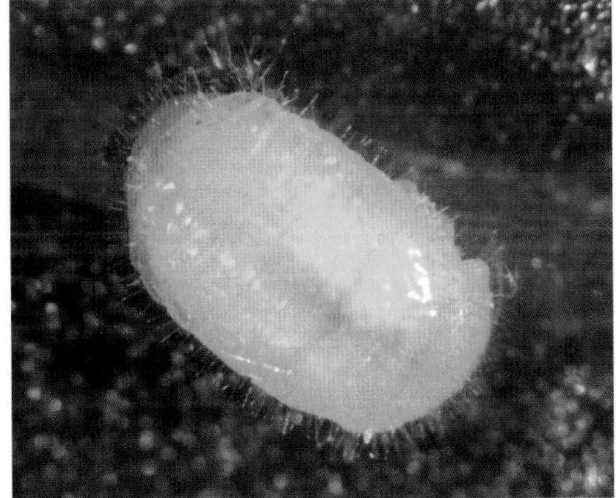

Figure 166. *Rhyzobius litura* pupa.
Photo: Remy Poland.

Identification

Length: 2.5-3mm. *Background colour*: pale to dark brown. *Pattern*: variable, but often with dark U-shaped mark towards end of elytra. *Pronotum*: pale to dark brown. *Head colour*: pale to dark brown. *Leg colour*: pale to dark brown. *Other features*: hairy; long antennae.

Ecology

Habitats: grassland.

Host plants: low-growing vegetation, especially grasses and thistles.

Food: aphids.

Overwintering sites: low-growing vegetation (at or below ground level); grass tussocks; moss.

UK distribution status Widespread

UK distribution trend (1990-2010)
Decreasing

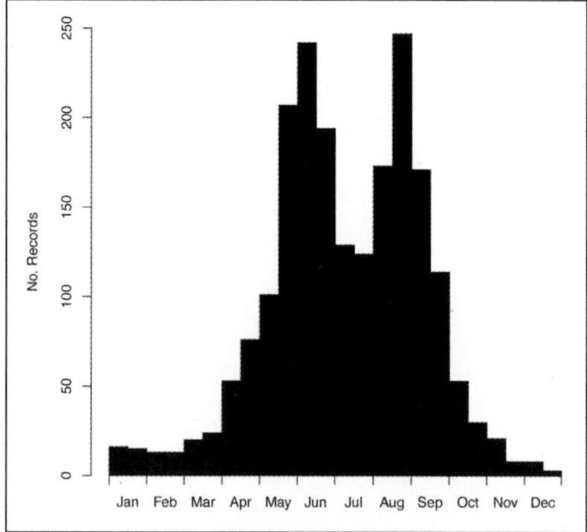

Figure 167. Phenogram for *Rhyzobius litura*.

Rhyzobius lophanthae (Blaisdell, 1892)

Synonyms *Rhizobius lophanthae*
Rhizobiellus lophanthae

Number of records 10
Number of 10km squares 4

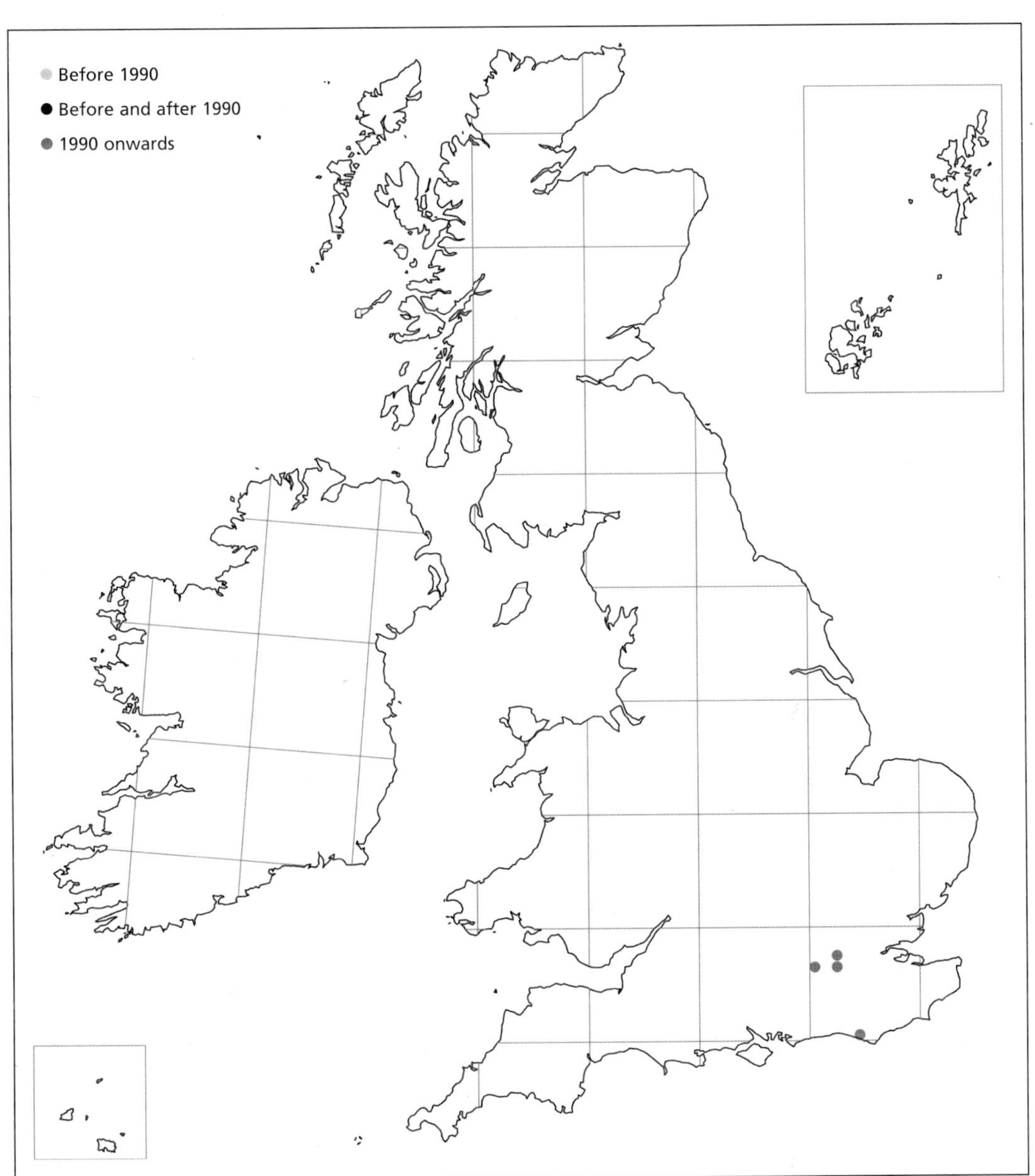

Map 35. Distribution (10km) of *Rhyzobius lophanthae*.

Rhyzobius lophanthae is native to Australia. It was widely used in Europe throughout the 20th century as a biological control agent of armoured scale insects, initially in Italy in 1908 (Roy & Migeon, 2010). The species is widespread around the Mediterranean basin. It was first found in Britain by D.A. Coleman, crawling up the trunk of an ash tree in Morden Park, Surrey, in April 1999 (Booth, 2000). Recent sightings of *R. lophanthae* have been noted from Lewes (E. Sussex) and Woking (Surrey) in July 2007 (R. Hawkins, personal communication). This species has been recorded as breeding outdoors in several parts of London (Barclay, 2007), including Fulham and Chelsea. Seemingly restricted to London and south-east England, *R. lophanthae* is smaller than the other two *Rhyzobius* species found in Britain, and has different colouration.

Identification

Length: 2mm. *Background colour*: black. *Pattern*: none. *Pronotum*: dull orange. *Head colour*: dull orange. *Leg colour*: dull orange. *Other features*: entire dorsal surface covered in short hairs; very long antennae.

Ecology

Habitat: trees.

Host plants: very few records, but these from oak, ash and Leyland cypress.

Food: coccids, diaspidids.

Overwintering sites: unknown.

UK distribution status Very local

UK distribution trend (1990-2010) Stable (based on 100 records or less)

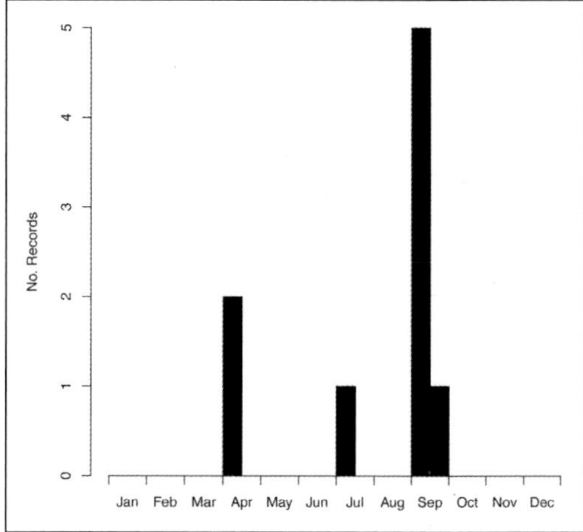

Figure 168. Phenogram for *Rhyzobius lophanthae*.

Clitostethus arcuatus (Rossi, 1794)

Synonyms *Scymnus arcuatus*

Number of records 32
Number of 10km squares 15

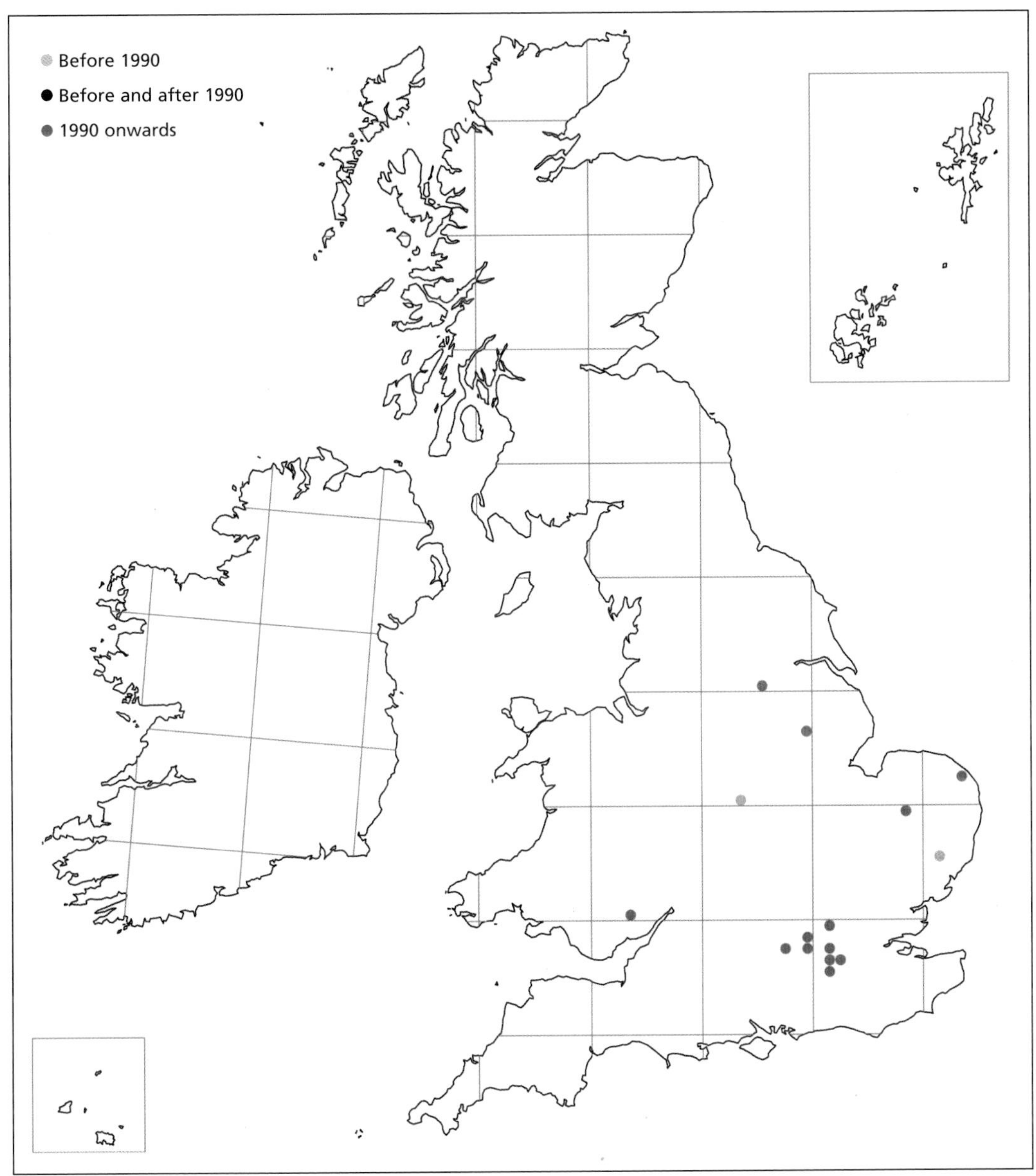

Map 36. Distribution (10km) of *Clitostethus arcuatus*.

Clitostethus arcuatus is a tiny, attractive ladybird with a distinctive horseshoe-shaped mark, easily visible when viewed through a hand lens. The species has most usually been found by beating ivy growing on trees such as oak (Hawkins, 2000). The very few records partly reflect this species' preference for warm climates; it is more common in Mediterranean countries.

Figure 169. *Clitostethus arcuatus* adult.
Photo: Gilles San Martin.

Figure 170. *Clitostethus arcuatus* adult.
Photo: Gilles San Martin.

Identification

Length: 1.2-1.5mm. *Background colour*: dark brown to black. *Pattern*: pale yellow/cream horseshoe-shaped mark in the centre of the elytra. *Pronotum*: dark brown but cream at sides, or sometimes mostly cream. *Head colour*: dark brown to black, or sometimes cream. *Leg colour*: cream. *Other features*: hairy.

Ecology

Habitats: coniferous and deciduous woodland or other habitats with trees.

Host plants: ivy (also recorded on honeysuckle, *Viburnum*, holly).

Food: aleyrodids (whitefly).

Overwintering sites: bark crevices and under bark of coniferous and deciduous trees.

UK conservation designation Endangered

UK distribution status Very local

UK distribution trend (1990-2010) Stable (based on 100 records or less)

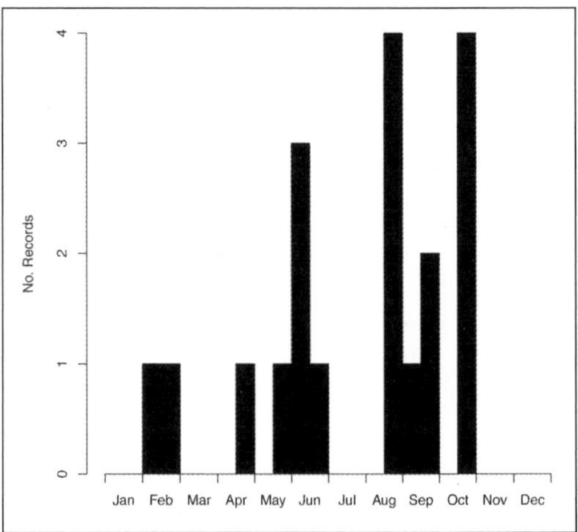

Figure 171. Phenogram for *Clitostethus arcuatus*.

Stethorus punctillum (Weise, 1891)

Synonyms *Scymnus punctillum*
Scymnus ater sensu auctt. Brit. partim non (Kugelann, 1794)
Scymnus minimus (Rossi, 1794) non (Müller, O.F., 1776)

Number of records 113
Number of 10km squares 75

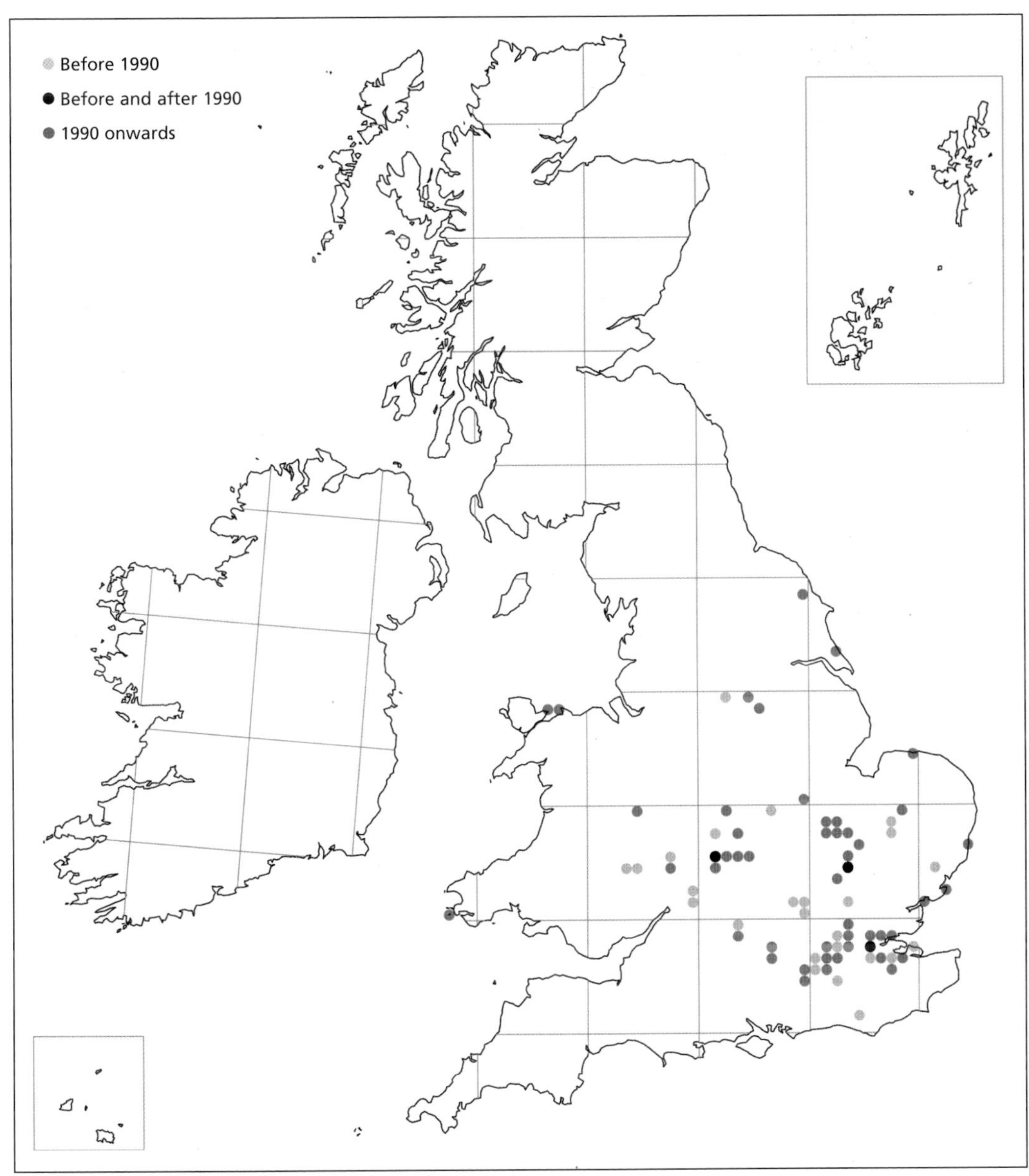

Map 37. Distribution (10km) of *Stethorus punctillum*.

Stethorus punctillum is our tiniest ladybird, and its varied habitat probably reflects that of its prey – spider mites, some of which are serious plant and fruit pests. It can be abundant and acts as a good pest-controller, for example in orchards, eating up to 150 spider mites each day (Kuznetsov, 1997). It is under-recorded due to its minute size, but is characteristically ladybird-like when viewed through a hand lens. *Stethorus punctillum* does not occur in Scotland or Ireland.

Figure 172. *Stethorus punctillum* adult.
Photo: Gilles San Martin.

Identification

Length: 1.3-1.5mm. *Background colour*: black. *Pattern*: none. *Pronotum*: black. *Head colour*: black with yellowish-brown mouthparts. *Leg colour*: black and yellowish-brown (at least tibiae yellowish-brown). *Other features*: antennae and mouthparts yellowish-brown; hairs towards tip of elytra lie parallel to suture (they diverge at an angle in *Scymnus* spp.) (Hawkins, 2000).

Ecology

Habitats: various, including deciduous woodlands, orchards, gardens, hedgerows, grasslands.

Host plants: various deciduous trees (especially fruit trees), gorse.

Food: Acari (spider mites), small aphids.

Overwintering sites: bark crevices and under bark; sheltered positions on deciduous trees; possibly leaf litter.

UK distribution status Very local

UK distribution trend (1990-2010) Stable

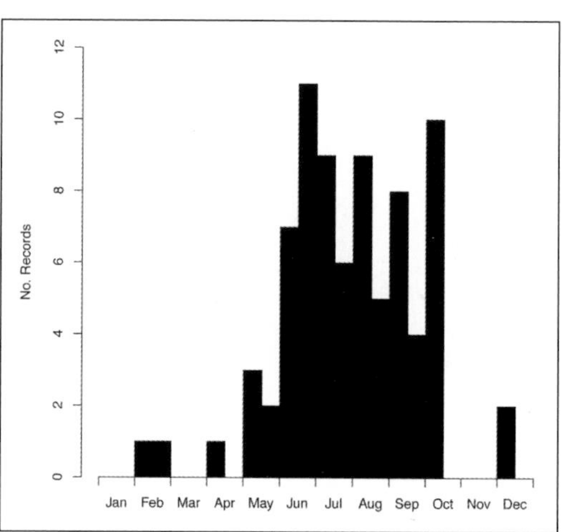

Figure 173. Phenogram for *Stethorus punctillum*.

Scymnus suturalis Thunberg, 1795

Subgenus *Pullus* Mulsant, 1846
Synonyms None

Number of records 546
Number of 10km squares 248

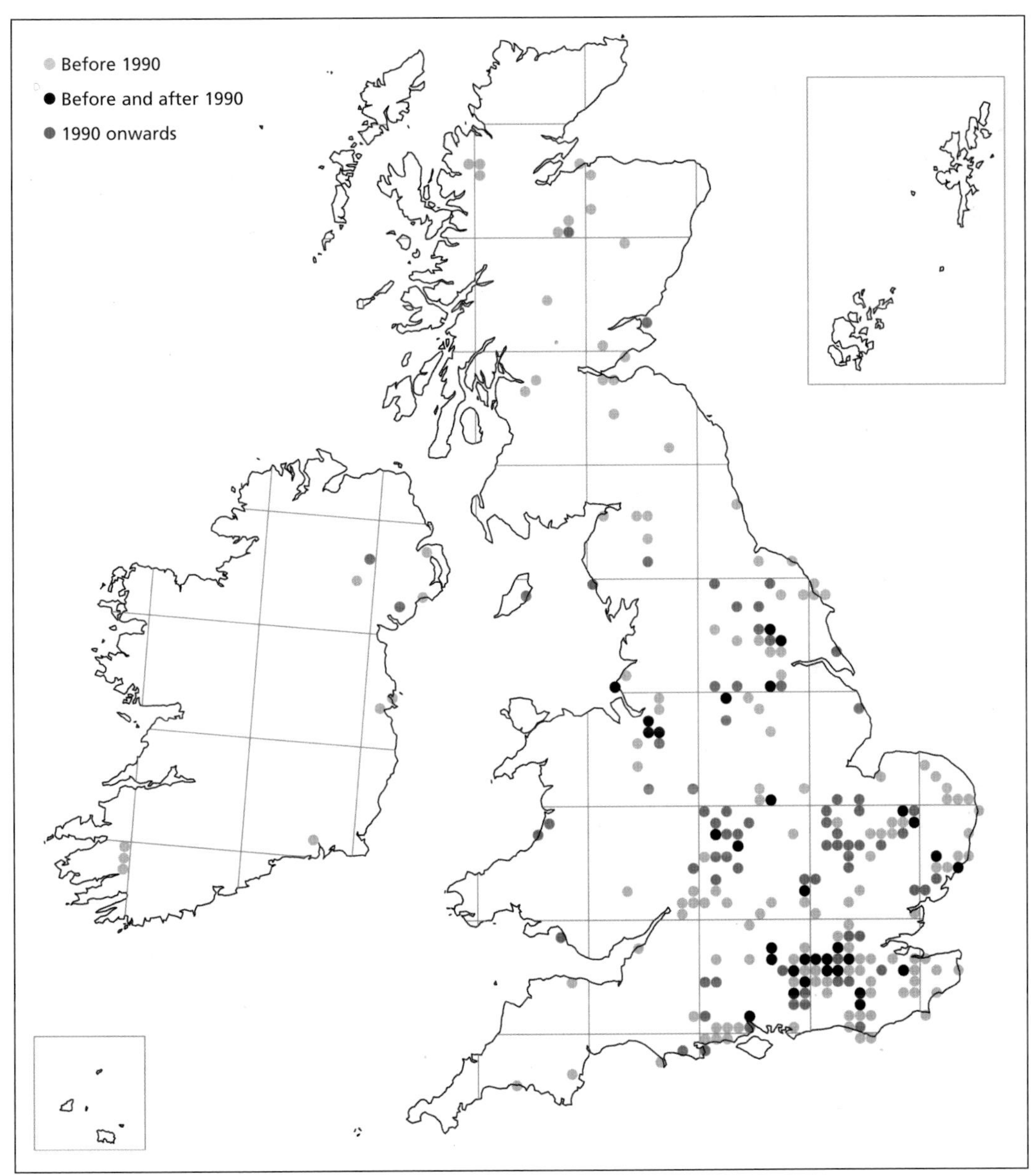

Map 38. Distribution (10km) of *Scymnus suturalis.*

Scymnus suturalis is a pine specialist that may sometimes be found on other conifers, and has occasionally been recorded on other plants such as ivy and oak. One of the commoner *Scymnus* species, it can be the most abundant ladybird on pines, where it is sometimes found in very large numbers. *Scymnus suturalis* is a very widespread species, with records scattered throughout Britain and Ireland. Its elytra are a rich brown colour, with a characteristic dark line running down the centre line.

Figure 174. *Scymnus suturalis* adult.
Photo: Gilles San Martin.

Figure 175. *Scymnus suturalis* adult.
Photo: Jo Bogaert.

Identification

Length: 1.5-2mm. *Background colour*: brown. *Pattern*: dark brown to black along centre line, especially at the top, thus sometimes forming a dark T-shape. *Pronotum*: black with brown tips. *Head colour*: black. *Leg colour*: brown.

Ecology

Habitats: coniferous woodlands and other habitats with coniferous trees.

Host plants: needled conifers, especially Scots pine and Douglas fir.

Food: adelgids, aphids.

Overwintering sites: sheltered positions on needled conifers, especially buds on Scots pine; moss.

UK distribution status Local

UK distribution trend (1990-2010) Stable

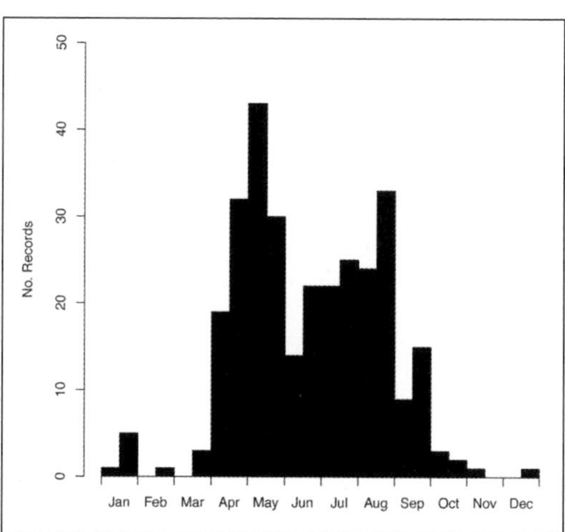

Figure 176. Phenogram for *Scymnus suturalis*.

Scymnus auritus Thunberg, 1795

Subgenus *Pullus* Mulsant, 1846
Synonyms *Scymnus capitatus* (Fabricius, 1798)

Number of records 476
Number of 10km squares 240

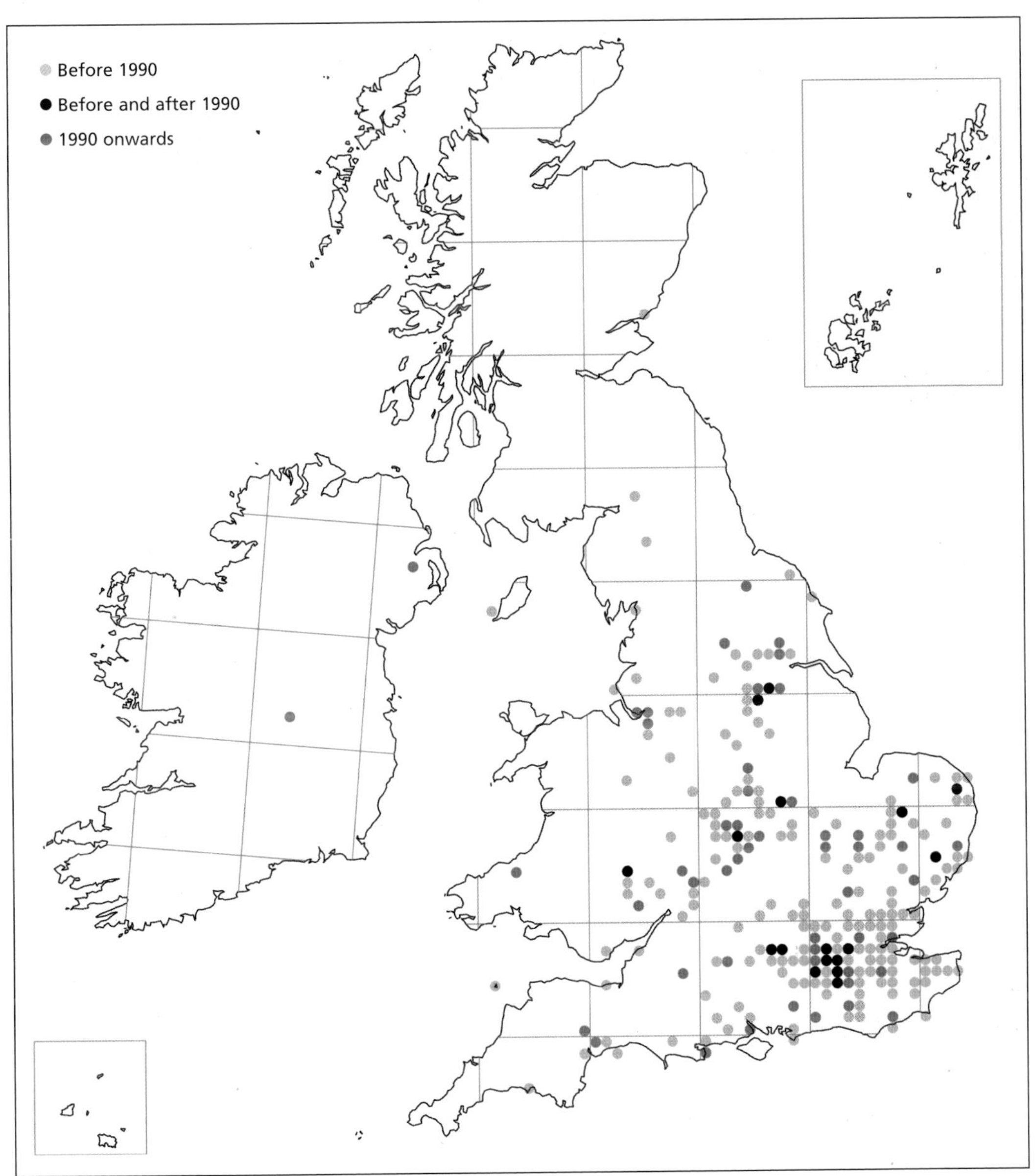

Map 39. Distribution (10km) of *Scymnus auritus*.

Scymnus auritus is a highly specialised feeder, eating aphid-like insects of the family Phylloxeridae, and is usually found on oak trees. Depending on prey outbreaks, the distribution and abundance of *S. auritus* may vary substantially from year to year. Hawkins (2000) reported the species on sycamore and lime trees, although principally on oak. *Scymnus auritus* may act as a control for grape phylloxera, which can be a serious pest of vineyards and, indeed, almost destroyed the wine industry in France after it was accidentally introduced in 1860.

Figure 177. *Scymnus auritus* adult male.
Photo: Jo Bogaert.

Identification

Length: 2-2.3mm. *Background colour*: black. *Pattern*: hind margin of elytra is reddish-brown. *Pronotum*: black (with reddish-brown margin in male). *Head colour*: reddish (male); black (female). *Leg colour*: reddish-brown. *Other features*: tip of abdomen is reddish-brown.

Ecology

Habitats: deciduous woodland and other habitats with oak trees.

Host plants: oak; occasionally on other deciduous trees.

Food: phylloxera.

Overwintering sites: bark crevices and under bark of oak trees.

UK distribution status Local

UK distribution trend (1990-2010) Stable

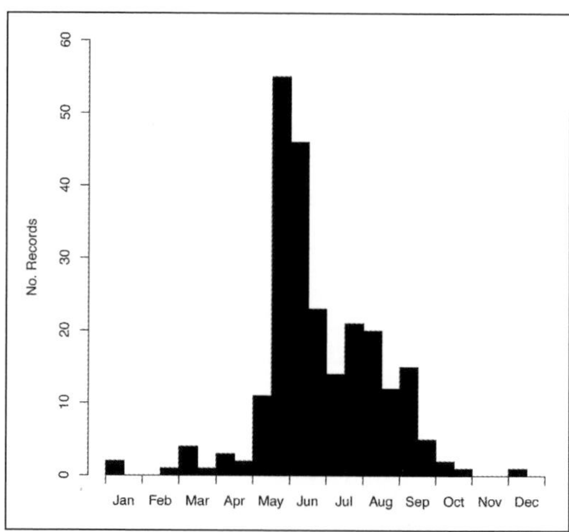

Figure 178. Phenogram for *Scymnus auritus*.

Scymnus frontalis (Fabricius, 1787)

Subgenus *Scymnus* Kugelann, 1794
Synonyms None

Number of records 394
Number of 10km squares 194

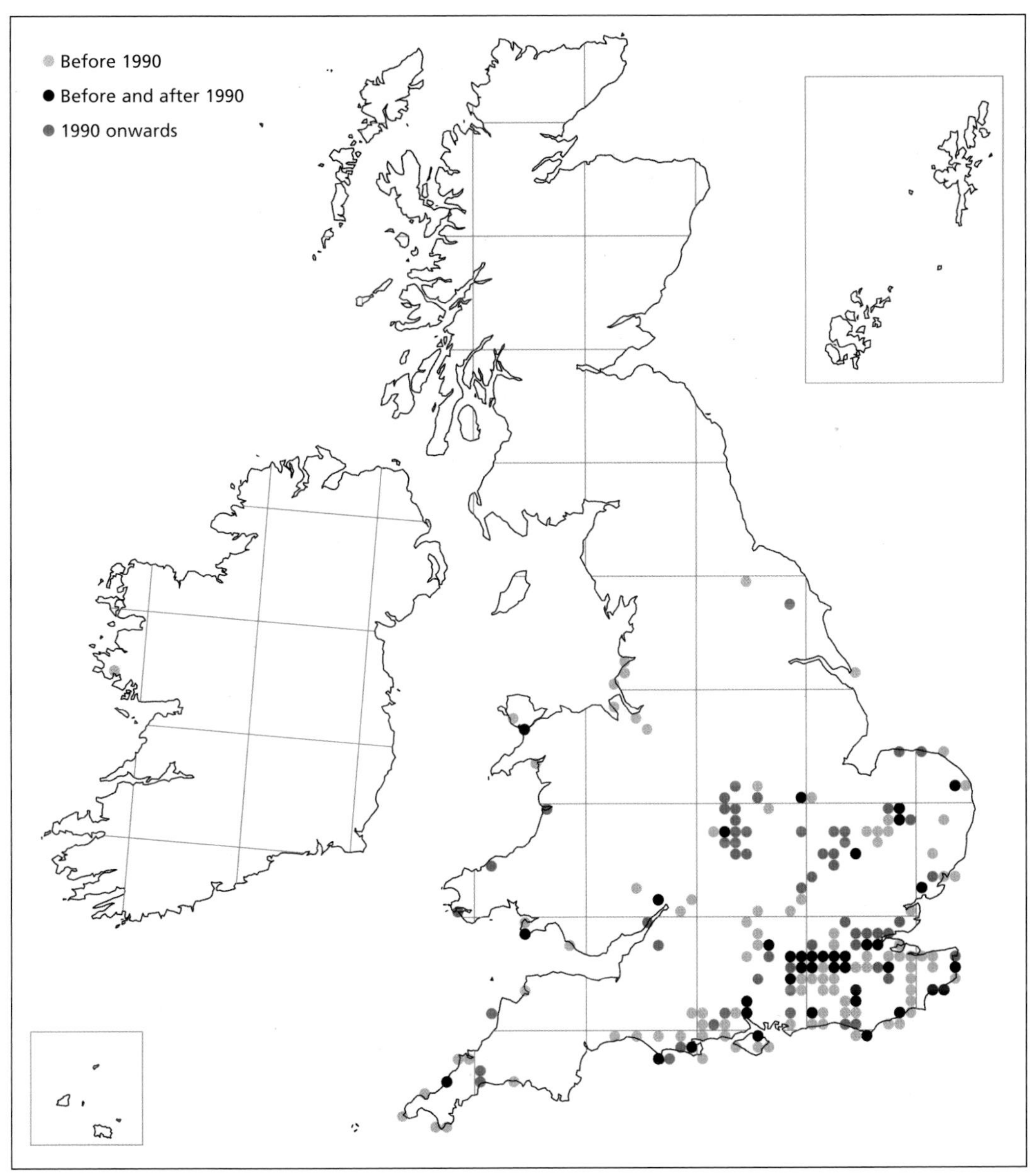

Map 40. Distribution (10km) of *Scymnus frontalis.*

Symnus frontalis is one of the largest of the *Scymnus* species, and one of the commonest, at least in south-east and central England. This species has a preference for dry soils and bare ground and this is reflected in the many coastal records. The presence of an elongate red spot on each elytron helps to make *S. frontalis* one of the more recognisable of our small ladybirds.

Figure 179. *Scymnus frontalis* adult. Photo: Jo Bogaert.

Figure 180. *Scymnus* species larva. Photo: Carlos Ricci and Gabriele Rondoni.

Identification

Length: 2.6-3.2mm. *Background colour*: black. *Pattern*: two elongate red spots towards the front of the elytra. *Pronotum*: black, with brown margins in male only. *Head colour*: brown (male); black (female); both with brown mouthparts. *Leg colour*: brown. *Other features*: hairy; rather elongate; pointed abdomen.

Ecology

Habitats: heathland and other dry habitats particularly on chalky or sandy soils, including dunes.

Host plants: low-growing vegetation including thistles and grasses.

Food: aphids.

Overwintering sites: leaf litter; grass tussocks; rosettes of perennial plants.

UK distribution status Local

UK distribution trend (1990-2010) Stable

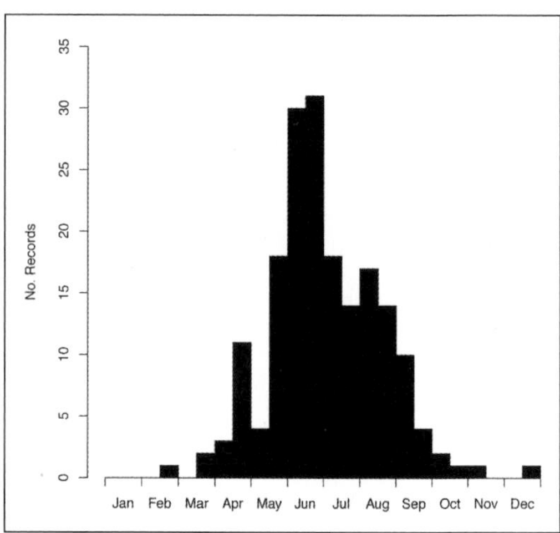

Figure 181. Phenogram for *Scymnus frontalis*.

Scymnus haemorrhoidalis Herbst, 1797

Subgenus *Neopullus* Sasaji, 1971
Synonyms None

Number of records 348
Number of 10km squares 195

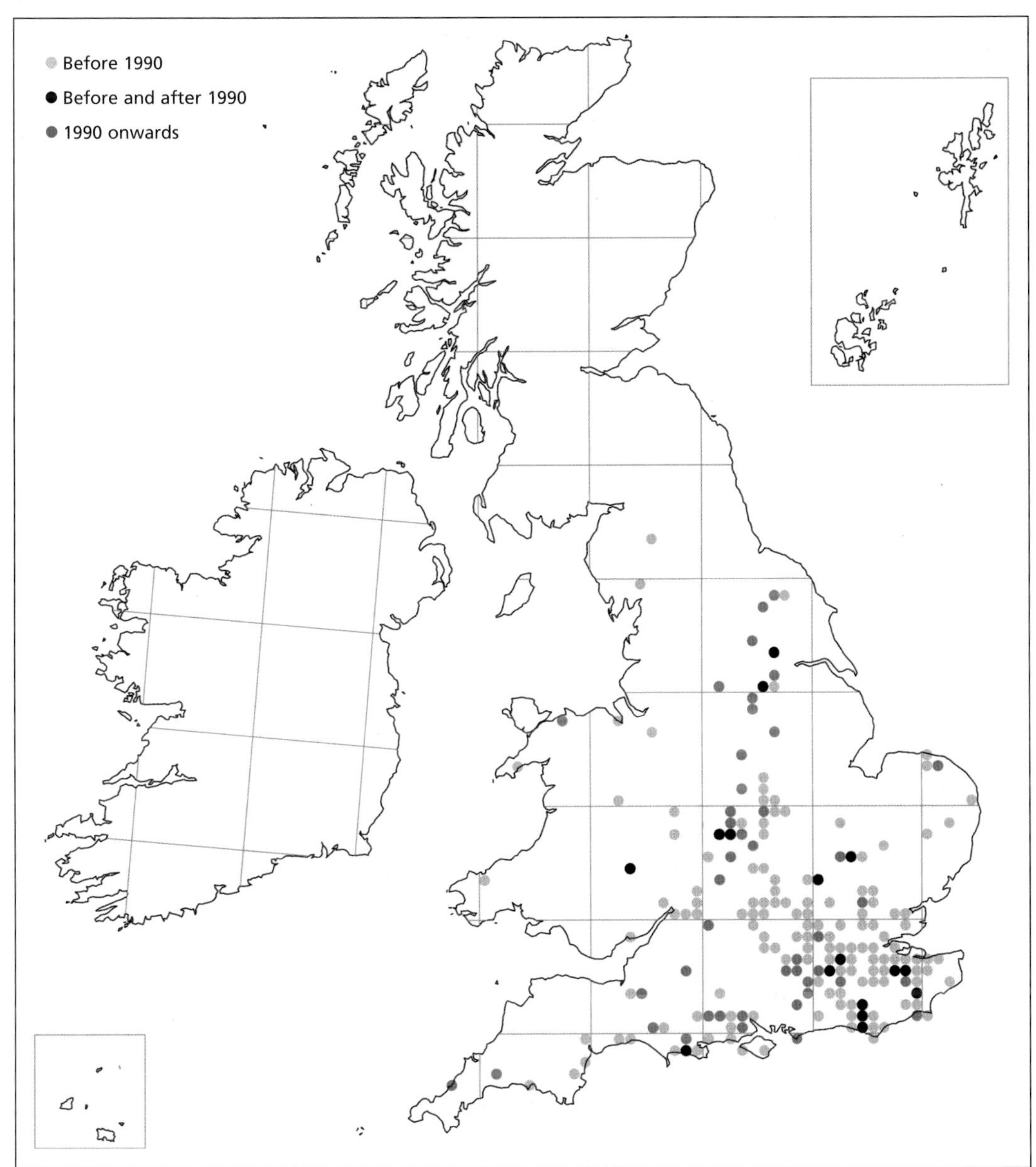

Map 41. Distribution (10km) of *Scymnus haemorrhoidalis*.

Supposedly a common species, Hawkins (2000) suggested that *Scymnus haemorrhoidalis* is difficult to find because it lives close to the ground, rather than higher up on low vegetation; hence it may be under-recorded. It is a widespread species in southern Britain, but we have no records from Scotland or Ireland. The elytra of this species have a distinctive broad red tip, and the head and pronotum are also mostly red.

Figure 182. *Scymnus haemorrhoidalis* adult. Photo: Jo Bogaert.

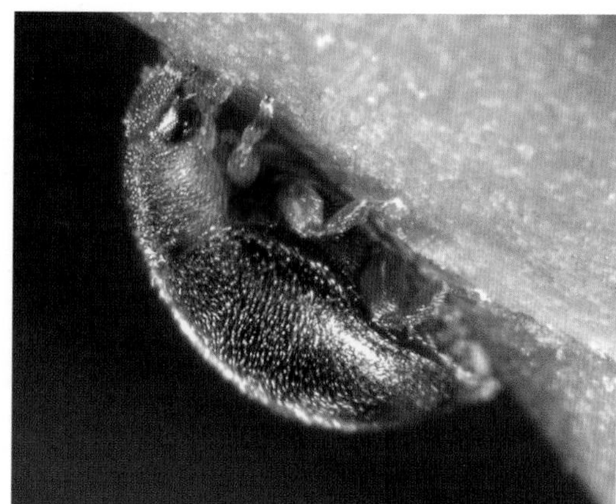

Figure 183. *Scymnus haemorrhoidalis* adult. Photo: Jo Bogaert.

Identification

Length: 1.8-2.2mm. *Background colour*: black. *Pattern*: broad reddish-brown patch at rear of elytra. *Pronotum*: black with reddish-brown front margin. *Head colour*: reddish. *Leg colour*: brown. *Other features*: hairy; tip of abdomen is reddish-brown.

Ecology

Habitats: damp habitats such as bogs, water margins and undisturbed grassland.

Host plants: low down on low-growing vegetation and shrubs; moss.

Food: aphids.

Overwintering site: low herbage; reeds; grass tussocks; leaf litter; moss; rosettes of perennial plants.

UK distribution status Local

UK distribution trend (1990-2010) Stable

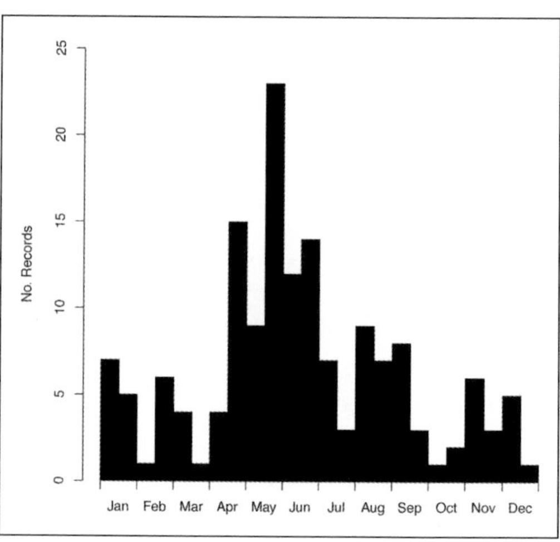

Figure 184. Phenogram for *Scymnus haemorrhoidalis*.

Scymnus femoralis (Gyllenhal, 1827)

Subgenus *Scymnus* Kugelann, 1794
Synonyms *Scymnus rubromaculatus* sensu auctt. Brit. partim non (Goeze, 1777)
Scymnus pygmaeus sensu auctt. Brit. partim non (Geoffroy in Fourcroy, 1785)

Number of records: 125
Number of 10km squares: 78

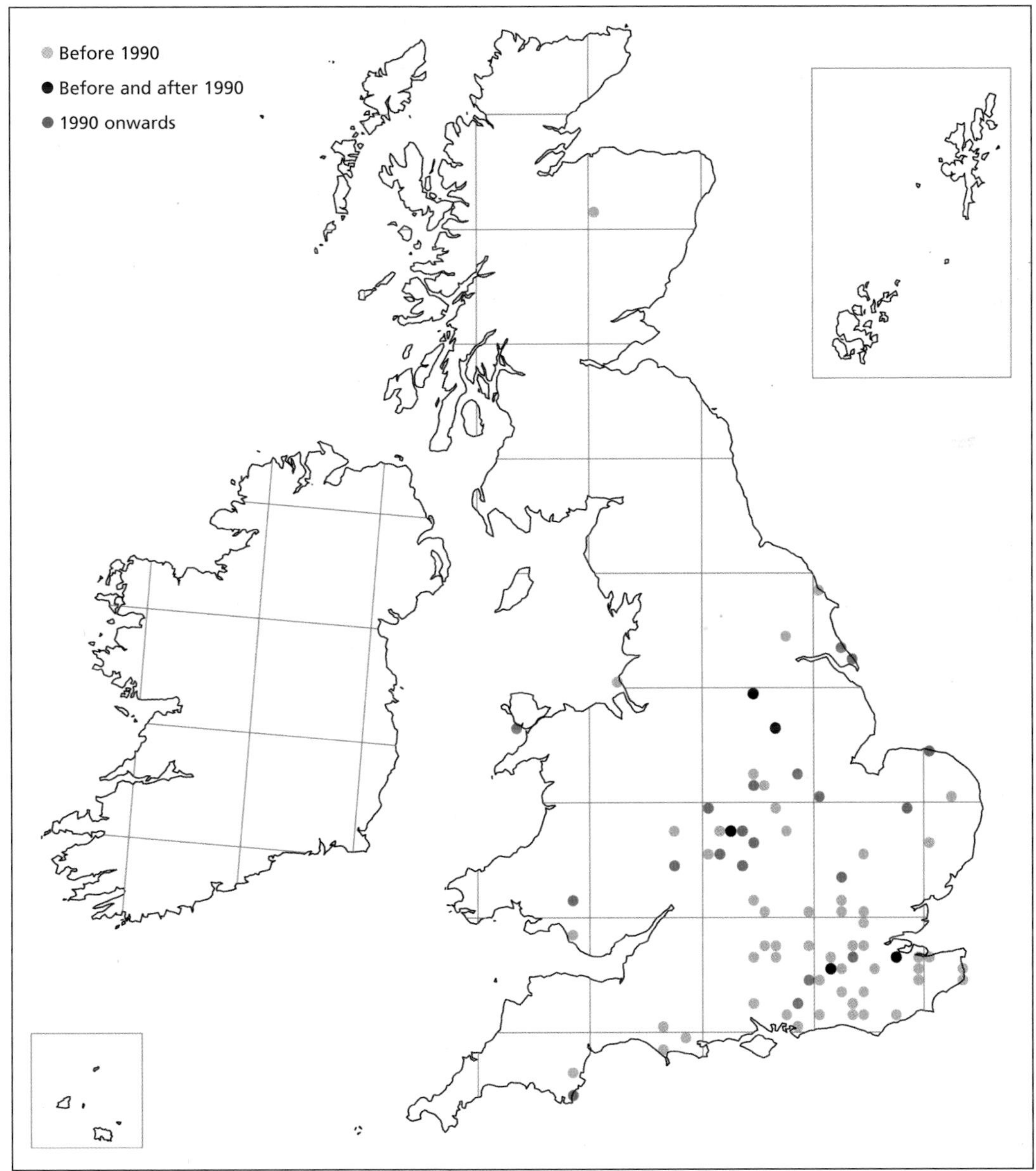

Map 42. Distribution (10km) of *Scymnus femoralis*.

Scymnus femoralis is very similar to *S. schmidti*, but more convex and a little smaller. It is a relatively uncommon species with few recent records, but its small size and preference for being low-down on vegetation may partly account for this. Like several of the inconspicuous ladybirds, this species shows marked sexual dimorphism, the male having a reddish-brown head and pronotum, while those of the female are black.

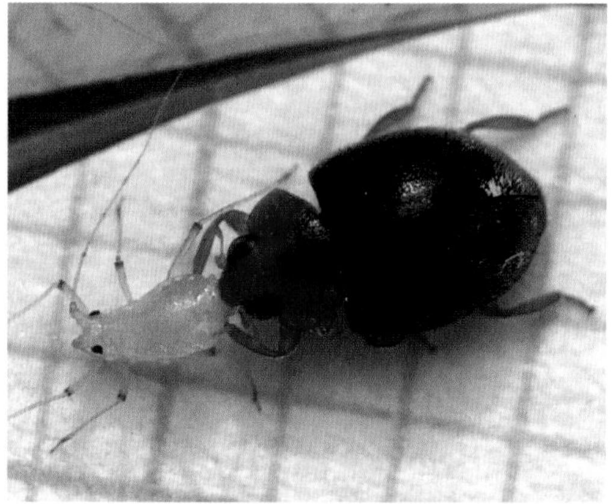

Figure 185. *Scymnus femoralis* adult male eating an aphid. Photo: Gerrian Tacoma-Krist.

Figure 186. *Scymnus femoralis* adult. Photo: Gerrian Tacoma-Krist.

Figure 187. *Scymnus femoralis* adult male. Photo: Gilles San Martin.

Figure 188. *Scymnus femoralis* adult female. Photo: Gilles San Martin.

Identification

Length: 1.8-2.2mm. *Background colour*: black. *Pattern*: none, or paler strip at rear of elytra. *Pronotum*: reddish-brown with black patch at base (male); black (female). *Head colour*: reddish-brown (male); black (female). *Leg colour*: reddish-brown. *Other features*: hairy; reddish-brown antennae and mouthparts.

Ecology

Habitats: heathland and other dry habitats particularly on chalky or sandy soils.

Host plants: low down on low-growing vegetation; occasionally on deciduous trees such as oak.

Food: aphids.

Overwintering sites: low herbage; moss.

UK conservation designation Nationally notable B

UK distribution status Very local

UK distribution trend (1990-2010) Stable

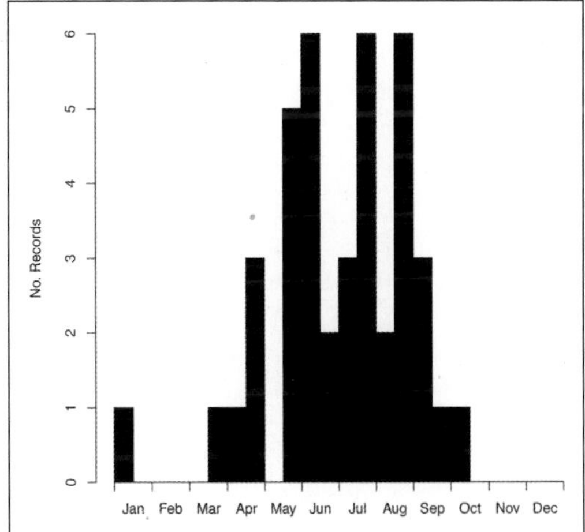

Figure 189. Phenogram for *Scymnus femoralis*.

Scymnus schmidti Fürsch, 1958

Subgenus *Scymnus* Kugelann, 1794
Synonyms *Scymnus pygmaeus* sensu auctt. Brit. partim non (Geoffroy in Fourcroy, 1785)
Scymnus frontalis var. *immaculatus* sensu auctt. Brit. partim non Suffrian, 1843
Scymnus mimulus Capra & Fürsch, 1967

Number of records 142
Number of 10km squares 73

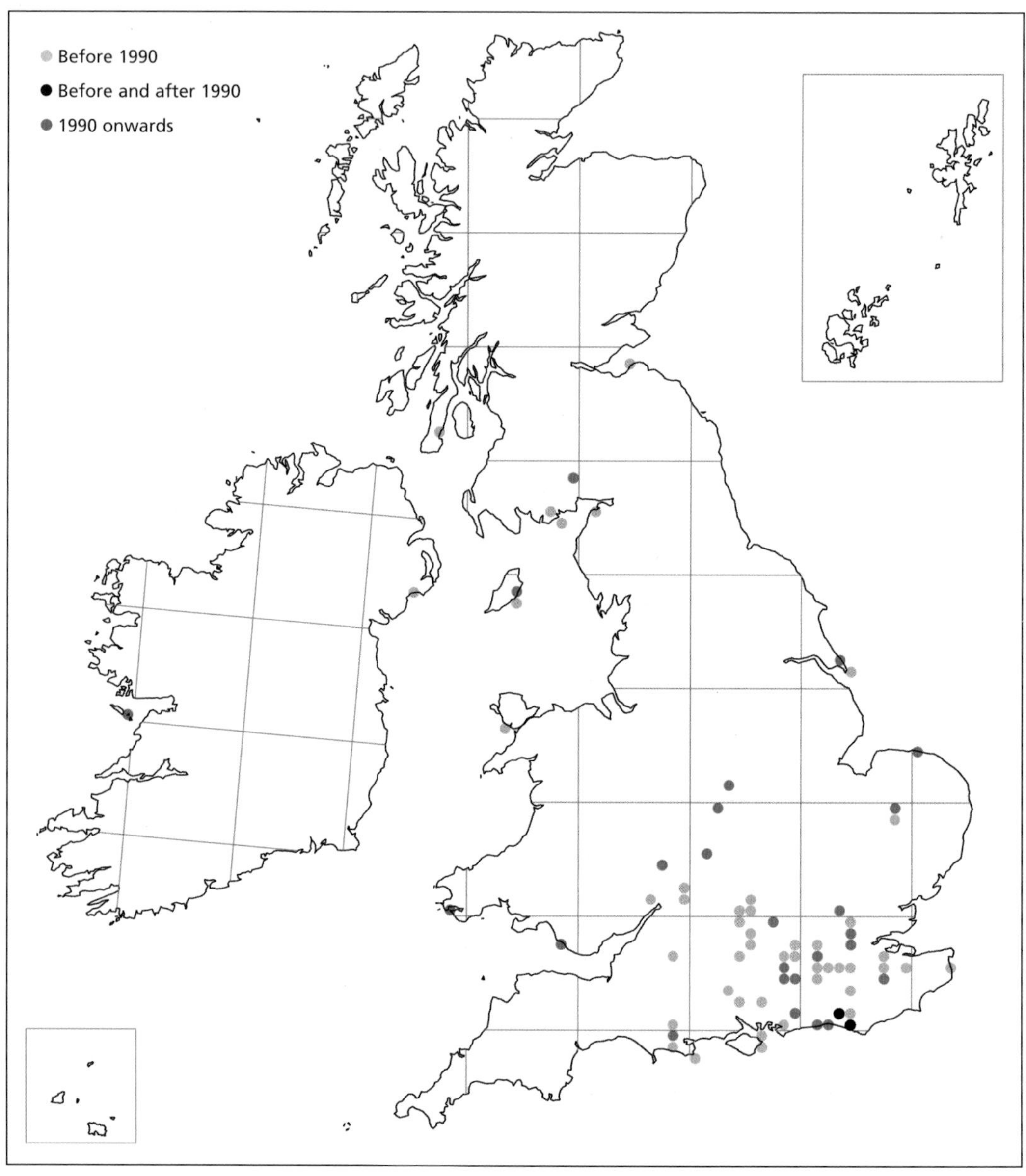

Map 43. Distribution (10km) of *Scymnus schmidti*.

Scymnus schmidti is similar to, but rather larger and less convex than *S. femoralis*, which is found in similar dry habitats. The pronotal patterns of the male also differ, those of *S. schmidti* being predominantly black, rather than reddish-brown. Outside of southern and central England, the records of *S. schmidti* are sparse and nearly all coastal.

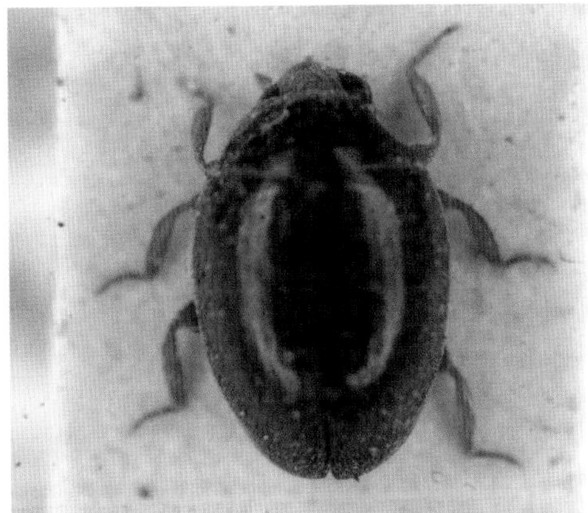

Figure 190. *Scymnus schmidti* adult male. Photo: Remy Poland.

Identification

Length: 2.4-2.6mm. *Background colour*: black. *Pattern*: none, or thin reddish margin at rear. *Pronotum*: black, with reddish anterior margins in male. *Head colour*: reddish (male); black (female). *Leg colour*: brown (male); black with brown tibiae (female). *Other features*: hairy.

Ecology

Habitats: dry grassland, dunes, heathland and chalk grassland.

Host plants: low down in low-growing vegetation.

Food: aphids.

Overwintering sites: low herbage; leaf litter.

UK conservation designation Nationally notable B

UK distribution status Very local

UK distribution trend (1990-2010) Stable

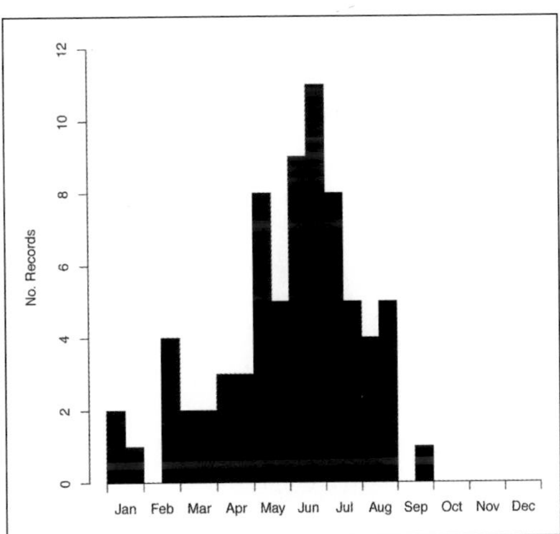

Figure 191. Phenogram for *Scymnus schmidti*.

Scymnus nigrinus Kugelann, 1794

Subgenus *Scymnus* Kugelann, 1794
Synonyms None

Number of records 110
Number of 10km squares 67

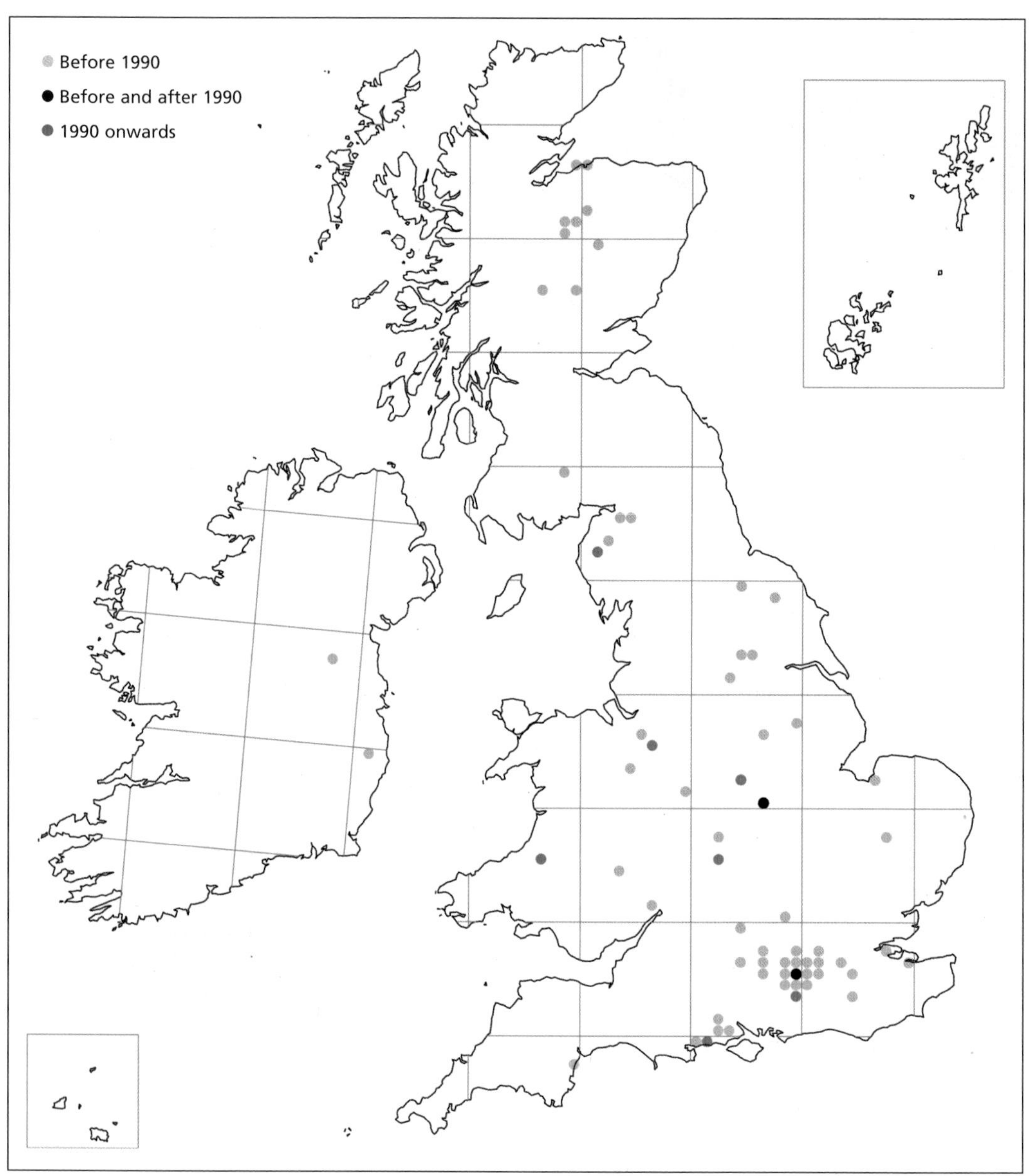

Map 44. Distribution (10km) of *Scymnus nigrinus*.

A rather specialist ladybird, Hawkins (2000) reported *Scymnus nigrinus* in Surrey almost exclusively from young pine trees. The habitat outlined by Majerus (1994) is rather broader, and in addition to pine trees, we have a few records of *S. nigrinus* on gorse, larch and even oak. However, there are very few recent records of the species. In Britain, *S. nigrinus* is the only species of its genus that is entirely black.

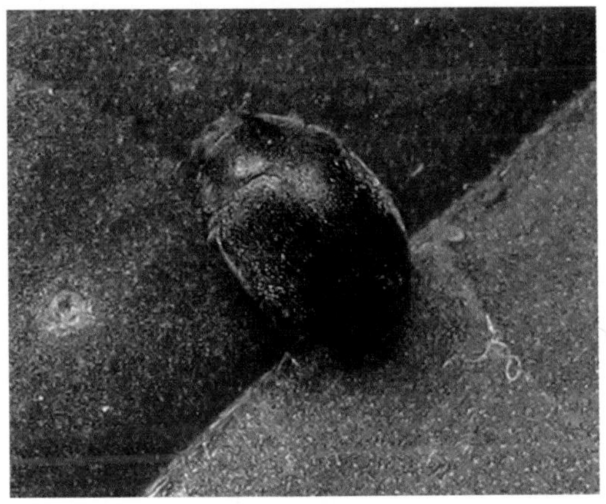

Figure 192. *Scymnus nigrinus* adult. Photo: Peter Brown.

Figure 193. *Scymnus nigrinus* adult. Photo: Remy Poland.

Identification

Length: 2-2.8mm. *Background colour*: black. *Pattern*: none. *Pronotum*: black. *Head colour*: black. *Leg colour*: black with pale to dark brown tarsi. *Other features*: hairy.

Ecology

Habitats: coniferous woodland and other habitats with coniferous trees.

Host plants: needled conifers, especially Scots pine trees; gorse.

Food: aphids, adelgids.

Overwintering sites: needled conifers, especially Scots pine trees – usually in bark crevices, in sheltered positions around buds and cones, or in cones.

UK distribution status Very local

UK distribution trend (1990-2010) Stable

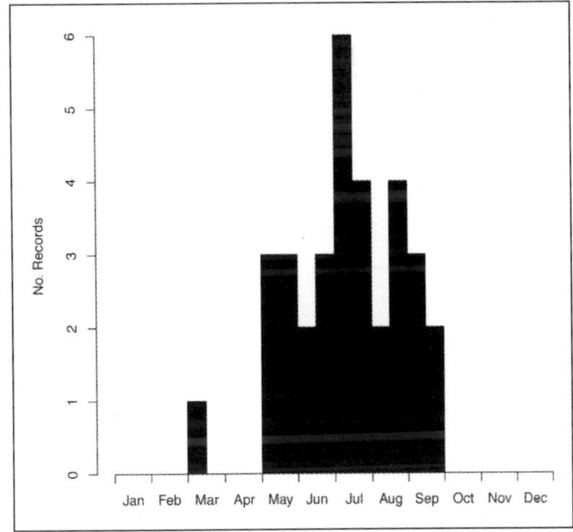

Figure 194. Phenogram for *Scymnus nigrinus*.

Scymnus limbatus Stephens, 1832

Subgenus *Neopullus* Sasaji, 1971
Synonyms *Scymnus testaceus* sensu auctt. Europ. ante 1967 non Motschulsky, 1837

Number of records: 77
Number of 10km squares: 51

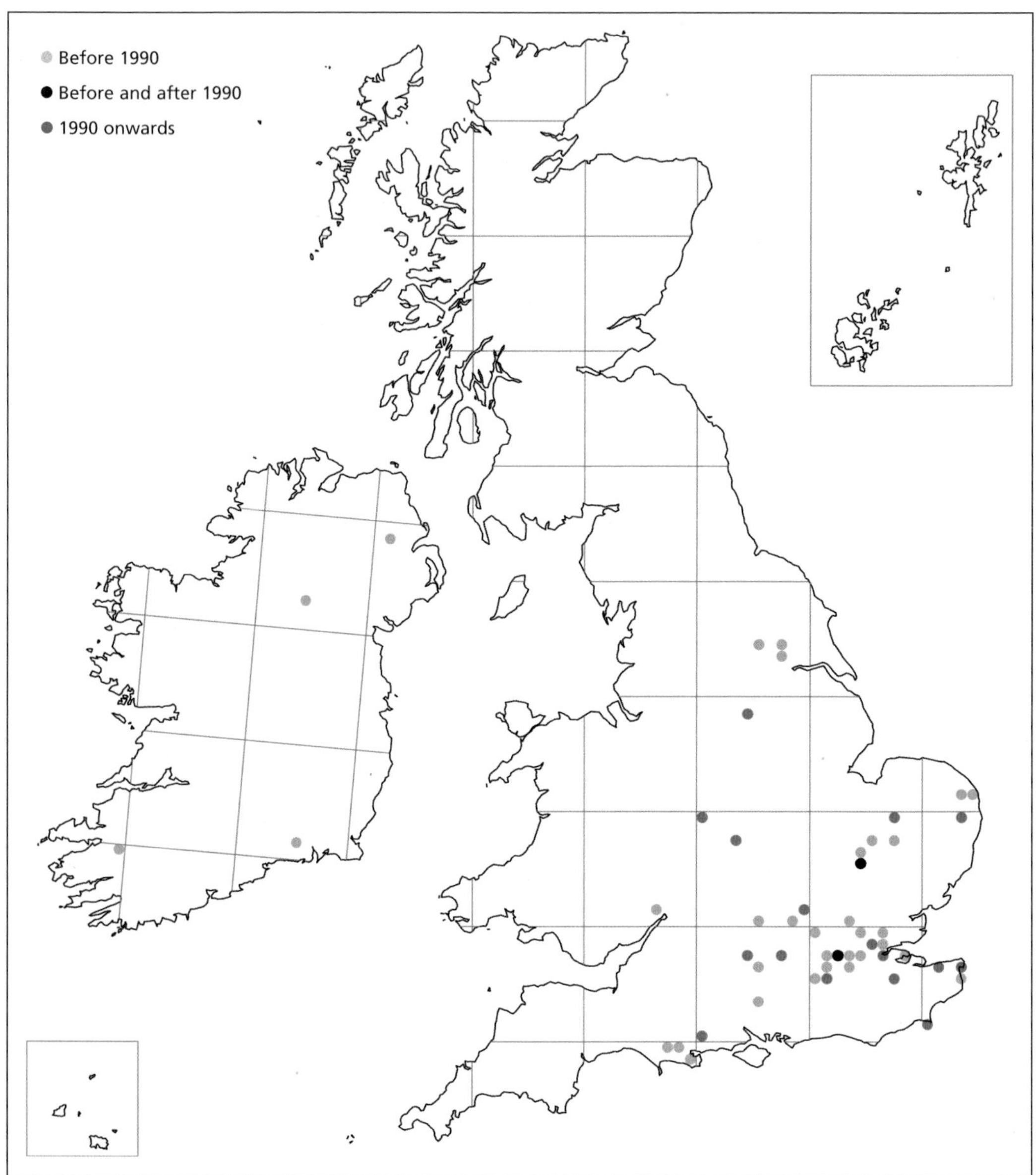

Map 45. Distribution (10km) of *Scymnus limbatus*.

Scymnus limbatus is similar to *S. suturalis*, but found in a distinctly different habitat; whilst *S. limbatus* is a species of deciduous trees in marshy habitats, *S. suturalis* is a conifer specialist. *Scymnus limbatus* is an uncommon species and there are very few recent records of it. All but one of our records came from England, the exception being a record from Summerhill, County Fermanagh, Northern Ireland, in 1905.

Figure 195. *Scymnus limbatus* adult.
Photo: Jo Bogaert.

Identification

Length: 1.6-2mm. *Background colour*: brown. *Pattern*: a broad dark brown to black strip running along the centre line, widening at the top and bottom. *Pronotum*: dark brown to black. *Head colour*: dark brown to black. *Leg colour*: brown. *Other features*: hairy.

Ecology

Habitats: deciduous trees in marshy habitats.

Host plants: willows; poplars; sometimes other deciduous trees such as elm.

Food: aphids, coccids.

Overwintering sites: bark crevices and under bark of willows and poplars.

UK conservation designation Nationally notable B

UK distribution status Very local

UK distribution trend (1990-2010) Stable (based on 100 records or less)

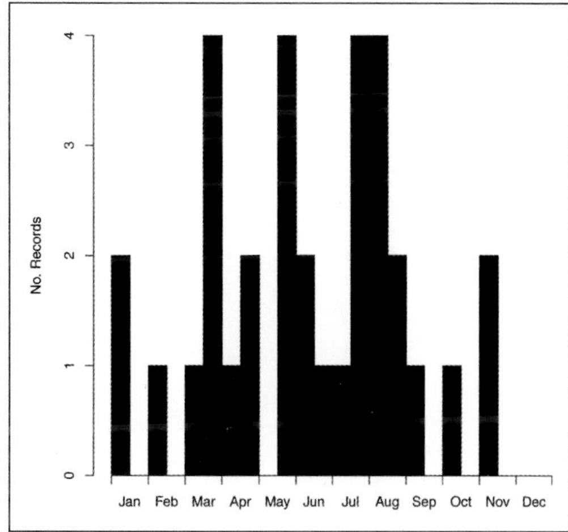

Figure 196. Phenogram for *Scymnus limbatus*.

Scymnus interruptus (Goeze, 1777)

Subgenus *Scymnus* Kugelann, 1794
Synonyms None

Number of records 20
Number of 10km squares 9

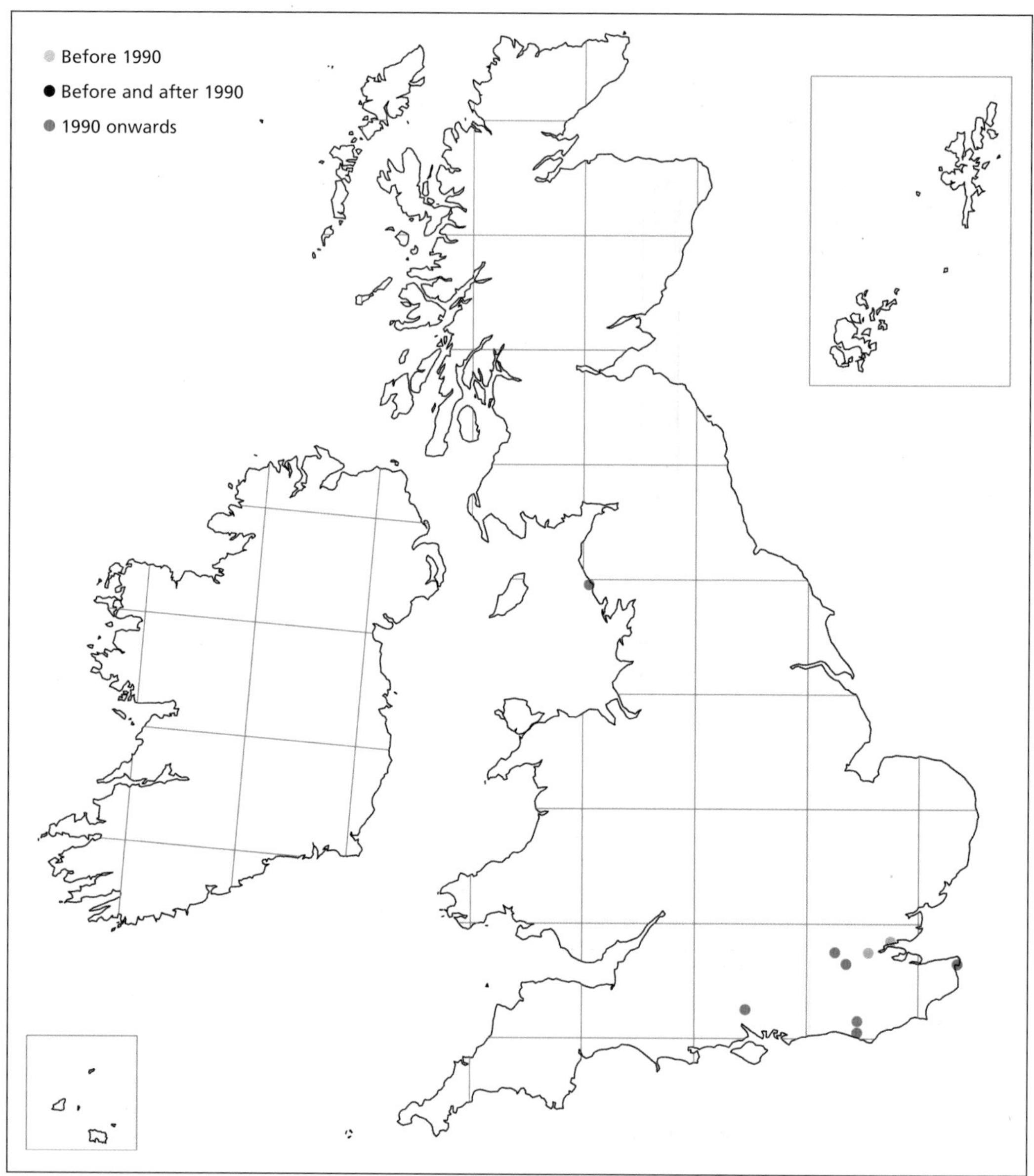

Map 46. Distribution (10km) of *Scymnus interruptus*.

Scymnus interruptus is a relatively common species in parts of continental Europe, including western France, where it occurs in diverse habitats including gardens and houses (le Monnier & Livory, 2003) and in Portugal, in citrus groves (Magro & Hemptinne, 1999). However, we have very few records of the species, most of them contributed by Peter Hodge. With the exception of a single record from 1986, all records are from 1996 or later. Most of the records are coastal, all but one coming from south-east England, suggesting that *S. interruptus* is an occasional migrant from Europe, rather than established in Britain. Several of the records reported the species on ivy. *Scymnus interruptus* tends to have a prominent triangular-shaped red spot on each elytron.

Figure 197. *Scymnus interruptus* adult.
Photo: Jo Bogaert.

Figure 198. *Scymnus interruptus* adult.
Photo: Peter Brown.

Identification

Length: 1.5-2.2 mm. *Background colour*: black. *Pattern*: two red spots (roughly triangular in shape) at the front edges of the elytra. *Pronotum*: black. *Head colour*: black. *Leg colour*: brown. *Other features*: hairy.

Ecology

Habitats: diverse, including gardens, on hedges or trees.

Host plants: unknown in Britain, but possibly include ivy.

Food: pseudococcids (mealybugs), diaspidids.

Overwintering sites: unknown.

UK distribution status Very local

UK distribution trend (1990-2010) Stable (based on 100 records or less)

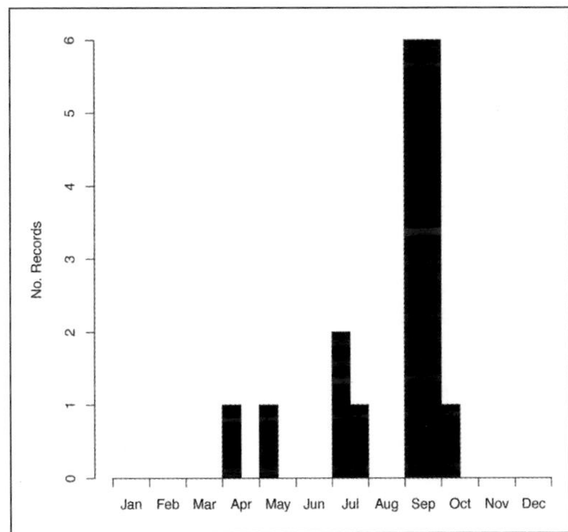

Figure 199. Phenogram for *Scymnus interruptus*.

Nephus redtenbacheri (Mulsant, 1846)

Synonyms *Scymnus testaceus* sensu auctt. Brit. non (Motschulsky, 1837)
Scymnus mulsanti (Waterhouse, G.R., 1862)
Scymnus lividus (Bold, 1872)
Scymnus limonii (Donisthorpe, 1903)

Number of records 393
Number of 10km squares 226

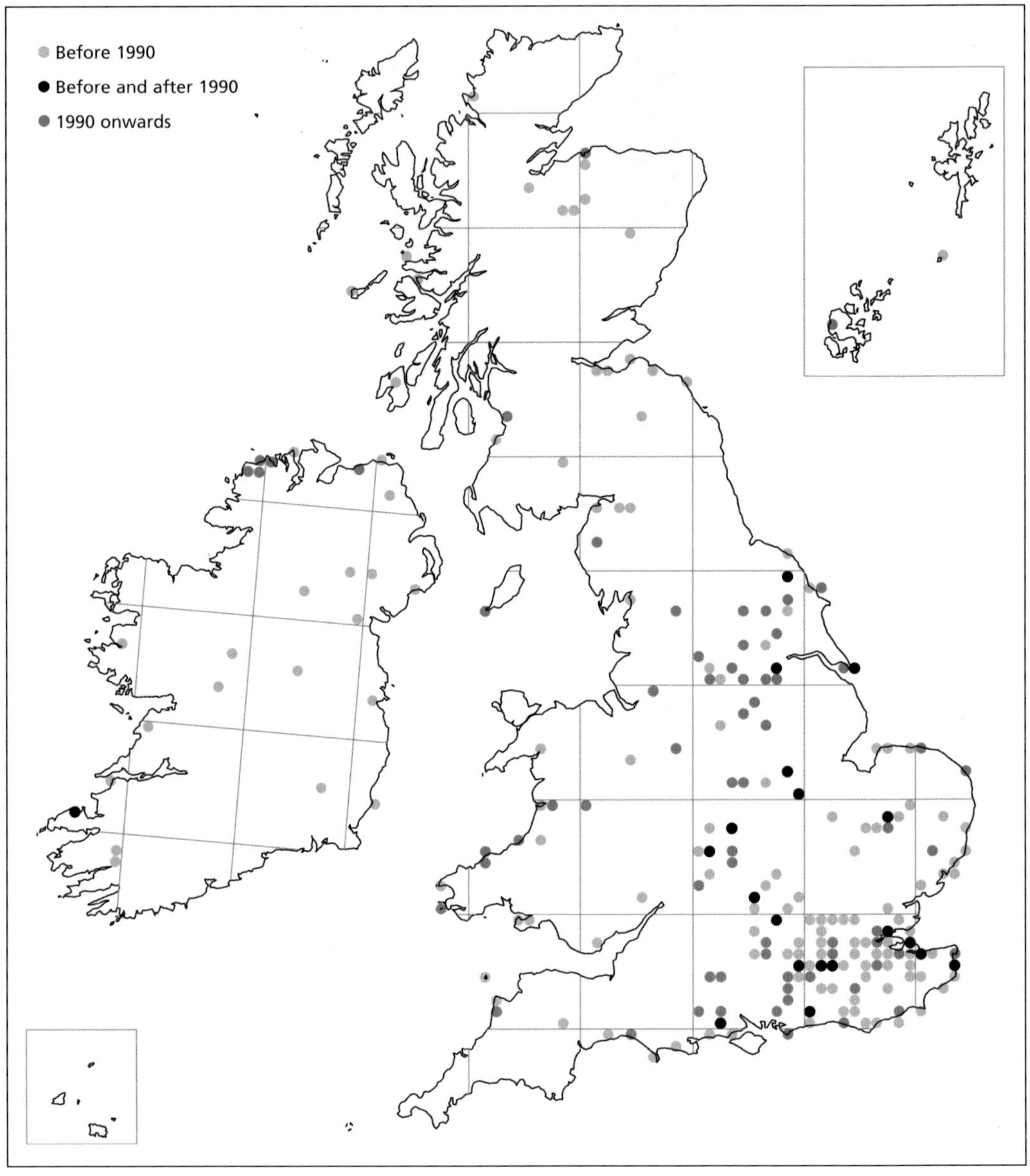

Map 47. Distribution (10km) of *Nephus redtenbacheri*.

Nephus redtenbacheri is a habitat generalist that is widespread across Britain and Ireland. It is reported to feed on both mealybugs (a type of mobile scale insect) and aphids (Kuznetsov, 1997). *Nephus redtenbacheri* may tend to favour coastal habitats, including dunes, but there are also many inland records of the species. Its black elytra bear characteristic kidney-shaped reddish-brown patches.

Figure 200. *Nephus redtenbacheri* adult. Photo: Jo Bogaert.

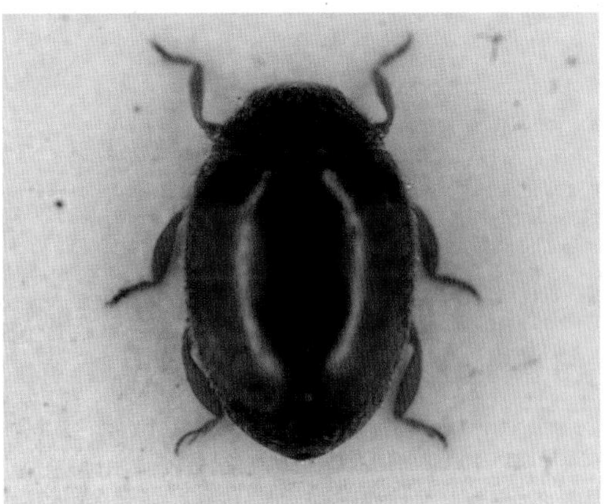

Figure 201. *Nephus redtenbacheri* adult. Photo: Remy Poland.

Identification

Length: 1.3-2.3mm. *Background colour*: black. *Pattern*: two large elongate reddish-brown ill-defined patches. *Pronotum*: black. *Head colour*: black. *Leg colour*: light to dark brown. *Other features*: hairy.

Ecology

Habitats: undisturbed grassland, dunes, heathland, bogs, quite often coastal.

Host plants: low-growing vegetation.

Food: pseudococcids (mealybugs), coccids, aphids.

Overwintering sites: low herbage; leaf litter; moss.

UK distribution status Local

UK distribution trend (1990-2010)
Decreasing

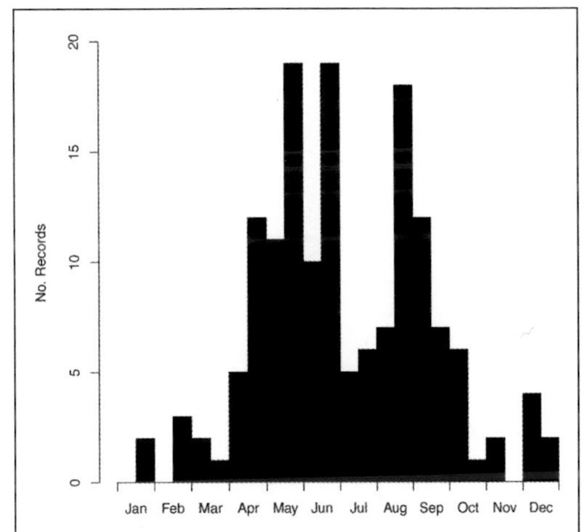

Figure 202. Phenogram for *Nephus redtenbacheri*.

Nephus quadrimaculatus (Herbst, 1783)

Synonyms *Nephus pulchellus* (Herbst, 1797)
Scymnus quadrimaculatus (Herbst, 1783)
Scymnus pulchellus (Herbst, 1797)

Number of records 101
Number of 10km squares 41

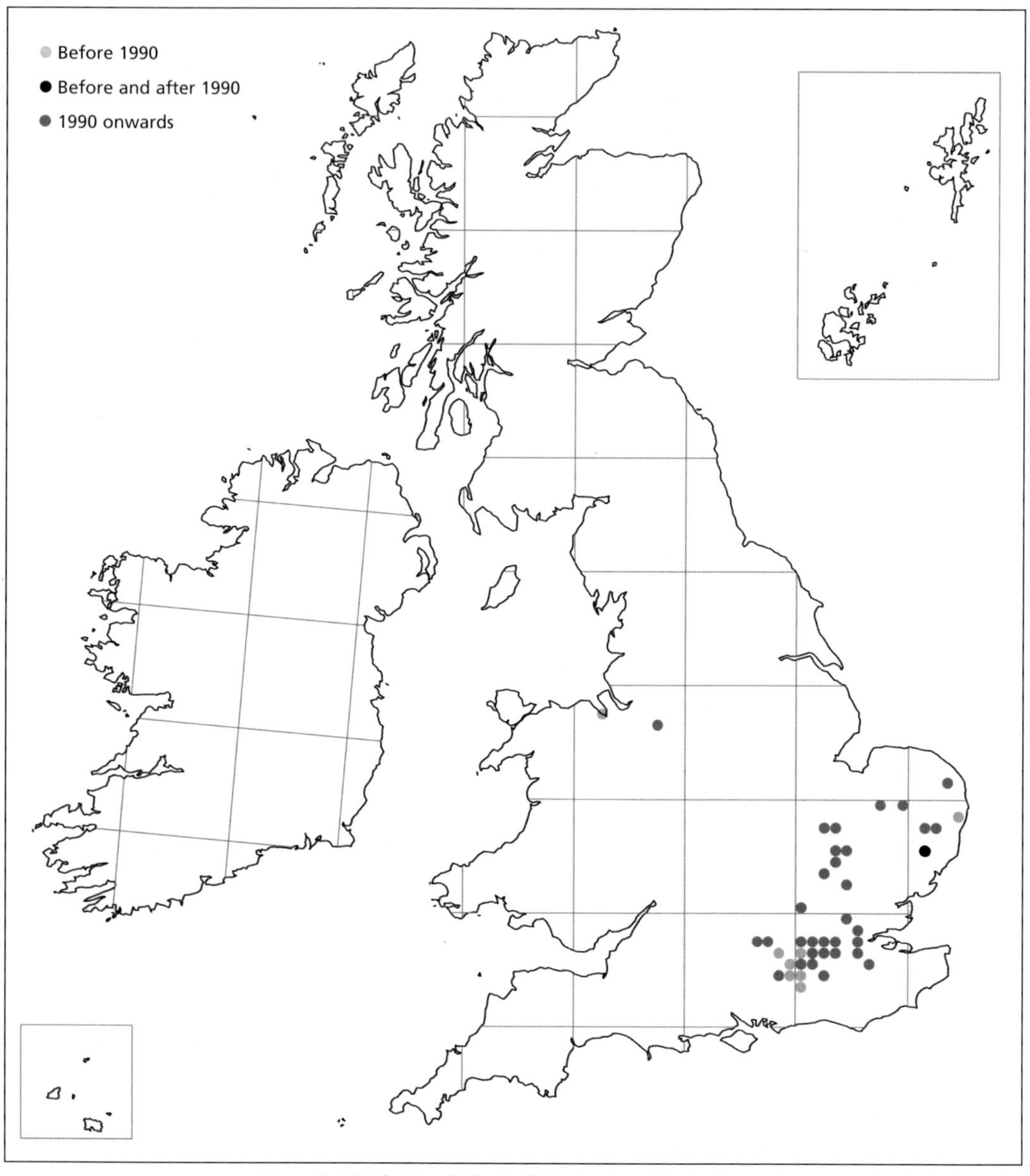

Map 48. Distribution (10km) of *Nephus quadrimaculatus.*

The uncommon ladybird *Nephus quadrimaculatus* is nearly always found in association with ivy. It can be found, sometimes in large numbers, in patches of ivy on garden walls and trees, as well as in woodlands. Once considered a rare species, with most records coming from Suffolk, it was found during the 1990s in other south-eastern counties, particularly Surrey, where it is now common. It is still largely restricted to south-east England, and three-quarters of our records have been made since 2000, suggesting that the species may still be increasing. As its name suggests, this species bears four distinctive markings on its elytra.

Figure 203. *Nephus quadrimaculatus* adult. Photo: Gilles San Martin.

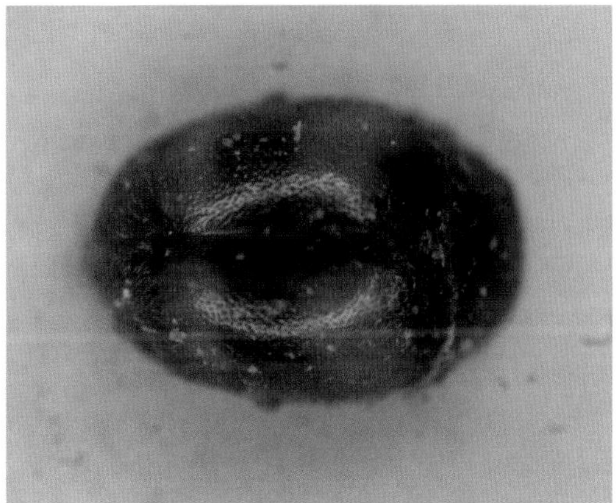

Figure 204. *Nephus quadrimaculatus* adult. Photo: Remy Poland.

Identification

Length: 1.5-2mm. *Background colour*: black. *Pattern*: two pairs of reddish-brown kidney-shaped spots, the anterior pair being larger than the posterior pair. *Pronotum*: black. *Head colour*: black. *Leg colour*: pale. *Other features*: hairy; abdomen has a reddish-brown tip.

Ecology

Habitats: gardens, woodlands and other habitats where ivy is prevalent.

Host plants: ivy.

Food: coccids.

Overwintering sites: probably in ivy.

UK conservation designation Vulnerable

UK distribution status Very local

UK distribution trend (1990-2010) Stable (based on 100 records or less)

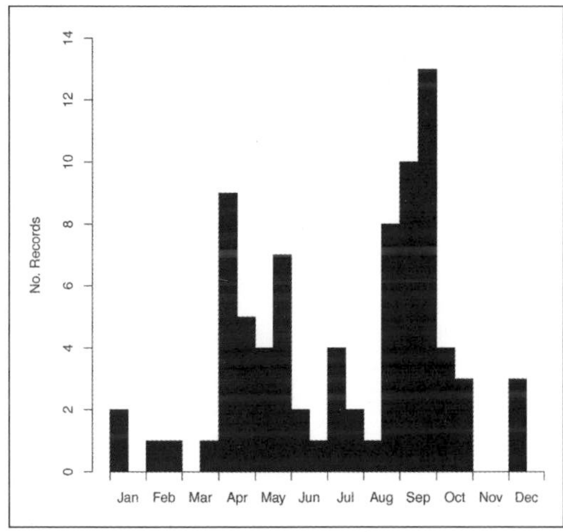

Figure 205. Phenogram for *Nephus quadrimaculatus*.

Nephus bisignatus (Boheman, 1850)

Synonyms *Scymnus bisignatus*
Nephus bohemani (Stenius, 1952)

Number of records 4
Number of 10km squares 3

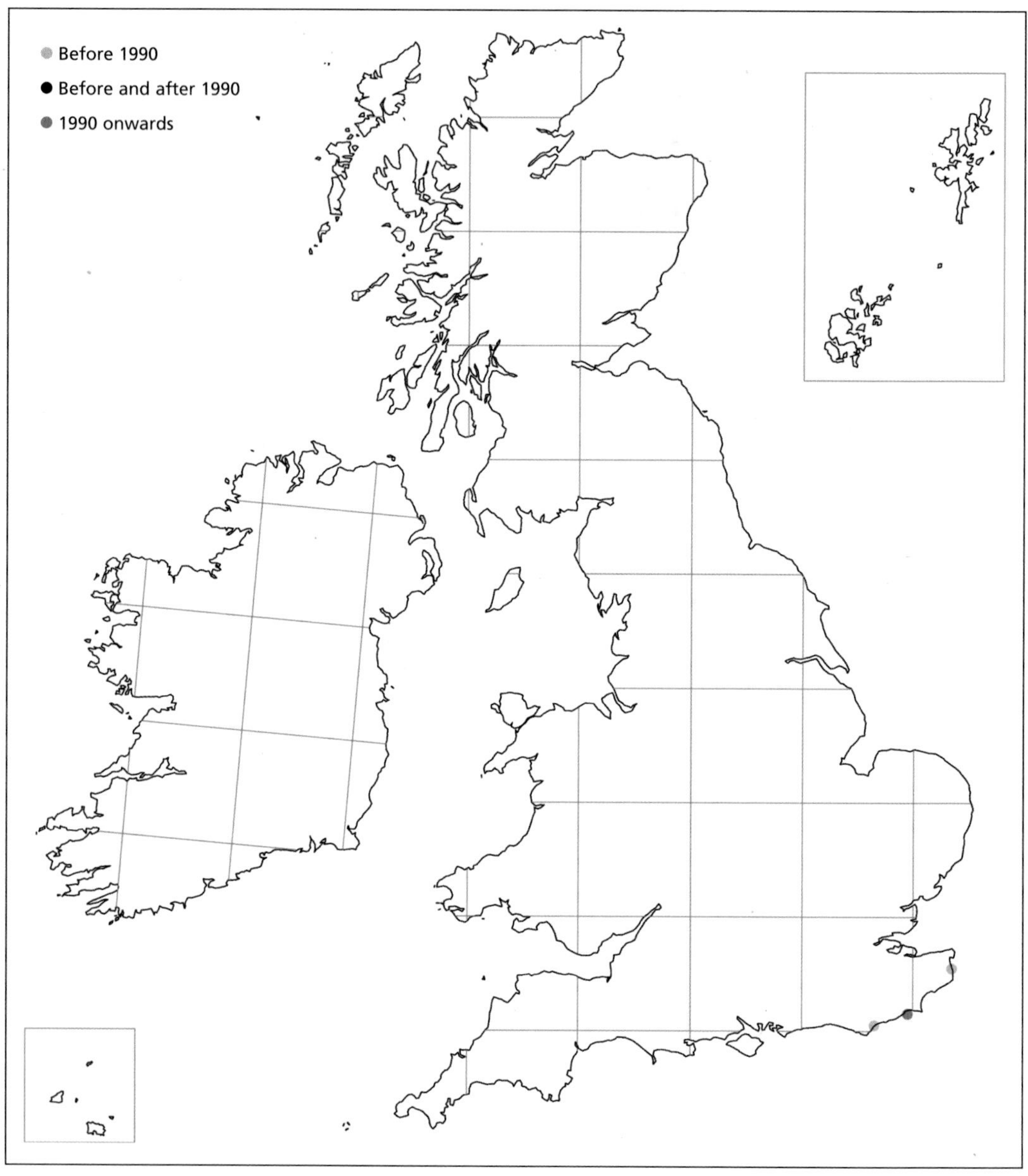

Map 49. Distribution (10km) of *Nephus bisignatus*.

Nephus bisignatus is now thought to be extinct in Britain (Majerus, 1994), although there is a single recent record, from Rye Harbour, East Sussex, in May 1996. Other than that we only know of two localities for the species (Deal, East Kent, and Pevensey Bay, East Sussex), both from pre-1940 museum records. In Europe, *N. bisignatus* has a wide distribution, including Scandinavia, the Netherlands, Germany, southern France, Italy, Portugal and Greece (Kontodimas *et al.*, 2007) and can be important in controlling mealybug populations, for example in vineyards.

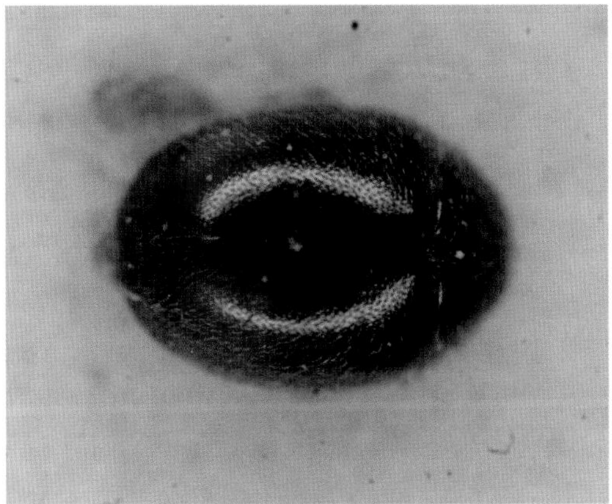

Figure 206. *Nephus bisignatus* adult.
Photo: Remy Poland.

Identification

Length: 1.5-2mm. *Background colour*: black. *Pattern*: two reddish-brown spots towards base of elytra. *Pronotum*: black. *Head colour*: black. *Leg colour*: brown. *Other features*: fine reddish-brown margin to base of elytra.

Ecology

Habitats: woodlands and other habitats with trees.

Host plants: possibly Leyland cypress and other related species.

Food: coccids, pseudococcids (mealybugs).

Overwintering sites: unknown.

UK conservation designation Extinct

UK distribution status Extinct

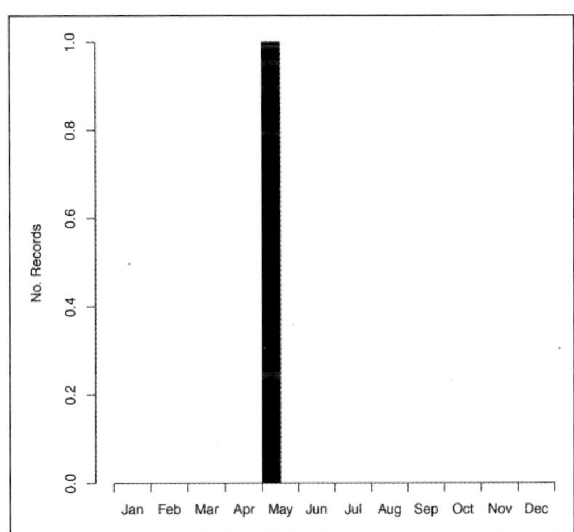

Figure 207. Phenogram for *Nephus bisignatus*.

Hyperaspis pseudopustulata Mulsant, 1853

Synonyms *Hyperaspis reppensis* sensu auctt. Brit. non (Herbst, 1783)

Number of records 134
Number of 10km squares 83

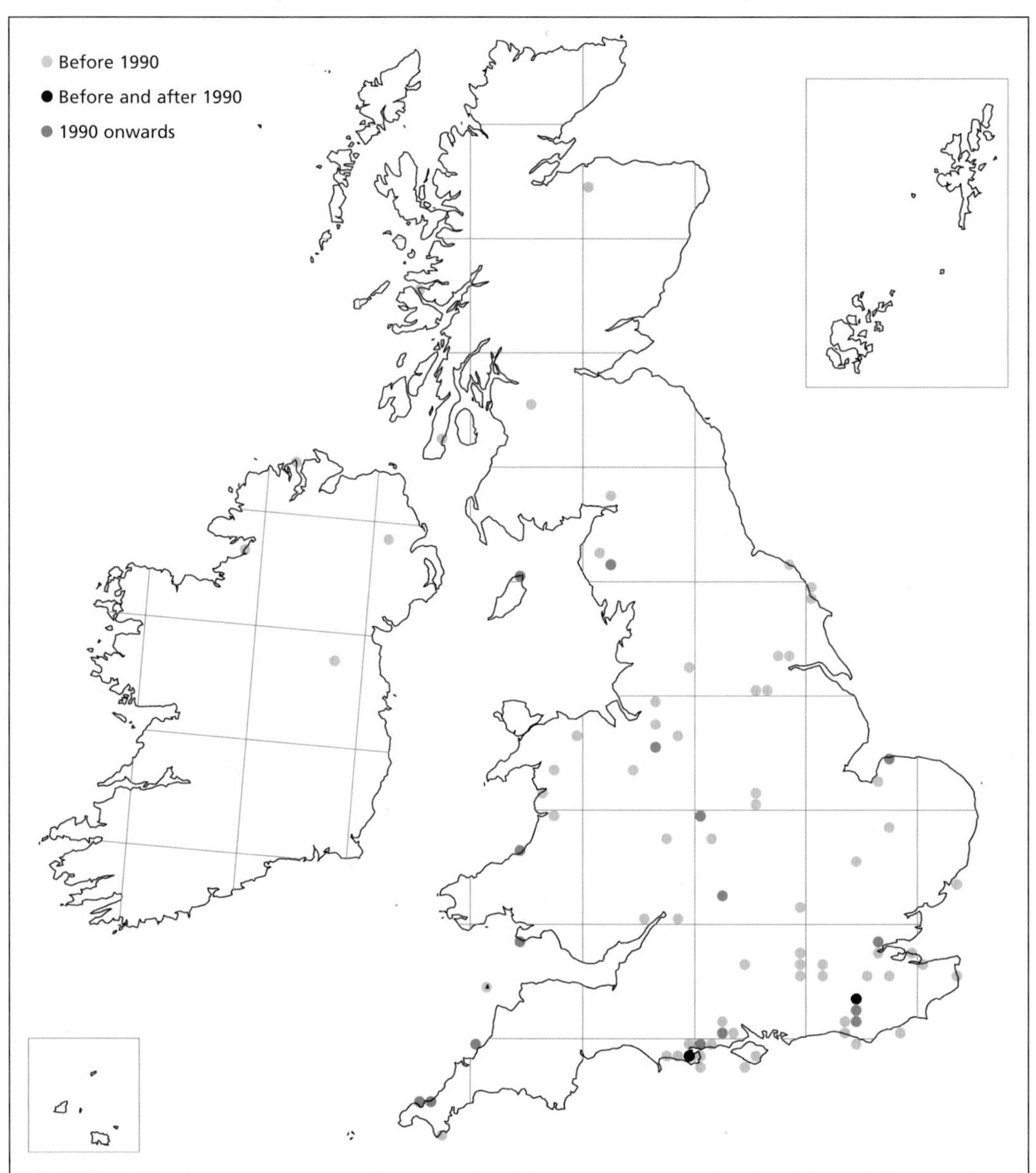

Map 50. Distribution (10km) of *Hyperaspis pseudopustulata.*

Unlike the other inconspicuous ladybirds, *Hyperaspis pseudopustulata* is shiny, hairless and reasonably large, and is easily recognisable as a ladybird. It is black with two small orangey-red spots towards the tips of the elytra. However, it is not an easy insect to find. Whilst *H. pseudopustulata* is widespread in England and Wales, there are few recent records of it there, and no recent records from Scotland or Ireland.

Figure 208. *Hyperaspis pseudopustulata* adult. Photo: Richard Comont.

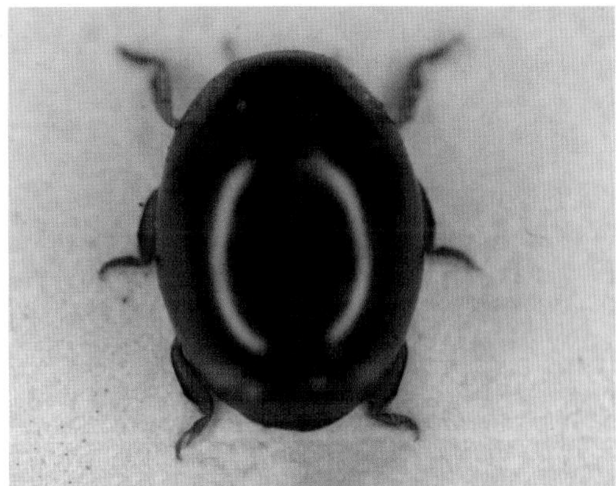

Figure 209. *Hyperaspis pseudopustulata* adult. Photo: Remy Poland.

Identification

Length: 3-4mm. *Background colour*: black. *Pattern*: two orangey-red spots near tips of elytra. *Pronotum*: black with an orangey-red anterior margin. *Head colour*: black and red. *Leg colour*: black and brown. *Other features*: hairless; mouthparts and antennae brown.

Ecology

Habitats: diverse but often coastal or wet habitats.

Host plants: low vegetation at water margins including reed and reedmace.

Food: aphids.

Overwintering sites: leaf litter and moss.

UK distribution status Very local

UK distribution trend (1990-2010) Stable

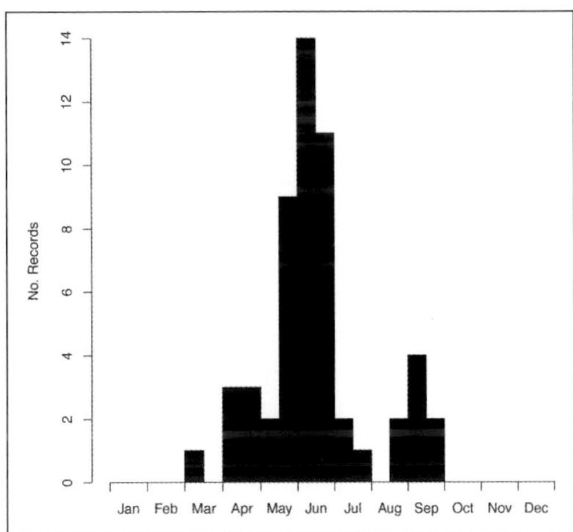

Figure 210. Phenogram for *Hyperaspis pseudopustulata*.

Occasional species and potential new arrivals

There are many more ladybird species in continental Europe than in Britain and Ireland; for example, the Netherlands has at least twenty more species than Britain. Some of these species have the capability to reach and survive in parts of south-east England, if not elsewhere in Britain and Ireland. Here, we outline several species that could become established in future years, plus others that formerly occurred in Britain.

Vibidia duodecimguttata was formerly on the British list of ladybird species and it has been recorded in England, Scotland and Ireland. However, all but one of the few records date back to the early 20th century or before. The most recent record in the BRC Coccinellidae Recording Scheme database is from Barna, on the west coast of Ireland, in 1973. *Vibidia duodecimguttata*, sometimes known as the 12-spot ladybird, is common in continental Europe but has probably only ever been an occasional migrant in Britain and Ireland (Majerus, 1994). It resembles the orange ladybird, but is smaller and generally has two fewer spots on each elytron. The similarities between these two species do not end there, as both feed on mildews and are usually found on deciduous trees.

Figure 211. *Vibidia duodecimguttata* adult.
Photo: Peter Brown.

Figure 212. *Cynegetis impunctata* adult.
Photo: Peter Brown.

Cynegetis impunctata was reported for the first time in Britain in 2006, when a single adult of the species was apparently found in Martin Down, Hampshire. Unfortunately this record was provided with photographic evidence only; a specimen is required for confirmation because this small red-brown and slightly hairy species resembles an unspotted 24-spot ladybird. However, *C. impunctata* was reported by Majerus (1994) to be abundant around the French terminus of the Channel Tunnel, and he argued that it was a strong candidate for immigration to Britain. It is likely to arrive as an accidental import on a ferry, car or train from Europe, rather than of its own accord, particularly as the species seems to lack the ability to fly (Kuznetsov, 1997). No further reports of the species have been received, so there is no evidence that it is established in Britain or Ireland.

Calvia decemguttata was recorded in Killarney, Ireland in 1927 and is known from a single 19th century record in the west of England (Majerus, 1994). *Calvia decemguttata* resembles the congeneric cream-spot ladybird and the orange ladybird, but generally has ten spots. It is roughly the same size as these species and, like the cream-spot ladybird, is an aphid-feeding species found on deciduous trees.

Figure 213. *Calvia decemguttata* adult.
Photo: Peter Brown.

Figure 214. *Oenopia conglobata* adult.
Photo: Peter Brown.

Oenopia conglobata is a pink ladybird that is common in trees in continental Europe, including coastal areas of Belgium and France (Majerus, 1994). Thus, although we have no records of this species in Britain or Ireland, it would not be surprising if this situation changes in the future.

Exochomus nigromaculatus is a black ladybird (with two orange-red markings on the pronotum, and orange-red legs) about the same size as its closest relation in Britain, the pine ladybird. *Exochomus nigromaculatus* is a species of dry heathland in continental Europe. The species had not been recorded in Britain since the 1830s until it was found near Doncaster in 1967 (Skidmore, 1985). We have no recent records of the species.

Natural enemies of ladybirds

"In spring 1999 I collected, on a loggia in the built-up area of Vienna, a two-spot ladybird with strikingly furred elytra. The greenish fur turned out to be a mass development of the fungus of the order Laboulbeniales, Hesperomyces virescens. *Another coccinellid parasite came to light when I lifted the beetle's wings: Acari of the family Podapolipidae, attached to the inner surface of the elytra. By picking up a single common beetle on my doorstep, I had happened to detect both a fungus and a mite species new to Austria."* Erhard Christian, 2001.

There are a number of predators, parasitoids, parasites and pathogens that exploit ladybirds as a source of nutrition and are, therefore, referred to as 'natural enemies'. Many species of ladybird contain a variety of bitter-tasting, toxic alkaloids and this, coupled with their bright 'warning' colours (aposematism), deters many potential natural enemies. About 50 different alkaloids have been identified in ladybirds. These are produced in the haemolymph and distributed throughout the ladybird's body. Ladybirds secrete haemolymph through the process of 'reflex bleeding', commonly observed as yellow droplets from the tibio-femoral (leg) articulations in adults, and pores in the dorsal surface of larvae and pupae. Immature stages of the Epilachninae (24-spot and bryony ladybirds) exude defensive secretions through glandular hairs. Methylalkylpyrazines are also present in ladybird reflex blood and the characteristic odour of ladybird reflex blood is attributed to the pyrazines, and provides an additional defence signal alongside the warning colouration. Pyrazines are generally absent from cryptic (inconspicuous) ladybirds (Daloze *et al.*, 1995).

Ladybirds also possess a number of physical defences. The elytra of adult ladybirds provide good protection. Similarly, ladybird pupae have relatively hard cuticles and some species retain the final larval skin which provides additional protection. Some immature stages are defended by spiny projections or wax covers (Majerus *et al.*, 2007). The abdominal tergites of ladybird pupae, as is the case for many Coleoptera, have heavily sclerotized margins between deep intersegmental clefts forming 'gin traps'; when a pupa is disturbed it raises and drops its body rapidly; the gin traps act as jaws.

The few natural enemies that overcome the defences of ladybirds are taxonomically diverse and have fascinating life histories.

Vertebrate predators

There are reports that ladybirds have been eaten by various vertebrate and invertebrate predators, despite their anti-predator defences. Fish, amphibians, reptiles, birds and mammals have all been listed as predators of ladybirds, but most research has been on birds. Birds that feed on the wing, such as swifts, swallows and housemartins, often ingest ladybirds (Majerus & Majerus, 1997a).

Invertebrate predators

Ladybirds are frequently found in the webs of spiders but are not generally thought to be consumed by the spider. Hunting spiders rarely attack Coleoptera species (Nentwig, 1986). Phytophagous (plant-feeding) ladybirds are prey to a number of predatory insects including

Coleoptera (predatory Coccinellidae, Carabidae, Cantharidae), Hemiptera (Anthocoridae, Nabidae, Reduviidae, Pentatomidae, Lygaeidae), Neuroptera (Chrysopidae, Myrmeleontidae), Lepidoptera (larvae of some Noctuidae), Dermaptera (Forficulidae) and Hymenoptera (Formicidae). Predatory ladybirds prey on one another and are also prey to other insects such as lacewings, gomphid dragonflies (Odonata: Gomphidae), robber flies (Diptera: Asilidae) and vespid wasps (Hymenoptera: Vespidae). Ants occasionally kill predatory ladybirds, although it is more common for ant-ladybird interactions to be competitive rather than predatory. The myrmecophilous (ant-loving) ladybirds are, of course, an exception to this and are ignored by the ants, so gaining access to prey resources defended from other predators.

Figure 215. Harlequin ladybird caught in the web of a garden spider.
Photo: Mathew Killen.

Parasitoids

Ladybirds are attacked by a number of taxonomically diverse insect parasitoids. In some cases, the parasitoids are restricted to hosts within the Coccinellidae, while others have a broad host range, parasitising members of various insect families and orders. In addition, the primary parasitoids are often themselves host to many secondary parasitoids or 'hyperparasitoids'. More than 150 parasitoids have been reported associated with ladybirds worldwide (Ceryngier *et al.*, in press) and 40 of these are considered to be hyperparasitoids. Most parasitoid records relate to the subfamilies Coccinellinae, Epilachninae, Chilocorinae and Scymninae; indeed there are 52 parasitoid species recorded from Epilachninae. Parasitoids have been encountered in all developmental stages of ladybirds but larvae and pupae are attacked more often than eggs and adults. The four most commonly observed parasitoids in Britain are *Phalacrotophora fasciata* and *P. berolinensis* (Diptera), and *Oomyzus scaposus* and *Dinocampus coccinellae* (Hymenoptera).

Dinocampus coccinellae Förster (Hymenoptera: Braconidae, Euphorinae)

Synonyms *Dinocampus terminatus* (Nees)
Perilitus americanus Riley
P. coccinellae (Schrank)
P. terminatus (Nees)

Dinocampus is a genus of a single species. *Dinocampus coccinellae* has a worldwide distribution including all continents except Antarctica and has been reported to parasitise 40 ladybird species worldwide (13 in Britain). *Dinocampus coccinellae* is generally considered a solitary parasitoid of adult ladybirds of the subfamily Coccinellinae; however, the pine ladybird (Chilocorinae) has recently been recorded as a host (R. Poland & R. Comont, personal observation). Ladybird larvae and pupae have occasionally been reported as successful hosts to *D. coccinellae*. The level of parasitisation of ladybirds by *D. coccinellae* fluctuates considerably with locality, season and host. Parasitisation rates in Scotland were shown in one study to exceed 70% (Geoghegan *et al.*, 1997), but lower prevalence is more usual. Mean parasitisation rates can vary between 20% for 11-spot, cream-streaked and 7-spot ladybirds, to 9.7% for 5-spot ladybirds and rates below 5% for nine other species (Majerus, 1997).

Figure 216. *Dinocampus coccinellae* larva emerging from a 7-spot ladybird. Photo: Paul Brothers.

Figure 217. *Dinocampus coccinellae* larva spinning cocoon after emerging from a 7-spot ladybird. Photo: Rachael Hardie.

Figure 218. *Dinocampus coccinellae* pupa with 7-spot ladybird host. Photo: Remy Poland.

Figure 219. *Dinocampus coccinellae* adult and pupa with harlequin ladybird host. Photo: Richard Comont.

Identification

Larva: yellow maggot (10mm long) usually emerging from underside of the adult host. *Pupa*: straw-brown coloured silken cocoon (5mm long) spun between the legs of the host. *Adult*: small black and brown wasp (5mm long) with characteristic dark spot located midway at the top of the membranous forewing.

Ecology

Geographic range: worldwide; native range considered to be Europe and also possibly North America.

Host range: usually adult ladybirds within the subfamily Coccinellinae. Unlike most parasitoids, *D. coccinellae* larvae do not feed directly on the host tissues after the first instar but instead feed on cells derived from the parasitoid egg called teratocytes.

Reproduction: production of females from unfertilised eggs (thelytokous parthenogenesis) but males are produced on rare occasions and some strains produce males or females from unfertilised eggs (deuterotokous parthenogenesis).

Voltinism: multivoltine (two to three generations per year).

Overwintering: first-instar larva, or occasionally as an egg, within its host.

Life cycle: development can take place in both active hosts (lasting two to three weeks) and in dormant hosts (parasitoid diapauses with the host). The parasitoid egg hatches within the host's body and the emergent larva passes through three instars. The final-instar larva emerges from the host ladybird through the abdomen. It then spins a silken cocoon between the legs of the host and pupates. The ladybird usually dies within a few days from starvation. The duration of the pupal stage of *D. coccinellae* is about seven to ten days.

UK distribution status Ubiquitous

Phalacrotophora Enderlein (Diptera: Phoridae)

There are more than 50 described species within the genus *Phalacrotophora* but only two species are regularly recorded in Britain as gregarious endoparasitoids of ladybird pupae: *P. fasciata* and

Figure 220. *Phalacrotophora* investigating pre-pupal harlequin ladybird. Photo: Remy Poland.

Figure 221. *Phalacrotophora* investigating pre-pupal harlequin ladybird. Photo: Remy Poland.

Figure 222. *Phalacrotophora* ovispositing. Photo: Michael Majerus.

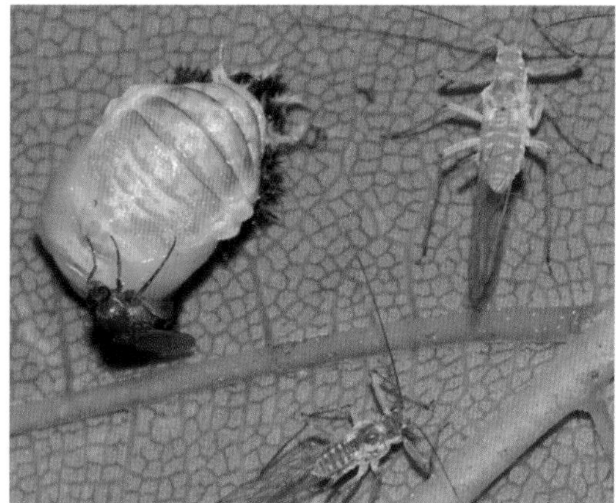

Figure 223. *Phalacrotophora* investigating a newly formed harlequin ladybird pupa. Photo: Brian Reid.

P. berolinensis. A further European species, *P. beuki*, described in 1997 (Disney & Beuk, 1997), was recognised as a monophagous parasitoid of eyed ladybirds (Durska *et al.*, 2003). The rate of parasitisation varies from year to year between host species and localities. Very high rates of parasitisation have been reported: for example, 80% for 7-spot ladybirds by *P. fasciata* and *P. berolinensis* (Disney *et al.*, 1994). Interestingly, a single host can be parasitised by both *P. fasciata* and *P. berolinensis* – a case of interspecific 'superparasitism'.

Identification

Final-instar larva: small (3mm) maggot (usually three to twelve per host depending on host size). *Pupa*: small (2-3mm) brown cocoons. *Adult*: *P. fasciata* and *P. berolinensis* are small (3mm) brown flies and can only be reliably distinguished by genitalia examination, although the first segment of the hind foot (metatarsus) of *P. fasciata* tends to be broader and darker than the narrower, yellow-brown metatarsus of *P. berolinensis*.

Ecology

Geographic range: worldwide.

Host range: ladybird pupae (although, rarely, pre-pupae can also be successfully parasitised) within the subfamily Coccinellinae.

Voltinism: multivoltine.

Overwintering: on the soil surface or upper soil layers as adults within the puparia.

Life cycle: adult female locates a ladybird pre-pupa, attracts males, mates and then lays eggs either on or just under the surface of the pupa. The eggs hatch within 24 hours and the larvae then enter the host and development proceeds rapidly (two to 12 days). Final-instar parasitoid larvae leave the ladybird pupa ventrally between the head and thorax, dropping to the ground where they pupate on the surface or in the upper soil layer. The flies either emerge as adults after 15-25 days or overwinter (Disney & Chazeau, 1990; Disney *et al.*, 1994). The number of individual parasitoids developing in a single host is related to host size. So, in pupae of large hosts such as eyed and 7-spot ladybirds, an average of seven to ten larvae are usually reported (although more than 20 have been recorded from a single host); in contrast, only two to three develop from 2-spot ladybirds (Disney, 1979; Disney *et al.*, 1994). There is also a trade-off between the number of larvae developing and their size; the more larvae that develop within a host, the smaller each individual larva.

UK status In south and south-east England *P. fasciata* is ubiquitous, and elsewhere *P. berolinensis* is ubiquitous

Oomyzus scaposus (Thomson) (Hymenoptera: Eulophidae, Tetrastichinae)

Synonyms *Tetrastichus coccinellae* Kurdjumov
T. melanis Burks
T. sexmaculatus Chandy Kurian
Syntomosphyrus taprobanes Waterston

Oomyzus scaposus (a wasp of the group commonly called chalcids) is thought to be the most widely distributed and common of all ladybird larval and pupal parasitoid species. It occurs in the Nearctic, Palaearctic, Oriental and Australasian regions, with reports from high latitudes in the Northern Hemisphere, even beyond the Arctic Circle, through the tropics to temperate areas in the Southern Hemisphere.

A related gregarious parasitoid that resembles *O. scaposus* is *Aprostocetus neglectus*. It can be distinguished by the presence of 6-7 setae on the upper surface of the submarginal vein, as opposed to the one present for *O. scaposus*. There is very little known about the ecology of this parasitoid other than it parasitises pupae and, occasionally, late larval stages of ladybirds. There are records in Britain from two host species: pine ladybird (Sheffield in 2002) and *Adalia* spp. (Oxfordshire, 2010; R. Comont, personal observation). It is widespread across continental Europe, where it has also been recorded from the heather ladybird.

Figure 224. Exit hole in a 7-spot pupa formed by emerging *Oomyzus scaposus*. Photo: Remy Poland.

Figure 225. *Oomyzus scaposus* adult. Photo: Remy Poland.

Identification

Species within the Tetrastichinae are extremely difficult to determine taxonomically (LaSalle 1993) and, accordingly, records should be treated with caution. Larval and pupal stages are within the host. *Adult*: Small (2 mm) black-bodied wasps.

Ecology

Geographic range: worldwide.

Host range: wide. Many ladybird species including Coccinellinae, Chilocorinae, and Scymninae but there also reports of infection of *Chrysopa* spp. (Neuroptera: Chrysopidae).

Voltinism: multivoltine.

Overwintering: diapauses as prepupae inside the dead host.

Life cycle: Female O. *scaposus* usually lay eggs in third- and fourth-instar ladybird larvae. The female may oviposit up to three times into the same host and then feeds on the fluid exuding from the oviposition holes in the host (Semyanov, 1986). Many O. *scaposus* individuals can develop successfully within a single host (up to 47 individuals in 7-spot ladybirds) and emerge as adult wasps, usually from the pupal stage of the host, after about 15 to 20 days. The wasps are sexually mature at emergence and mate within a few minutes of emerging (Iperti, 1964).

UK distribution status Ubiquitous

Medina (= Degeeria) separata (Meigen) (Diptera: Tachinidae)

There is one additional parasitoid worthy of brief mention, the endoparasitoid *Medina (= Degeeria) separata*. This species has commonly been misidentified as M. *luctuosa*, but M. *luctuosa* is specific to adult chrysomelids of the genus *Haltica*. Therefore, such records are doubtful and most likely to be M. *separata*. *Medina separata* has been recorded from 10-spot, cream-spot and eyed ladybirds in Britain, and from a range of other species in continental Europe, including 2-spot, 14-spot, larch and pine ladybirds. *Medina luctuosa* has been reported from harlequin ladybirds in Korea (Kenis *et al.*, 2008), but the true identity of this parasitoid is most likely to be M. *separata* (Tschorsnig & Herting, 1994). The eggs of the parasitoid are thought to be laid singly because only one larva will develop in a host. The adult host is killed when the parasitoid consumes its vital organs. The parasitoid larva emerges through the upper abdominal wall, and pupates in the soil, emerging about a week later. This rarely reported parasitoid is certainly one to look out for.

Mites (Acari)

Mites found on ladybirds can be truly parasitic or phoretic (simply hitchhiking between hosts). This latter, phoretic group includes species in the order Astigmata which prey on coccids and other hemipterans. The parasitic mites recorded from ladybirds include some generalist species, such as *Leptus ignotus*, that parasitise a wide variety of arthropods (Hurst *et al.*, 1997) and mites of the genus *Coccipolipus* that specialise on ladybirds.

Coccipolipus Husband (Prostigmata: Podapolipidae)

The mite genus *Coccipolipus* includes 14 species known to be parasitic on ladybirds. Many of these mite species are tropical, but the most understood is the widely distributed *Coccipolipus hippodamiae* (recorded from the United States, Russia, central and eastern Europe and the Democratic Republic of Congo). This species is the causative agent of a sexually transmitted disease which results in sterility of female hosts (Webberley *et al.*, 2006). *Coccipolipus hippodamiae* has recently been found infecting the invasive alien harlequin ladybird in parts of North America and Europe; infection causes females to become sterile within three weeks (Rhule *et al.*, 2010).

Figure 226. Various life stages of *Coccipolipus hippodamiae* on the underside of a ladybird wingcase. Photo: Emma Rhule.

Identification

Larva: small pale mites with legs. *Adult*: sedentary orange mite with central white stripe.

Ecology

Geographic range: worldwide. *Coccipolipus hippodamiae* is considered to be absent from ladybirds in Britain (although this mite has occasionally been reported from scarce 7-spot ladybirds), also coastal areas of north-west continental Europe, and is scarce in Scandinavia, due to limited intergenerational mating of the ladybird (Majerus, 1994).

Host range: wide. Many ladybird species including Coccinellinae, Epilachninae and Chilocorinae.

Voltinism: multivoltine.

Overwintering: all stages on the underside of the host elytra.

Life cycle: All stages of *C. hippodamiae* live on the underside of the elytra of ladybirds (Majerus, 1994), where the adult females feed on host haemolymph by embedding their jaws into the elytra or, on occasions, the abdomen. The motile mite larvae emerge from eggs and migrate between hosts during sexual contact (Webberley & Hurst, 2002) and, on rare occasions, through close proximity during host overwintering. Larvae, arriving on a new host, metamorphose into adults after attachment by their mouthparts to the host. Thereafter, adult mites are entirely sedentary. These mites can only establish within a host population if there are high levels of promiscuity and overlapping generations.

UK distribution status Not established

Nematodes

Studies have demonstrated that ladybirds may be susceptible to entomopathogenic nematodes belonging to several families, such as Steinernematidae (Shapiro-Ilan & Cottrell, 2005), Heterorhabditidae (Shapiro-Ilan & Cottrell, 2005), Allantonematidae (Iperti, 1964) or Mermithidae (Iperti, 1964). However, only the members of the latter two families have been reported to parasitise ladybirds in the wild.

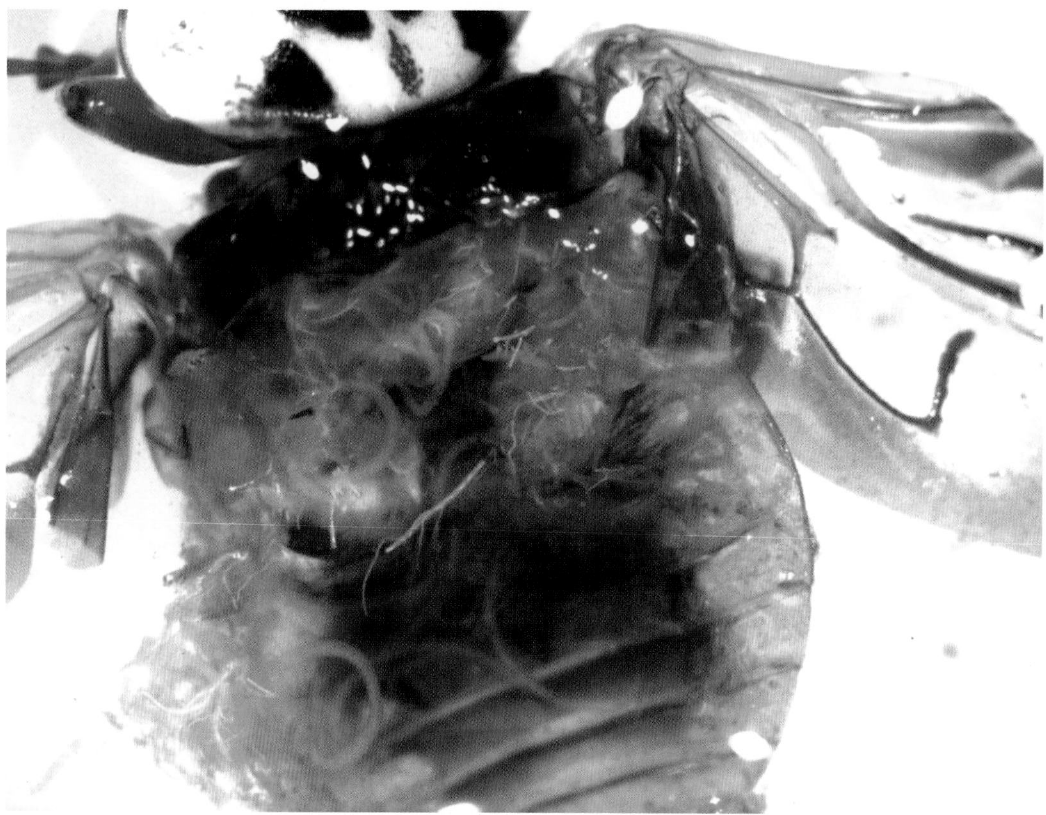

Figure 227. Nematode worms emerging from a ladybird.
Photo: Remy Poland.

Allantonematidae (Tylenchida)

Parasitilenchus coccinellinae (Allantonematidae) has been reported from 14-spot, 2-spot, and Adonis' ladybirds and also *Oenopia conglobata*, and *Hippodamia* (*Semiadalia*) *undecimnotata* in Europe (Iperti, 1964). Recently, a tylenchid nematode has also been found infecting harlequin ladybirds in North America, although the species is yet to be confirmed (R. Poland, personal observation). Over 100 adult female *P. coccinellinae* and up to 10 000 larvae and young adults can be found within a single host (Iperti & van Waerebeke, 1968). The transmission method of this nematode is unknown. *Parasitilenchus coccinellinae* does not usually result in host death, but does consume host resources and retards maturation of the ovaries (Ceryngier & Hodek, 1996).

There is one report of allantonematid nematodes of the genus *Howardula* infecting 2-spot ladybird larvae in England (Hariri, 1965). Interestingly, this nematode did not seem to alter the host gonads, as is the case with other allantonematids, but resulted in a reduction in size of host fat bodies.

Mermithidae (Mermithida)

The immature stages of several members of the Mermithidae are solitary endoparasites of adult ladybirds including Adonis', 14-spot and 7-spot ladybirds (Iperti, 1964). These nematodes reduce the weight, respiratory rate, host ovary growth and the size of the fat body of their hosts. The behaviour of infected females is altered as the parasite develops (they do not mate, eat fewer aphids and become hyperactive). Ultimately, infection causes paralysis and death of the host within about 17 days and the worm emerges.

Fungal pathogens

Hypocreales (Ascomycota)

Fungal pathogens of the order Hypocreales are widely regarded as important natural enemies of ladybirds, but their role in regulating ladybird populations is poorly understood (Roy & Cottrell, 2008). The hypocrealean fungi that have been found infecting ladybirds include: *Beauveria bassiana*, *Metarhizium anisopliae*, *Isaria farinosa* (= *Paecilomyces farinosus*), *I. fumosorosea* (= *P. fumosoroseus*) and *Lecanicillium* (= *Verticillium*) *lecanii*. The most well-studied genus of hypocrealean fungi infecting ladybirds is *Beauveria* (Roy & Cottrell, 2008); indeed *B. bassiana* is widely reported as a major mortality factor of overwintering ladybirds.

Beauveria bassiana (Balsamo) Vuillemin (Ascomycota: Hypocreales)

Identification

Small, white, round spores approximately 3 μm diameter produced at the end of hyphae. At late stages of infection, as these spores emerge, individual ladybirds appear white and fluffy.

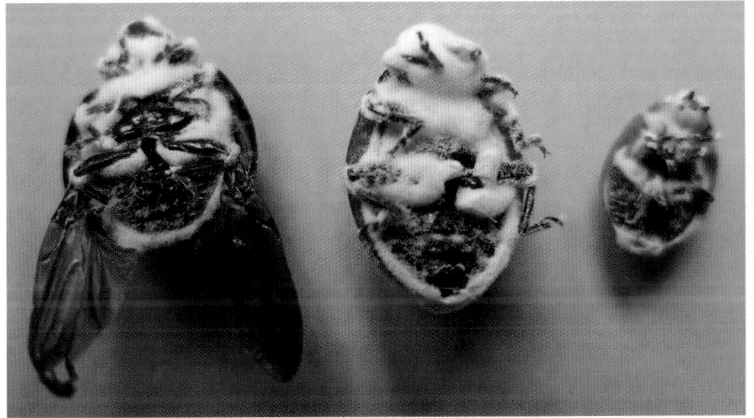

Figure 228. *Beauveria bassiana* infection (late stage) of (left to right) harlequin, 7-spot and 2-spot ladybird adults. Photo: Helen Roy.

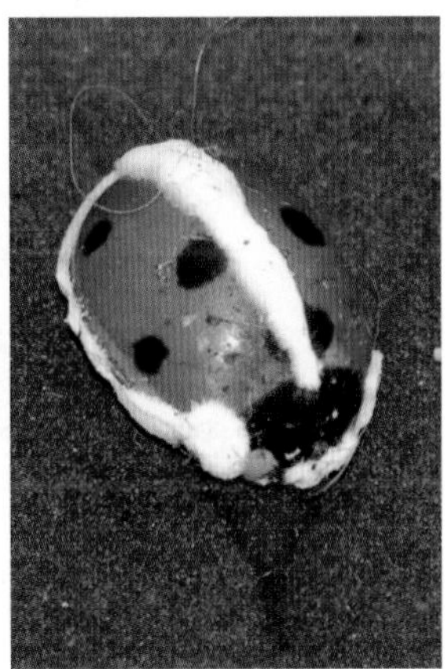

Figure 229. *Beauveria bassiana* infecting a 7-spot ladybird collected in the field. Photo: Richard Comont.

Ecology

Geographic range: worldwide.

Host range: wide. Many insect orders including Coleoptera.

Overwintering: spores remain dormant in the soil, on vegetation or in host individuals.

Life cycle: Hypocrealean entomopathogens produce infective spores (conidia) that attach, germinate and penetrate directly through the host cuticle. They utilise the host as a nutritional resource, proliferating within the host in many forms: protoplasts, blastospores and hyphal bodies. The fecundity of the host can be affected throughout the infection cycle but eventually the host is killed. After host death, the fungus produces infective conidia for further transmission, or, in the absence of new hosts or under adverse environmental conditions, it produces resting structures, such as sexual or asexual resting spores, chlamydospores or mummified hosts.

UK distribution status Ubiquitous

Hesperomyces spp. (Ascomycota: Laboulbeniales, Laboulbeniaceae)

Laboulbeniales are obligate ectoparasites that can be found infecting many arthropod hosts, particularly Coleoptera (Weir & Hammond, 1997). Ladybirds are infected by several species of the genus *Hesperomyces*. The most common is *Hesperomyces virescens*.

Hesperomyces virescens Thaxter (Laboulbeniales: Ascomycetes)

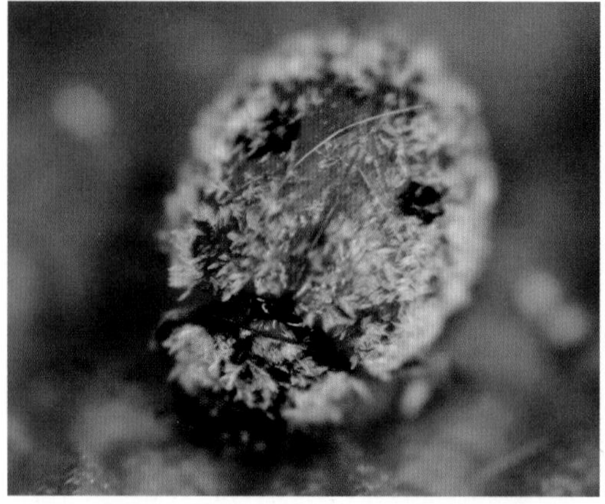

Figure 230. *Hesperomyces virescens* infection of 2-spot ladybird. Photo: Michael Majerus.

Figure 231. *Hesperomyces virescens* infection on the head and pronotum of a *Scymnus femoralis* adult. Photo: Gilles San Martin.

Identification

Small (1 mm) yellow fruiting bodies (thalli) projecting from the adult ladybird, usually on the elytra of females and the ventral surface of males. The base of the thalli appears as a foot with a melanised holdfast.

Ecology

Geographic range: worldwide.

Host range: five ladybird genera (in Britain): *Harmonia*, *Chilocorus*, *Hippodamia*, *Adalia* and *Psyllobora*.

Overwintering: On the surface of the host.

Life cycle: Most Laboulbeniales do not penetrate the insect cuticle, although *Hesperomyces virescens*, the most commonly reported laboulbenialean on ladybirds produces a circular appressorium and penetrates the host cuticle through the production of rhizoids (Weir & Beakes, 1996). However, laboulbenialean fungi do not cause mortality of their hosts, but heavy infections can impede flight, mating, foraging and feeding (Nalepa & Weir, 2007). Contact during sexual reproduction is thought to be the major transmission mechanism of *H. virescens*. However, *H. virescens* thalli on overwintering 2-spot ladybirds were shown to be distributed at the margins and front edges of the elytra which can be explained by the direct contact during aggregation (Weir & Beakes, 1996).

UK distribution status Ubiquitous

Other pathogens

Nosema spp. (Microsporidia: Nosematidae)

Microsporidia are peculiar but fascinating intracellular pathogens with complex life cycles. Infection begins with a microsporidial spore in the host extruding a coiled tube, called the polar filament, which acts as a needle injecting the spore contents into the host cell. Inside the host cell, the intracellular stage (schizont) proliferates asexually and undergoes a sexual process to produce structures called sporonts. In the genus *Nosema*, each sporont gives rise to one spore (Ceryngier & Hodek, 1996). The spores can be transmitted horizontally (released into the environment and ingested) or vertically (mother to egg). Microsporidian species are often highly specific and not only infect single host species but specific tissues within the hosts, such as the fat body, midgut wall or the reproductive tissues. Infections by most microsporidia cause chronic diseases and so the host can appear asymptomatic. However, the body size, longevity and fecundity of infected individuals are often reduced and development time increased (Hajek, 2004).

Septate eugregarines (Apicomplexa: Eugregarinorida: Septatorina)

Eugregarines are large unicellular organisms (sometimes more than 0.5 mm in length) that are found within the alimentary canals, coelomic spaces and reproductive vesicles of many invertebrates (Rueckert & Leander, 2008). Several species within the eugregarine suborder Septatorina have been reported from the intestines of ladybirds. Most of them have been placed in the genus *Gregarina* of the family Gregarinidae.

Eugregarines are considered to be weak pathogens, destroying the intestinal cells in ladybirds, and are more common in regions with warm climates than in colder ones. Five aphidophagous ladybirds in SE France were reported harbouring eugregarines, and one of them, 14-spot ladybirds, at a prevalence of about 10% (Iperti, 1964).

Bacteria

Very little is known about the bacterial diseases of ladybirds, with the exception of male-killing bacteria (Majerus & Hurst, 1997). Male-killing bacteria are maternally inherited endosymbionts (within cells) which cause their hosts to produce female-biased sex ratios. They have now been identified in 14 ladybird host species, and are suspected to occur in five others. Bacteria from five different groups have been identified as male-killers of ladybirds (*Rickettsia*, *Wolbachia*, *Spiroplasma*, Flavobacteria and alpha-proteobacteria). *Adalia bipunctata* is host to four different male-killers (a *Rickettsia*, two species of *Wolbachia* and a *Spiroplasma*) and so is a particularly interesting species in which to study male-killing.

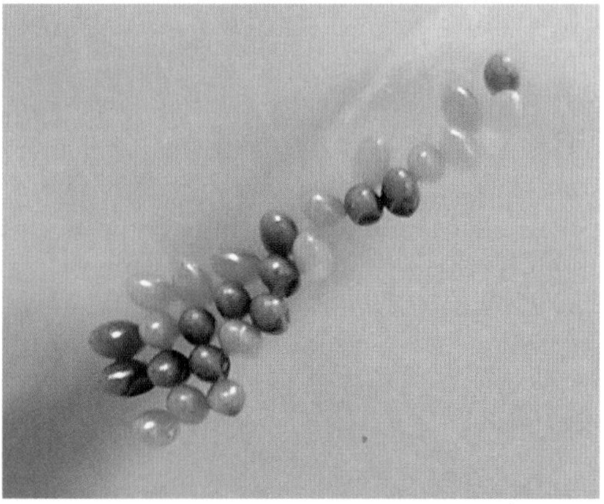

Figure 232. *Wolbachia* infection results in the death of most of the male offspring (yellow eggs) within a 2-spot ladybird egg clutch, consequently only half the eggs hatch (grey eggs). Photo: Helen Roy.

The evolutionary rationale of male-killing in the Coccinellidae seems clear. A male ladybird is an evolutionary 'dead-end' for a cytoplasmic endosymbiont because it cannot be vertically transmitted to the next generation. Therefore, it is advantageous for the symbionts to indirectly increase the fitness of their host by killing male hosts and favouring female hosts. In ladybirds, the endosymbiont causes death early in male embryonic development, and resources that would have been used by males are reallocated to their female siblings (Hurst, 1991; Majerus, 2003). Resource reallocation to females is achieved in two ways in ladybirds: lack of competition from male siblings, and consumption of their dead brothers upon hatching.

The aphidophagous ladybirds have a number of behavioural and ecological attributes that make them particularly prone to male-killer infection. Aphidophagous ladybirds lay their eggs in clutches and so the opportunity to eat a sibling egg, and gain an advantage in doing so, is high. Secondly, populations of their aphid prey fluctuate spatially and temporally. Finally, ladybirds are highly cannibalistic and consume sibling eggs (Majerus & Majerus, 1997b); daughters of infected females gain a survival advantage by feeding on their dead brothers.

Impact of natural enemies on ladybird populations

Two natural enemies are often considered among the most important causes of mortality in adult predatory ladybirds: the braconid parasitoid, *D. coccinellae*, and the entomopathogenic fungi, particularly *Beauveria* species. Some studies suggest that natural enemies exert stronger and more persistent effects on phytophagous ladybirds compared to predatory ladybirds, and coccidophagous species seem to be more affected than aphidophagous ones. However, information is scant and there is little conclusive evidence for top-down regulation of ladybird populations. Further studies are required to address the role that natural enemies play in the population dynamics of the Coccinellidae.

Introducing the Ladybird Parasite Survey

The parasites of ladybirds are, in many ways, as charismatic as the ladybirds themselves, and their fascinating life histories, with many intricacies still to be unraveled, contribute to this appeal. The braconid wasp, *D. coccinellae*, and the phorid flies, *Phalacrotophora* species, are easily recognisable in association with their ladybird hosts, and understanding the prevalence of these parasite species, temporally and spatially, would be valuable.

Bill Phillips has been studying ladybirds and their parasites in several field sites around Loughborough. His meticulous observations have led to some exciting finds in relation to fungal disease and the prevalence of parasitoids. It is always a delight to receive his photographs and field reports. He was one of the first people to observe emergence of *D. coccinellae* from a harlequin ladybird in the field. We hope that others will join the pursuit of monitoring ladybird parasites.

The arrival of the harlequin ladybird in Britain and Ireland provides a new emphasis for research on ladybird-parasite interactions. Theory suggests that invading species could escape the natural enemies from their native range and be less susceptible to those in the invaded range. Monitoring ladybird parasites provides a unique opportunity to compare the prevalence of parasites in native ladybirds and harlequin ladybirds. It is possible that we will observe native ladybird parasites adapting to this new arrival. These are exciting times for ladybird community dynamics and so, in May 2010, we launched the Ladybird Parasite Survey in association with BBC Breathing Places. Contributors are invited to complete a recording form and upload their results to the UK Ladybird Survey website: www.ladybird-survey.org

Recording *Phalacrotophora* and *Oomyzuz scaposus* (= *Tetrastichus coccinellae*)

Recorders are asked to collect ladybird pupae in late spring and summer and place them singly in a suitable container, after collecting information on the pupal habitat and location. The recorder then simply observes the pupae on a daily basis and records any changes. It is anticipated that in most cases an adult ladybird will emerge but the presence of a phorid or chalcid parasite will be clearly evident. Phorids will appear as 5 to 10 small (about 4 mm long) yellow fly larvae from the ladybird pupa which, over 24 hours, will turn into hard brown pupae. One adult fly should emerge from each fly pupa within one week. It is possible to identify the adults to species although this requires genitalia dissection. Chalcid wasp larvae develop inside the ladybird pupa and emerge as adults through a single exit hole, usually in the top of the pupa. Up to forty adult wasps, approximately 2 mm long, emerge from a single pupa.

Recording *Dinocampus coccinellae*

The braconid wasp, *D. Coccinellae*, is usually associated with adult ladybirds. A single yellow wasp, about 10 mm long, exits and spins a cocoon between the legs of the ladybird host. This parasite-host interaction can be observed in the field, particularly overwintered adult 7-spot ladybirds appearing in the spring.

Glossary of terms

Abdomen The second region of an insect containing the digestive tract and reproductive organs. Comprises a series of concave upper integumental plates (tergites) and convex lower integumental plates (sternites), held together by a tough flexible membrane.

Abdominal tergites Sclerotized (hardened) integumental (exoskeleton) plates on the upper part of the abdomen.

Adelgids Woolly aphids; insect family Adelgidae within the order Hemiptera (bugs).

Aleyrodids Whiteflies; insect superfamily Aleyrodoidea within the order Hemiptera (bugs).

Alkaloids Repellent chemicals contained within the ladybird's blood and secreted through reflex bleeding as defence.

Allantonematids Insect pathogenic worms (nematodes).

Anal cremaster The anal pore located at the tip of the last abdominal segment of an insect.

Anterior Front end of an insect.

Aphidophagous Feeds on aphids.

Aphids Greenfly or blackfly; insect superfamily Aphidoidea within the order Hemiptera (bugs).

Appressorium A flattened and thickened tip of a hyphal (fungal) branch, formed by some pathogenic fungi, that facilitates penetration of the host.

Arboreal Tree-dwelling.

Arrhenotoky Type of parthenogenesis in which only males are produced.

Bivoltine See Voltinism.

Chlamydospores Thick-walled, asexual fungal spore that is derived from a hyphal cell and can function as a resting (resistant) spore.

Chrysomelid Seed or leaf beetle; insect family Chrysomelidae.

Cicadellids Leafhoppers; insect family Cicadellidae within the order Hemiptera (bugs).

Coccidophagous Feeds on coccids.

Coccids Scale insects; insect superfamily Coccoidea within the order Hemiptera (bugs).

Congeneric Species within the same genus; e.g. 2-spot (*Adalia bipunctata*) and 10-spot (*Adalia decempunctata*).

Conidia Asexually produced fungal spore.

Coxa (plural coxae) First of five sections (coxa, trochanter, femur, tibia, tarsus) of an insect's leg.

Cuticle Outer skin that forms the exoskeleton.

Diapause A period during which growth or development is delayed and metabolic activity is reduced often in response to adverse environmental conditions.

Diaspidid Armoured scale insect; insect family Diaspididae within the order Hemiptera (bugs).

Dimorphism The same species possessing two distinct body types.

Dorsal Upper surface.

Dorsoventrally flattened Flattened from top to bottom (squashed in appearance).

Ecdysis Process of shedding outer skin (cuticle).

Eclosion Emergence of an insect larva from an egg or insect adult from a pupa.

Elytra (singular elytron) Wing cases (adapted second pair of wings).

Entomopathogen Insect pathogen such as fungus, bacteria, virus etc.

Entomophagous Feeds on insects.

Endosymbiont Symbiont (organism in a symbiotic (mutually beneficial) relationship) that lives within the body of the host without deleterious effect on it.

Exoskeleton External skeleton (integument) that supports and protects an insect's body.

Exudate Fluid oozed during reflex bleeding.

Femur (plural femora) Third of five sections (coxa, trochanter, femur, tibia, tarsus) of an insect's leg.

Genus (plural genera) Taxonomic rank above species, e.g. *Coccinella*.

Haemolymph Insect blood.

Head The first region of an insect, where the antennae, compound eyes and mouthparts are located; the major centre of the nervous system.

Hyphae Thread-like filaments of a fungus.

Integument External skeleton (exoskeleton) that supports and protects an insect's body.

Labial palps Insect mouthparts.

Mandibles Insect mouthparts.

Maxillary palps Insect mouthparts.

Metatarsus Final section of the tarsus.

Methylalkylpyrazine Repellent chemical contained within ladybird blood and secreted through reflex bleeding as defence.

Mildew Mould (fungus) often seen growing on plants.

Multivoltine See Voltinism.

Mycophagous Feeds on fungi (mould or mildew).

Myrmecophile Animal that lives with ants.

Parasitoid An insect that spends a part of its life attached to or within a host, which it often consumes and ultimately kills in the process.

Parthenogenesis Asexual reproduction by females where growth and development of embryos occurs without fertilization by a male.

Pentatomids Shieldbugs; insect family Pentatomidae within the order Hemiptera (bugs).

Phylloxera Small aphid-like insects; insect family Phylloxeridae within the order Hemiptera (bugs).

Phytophagous Feeds on plants.

Posterior The rear end of an insect.

Pronotum The first section of the thorax, which for ladybirds is often highly patterned and useful in identification.

Pseudococcids Mealybugs; insect family Pseudococcidae within the order Hemiptera (bugs).

Psyllids Jumping plant lice; insect superfamily Psylloidea within the order Hemiptera (bugs).

Quiescent Dormant or inactive state.

Reflex bleeding Defensive reaction in which reflex blood is exuded.

Reflex blood Insect blood (haemolymph) secreted through the process of 'reflex bleeding'; commonly observed as yellow droplets from the leg joints in adults, and pores in the dorsal surface of larvae and pupae.

Rhizoids Structures in fungi and some other organisms that function like a root in support or absorption.

Schizonts Cells that divide by a process called schizogony to form more (daughter) cells.

Sclerotized Hardened or armoured.

Sporonts Cells that are produced by a process called sporogony, particularly in the life cycle of various parasitic microorganisms.

Scutellum Posterior portion of the mesonotum of an insect thorax – a small shield-like plate at the front of the wing cases.

Senescence Biological ageing.

Tarsus (plural tarsi) Fifth of five sections (coxa, trochanter, femur, tibia, tarsus) of an insect's leg; effectively the foot. Each tarsus is itself divided into segments – four in the case of ladybirds.

Teratocytes Specialised cells produced by some parasitoids (such as *Dinocampus coccinellae*), that act as feeding cells for the developing parasitoid.

Thalli Body of a fungus that apparently lacks differentiation.

Thelytoky Type of parthenogenesis in which females are produced from unfertilized eggs.

Thorax Central section of an insect to which wings and legs are attached. Comprises a series of concave upper and convex lower integumental plates called the nota and pleura. The thorax can be divided into three separate sections – pro, meso- and metathorax. Consequently the nota and pleura are referred to as pronotum, mesonotum, metanotum and propleuron, mesopleuron and metapleuron.

Tibia (plural tibiae) Fourth of five sections (coxa, trochanter, femur, tibia, tarsus) of an insect's leg.

Trochanter (plural trochanters) Second of five sections (coxa, trochanter, femur, tibia, tarsus) of an insect's leg.

Tubercle Round nodule, small eminence or warty outgrowth.

Univoltine See Voltinism.

Ventral Lower surface.

Voltinism Number of generations completed in one year. For example, 7-spot ladybirds are univoltine (one generation completed in one year) and harlequin ladybirds are bivoltine (two generations completed in one year) or sometimes multivoltine (many generations completed in one year).

References

Babendreier, D., Aebi, A., Kenis, M. & Roy, H.E. eds. (2010). Working Group 'Benefits and Risks of Exotic Biological Control Agents'. Proceedings of the first meeting at Engelberg (Switzerland), 6-10 September, 2009. *IOBC WPRS Bulletin*, **58**.

Baldock, D.W. (2008). *Bees of Surrey*, Woking, Surrey Wildlife Trust.

Barclay, M.V.L. (2007). Coleoptera. *British Journal of Entomology and Natural History*, **20**, 179.

Booth, R.G. (2000). *Rhyzobius lophanthae*: Exhibit at BNHS Annual Exhibition 1999. *British Journal of Entomology and Natural History*, **13**, 173.

Brown, P.M.J., Adriaens, T., Bathon, H., Cuppen, J., Goldarazena, A., Hagg, T., Kenis, M., Klausnitzer, B.E.M., Kovar, I., Loomans, A.J.M., Majerus, M.E.N., Nedved, O., Pedersen, J., Rabitsch, W., Roy, H.E., Ternois, V., Zakharov, I.A. & Roy, D.B. (2008a). *Harmonia axyridis* in Europe: spread and distribution of a non-native coccinellid. *Biocontrol*, **53**, 5-21.

Brown, P.M.J., Roy, H.E., Rothery, P., Roy, D.B., Ware, R.L. & Majerus, M.E.N. (2008b). *Harmonia axyridis* in Great Britain: analysis of the spread and distribution of a non-native coccinellid. *Biocontrol*, **53**, 55-67.

Brown, P.M.J., Frost, R., Doberski, J., Sparks, T., Harrington, R. & Roy, H.E. (2011) Decline in native ladybirds in response to the arrival of *Harmonia axyridis*: early evidence from England. *Ecological Entomology* **36**, 231-240.

Brown, P.M.J., Thomas, C., Lombaert, E., Jeffries, D.L., Estoup, A. & Lawson Handley, L.J. (2012) The global spread of *Harmonia axyridis* (Coleoptera: Coccinellidae): distribution, dispersal and routes of invasion. *Biocontrol*, **56**(4): 623-642.

Ceryngier, P. & Hodek, I. (1996). Enemies of Coccinellidae. *Ecology of Coccinellidae* (eds I. Hodek & A. Honěk), pp. 319-350. Dordrecht, Kluwer Academic Publishers.

Ceryngier, P., Roy, H.E. & Poland, R.L. (in press) Natural enemies of ladybird beetles. *Ecology and behaviour of Coccinellidae* (eds I. Hodek, A. Honěk & H.F. van Emden), Wiley-Blackwell.

Cotton, D.C.F. (2006). Some ladybird (Coleoptera; Coccinellidae) records from Cos Sligo and Leitrim. *Irish Naturalists' Journal* **28**: 253-255.

Daloze, D., Braekman, J.C. & Pasteels, J.M. (1995). Ladybird defence alkaloids: structural, chemotaxonomic and biosynthetic aspects (Col.: Coccinellidae). *Chemoecology*, **5/6**, 173-183.

Disney, R.H.L. (1979). Natural history notes on some British Phoridae (Diptera) with comments on a changing picture. *Entomologist's Gazette*, **30**, 141-150.

Disney, R.H.L. & Chazeau, J. (1990). The recognition and biology of *Phalacrotophora quadrimaculata* (Diptera, Phoridae) parasitizing *Olla v-nigrum* (Coleoptera, Coccinellidae) used in attempts to control the leucaena psyllid. *Annales De Parasitologie Humaine Et Comparee*, **65**, 98-100.

Disney, R.H.L., Majerus, M.E.N. & Walpole, M.J. (1994). Phoridae (Diptera) parasitising Coccinellidae (Coleoptera). *Entomologist*, **113**, 28-42.

Disney, R.H.L. & Beuk, P.L.T. (1997). European Phalacrotophora (Diptera: Phoridae). *Entomologist's Gazette*, **48**, 185-192.

Dixon, A.F.G. (2000). *Insect predator-prey dynamics: ladybird beetles and biological control*, Cambridge, Cambridge University Press.

Duff, A.G. (2008). *Checklist of beetles of the British Isles*, Wells, Somerset, A.G. Duff.

Durska, E., Ceryngier, P. & Disney, R.H.L. (2003). *Phalacrotophora beuki* (Diptera : Phoridae), a parasitoid of ladybird pupae (Coleoptera : Coccinellidae). *European Journal of Entomology*, **100**, 627-630.

Ford, E.B. (1945). *Butterflies*, London, Collins.

Ford, E.B. (1955). *Moths*, London, Collins.

Geoghegan, I.E., Thomas, W.P. & Majerus, M.E.N. (1997). Notes on the coccinellid parasitoid *Dinocampus coccinellae* (Schrank) (Hymenoptera: Braconidae) in Scotland. *Entomologist*, **116**, 179-184.

Hajek, A. (2004). *Natural enemies: an introduction to biological control*, Cambridge, Cambridge University Press.

Hariri, G. (1965). Records of nematode parasites of *Adalia bipunctata* (L.) (Col., Coccinellidae). *Entomologist's Monthly Magazine*, **101**, 132.

Hawkins, R.D. (2000). *Ladybirds of Surrey*, Woking, Surrey Wildlife Trust.

Hodek, I., Iperti, G. & Hodkova, M. (1993). Long-distance flights in Coccinellidae (Coleoptera). *European Journal of Entomology*, **90**, 403-414.

Hodek, I. & Honěk, A. (1996). *Ecology of Coccinellidae*, Dordrecht, Springer.

Hodek, I. & Honěk, A. (2009). Scale insects, mealybugs, whiteflies and psyllids (Hemiptera, Sternorrhyncha) as prey of ladybirds. *Biological Control*, **51**, 232-243.

Hodek, I., Honěk, A. & van Emden, H.F. eds. (in press) *Ecology and behaviour of Coccinellidae*, Wiley-Blackwell.

Hurst, L.D. (1991). The incidences and evolution of cytoplasmic male killers. *Proceedings of the Royal Society of London Series B-Biological Sciences*, **244**, 91-99.

Hurst, G.D.D., Majerus, M.E.N. & Fain, A. (1997). Coccinellidae (Coleoptera) as vectors of mites. *European Journal of Entomology*, **94**, 317-319.

Iperti, G. (1964). Les parasites des Coccinelles aphidiphages dans les Alpes-Maritimes et les Basses-Alpes. *Entomophaga*, **9**, 153-180.

Iperti, G. & van Waerebeke, D. (1968). Description, biologie et importance d'une novelle espèce d'Allantonematidae (Nématode) parasite des coccinelles aphidophages: *Parasitilenchus coccinellinae*, n. sp. *Entomophaga*, **13**, 107-119.

Iperti, G. (1999). Biodiversity of predaceous Coccinellidae in relation to bioindication and economic importance. *Agriculture Ecosystems & Environment*, **74**, 323-342.

Kenis, M., Roy, H.E., Zindel, R. & Majerus, M.E.N. (2008). Current and potential management strategies against *Harmonia axyridis*. *Biocontrol*, **53**, 235-252.

Kirby, M. (2008). The ladybird, the scale and the spindle – a highly specialised relationship. *British Wildlife*, **19**, 193-196.

Klausnitzer, B. & Klausnitzer, H. (1997). *Marienkäfer (Coccinellidae)*, 4th ed. Magdeburg, Westarp Wissenschaften.

Kontodimas, D.C., Milonas, P.G., Stathas, G.J., Economou, L.P. & Kavallieratos, N.G. (2007). Life table parameters of the pseudococcid predators *Nephus includens* and *Nephus bisignatus* (Coleoptera: Coccinelidae). *European Journal of Entomology*, **104**, 407-415.

Kovář, I. (1996). Phylogeny. *Ecology of Coccinellidae* (eds I. Hodek & A. Honěk), pp. 19-32. Dordrecht, Kluwer Academic Publishers.

Kuznetsov, V.N. (1997). *Lady beetles of the Russian Far East*, Gainesville, The Sandhill Crane Press.

le Monnier, Y. & Livory, A. (2003). *Atlas des Coccinelles de la Manche*, Coutances, Manche Nature.

Magro, A. & Hemptinne, J.L. (1999). The pool of coccinellids (Coleoptera: Coccinellidae) to control coccids (Homoptera: Coccoidea) in Portuguese citrus groves. *Boletín De Sanidad Vegetal Plagas*, **25**, 311-320.

Majerus, M.E.N. & Kearns, P. (1989). *Ladybirds*, Slough, Richmond Publishing.

Majerus, M.E.N. & Williams, Z. (1989). The distribution and life-history of the orange ladybird (*Halyzia 16-guttata* L.) (Coleoptera: Coccinellidae) in Britain. *Entomologist's Gazette*, **40**, 71-78.

Majerus, M.E.N. (1994). *Ladybirds*, London, HarperCollins.

Majerus, M.E.N. (1995). *The current status of ladybirds in Britain: final survey report of the Cambridge Ladybird Survey – 1984-1994*, Cambridge, University of Cambridge.

Majerus, M.E.N. (1997). Parasitization of British ladybirds by *Dinocampus coccinellae* (Schrank) (Hymenoptera: Braconidae). *British Journal of Entomology and Natural History*, **10**, 15-24.

Majerus, M.E.N. & Hurst, G.D.D. (1997). Ladybirds as a model system for the study of male-killing symbionts. *Entomophaga*, **42**, 13-20.

Majerus, M.E.N. & Majerus, T.M.O. (1997a). Predation of ladybirds by birds in the wild. *Entomologist's Monthly Magazine*, **133**, 55-61.

Majerus, M.E.N. & Majerus, T.M.O. (1997b). Cannibalism among ladybirds. *Bulletin of the Amateur Entomologists' Society*, **56**, 235-248.

Majerus, M.E.N. (2002). *Moths*, London, HarperCollins.

Majerus, M.E.N. (2003). *Sex wars: genes, bacteria, and sex ratios*, Princeton, New Jersey, Princeton University Press.

Majerus, M.E.N., Roy, H.E., Brown, P.M.J., Ware, R.L. & Shields, C. (2006). *A guide to the ladybirds of the British Isles*, Shrewsbury, Field Studies Council.

Majerus, M.E.N., Sloggett, J.J., Godeau, J.F. & Hemptinne, J.L. (2007). Interactions between ants and aphidophagous and coccidophagous ladybirds. *Population Ecology*, **49**, 15-27.

Menzies, I.S. & Spooner, B.M. (2000). *Henosepilachna argus* (Geoffroy) (Coccinellidae, Epilachninae), a phytophagous ladybird new to the U.K., breeding at Molesey, Surrey. *The Coleopterist*, **9**, 1-4.

Minchin, D. (2010). A swarm of the seven-spot ladybird *Coccinella septempunctata* (Coleoptera: Coccinellidae) carried on a cruise ship. *European Journal of Entomology*, **107**, 127-128.

Morley, C. (1941). *Harmonia quadripunctata* new to Britain. *Transactions of the Suffolk Naturalists' Society*, **4**, 247.

Murchie, A.K., Moore, J.P., Moore, G.A. & Roy, H.E. (2008). The harlequin ladybird (Harmonia axyridis (Pallas)) (Coleoptera: Coccinellidae), found in Ireland. *Irish Naturalists' Journal* **29**: 25-26.

Nalepa, C.A. & Weir, A. (2007). Infection of *Harmonia axyridis* (Coleoptera: Coccinellidae) by *Hesperomyces virescens* (Ascomycetes: Laboulbeniales): role of mating status and aggregation behavior. *Journal of Invertebrate Pathology*, **94**, 196-203.

Nentwig, W. (1986). Non-webbuilding spiders: prey specialists or generalists? *Oecologia*, **69**, 571-576.

Pell, J.K., Baverstock, J., Roy, H.E., Ware, R.L. & Majerus, M.E.N. (2008). Intraguild predation involving *Harmonia axyridis*: a review of current knowledge and future perspectives. *Biocontrol*, **53**, 147-168.

Rhule, E.L., Majerus, M.E.N., Jiggins, F.M. & Ware, R.L. (2010). Potential role of the sexually transmitted mite *Coccipolipus hippodamiae* in controlling populations of the invasive ladybird *Harmonia axyridis*. *Biological Control*, **53**, 243-247.

Roy, H.E. & Cottrell, T.E. (2008). Forgotten natural enemies: Interactions between coccinellids and insect-parasitic fungi. *European Journal of Entomology*, **105**, 391-398.

Roy, H.E. & Wajnberg, E. eds. (2008a). *From biological control to invasion: the ladybird* Harmonia axyridis *as a model species*. Dordrecht, Springer.

Roy, H. & Wajnberg, E. (2008b). From biological control to invasion: the ladybird *Harmonia axyridis* as a model species. *Biocontrol*, **53**, 1-4.

Roy, H.E. & Migeon, A. (2010). Coccinellidae. *Arthropod invasions in Europe* (eds A. Roques, J.Y. Rasplus, W. Rabitsch, C. Lopez-Vaamonde, M. Kenis, W. Nentwig & D.B. Roy), Dordrecht, Springer.

Rueckert, S.I. & Leander, B.S. (2008). Gregarina: Gregarines. *The Tree of Life Web Project*, http://tolweb.org/Gregarina/124806/2008.09.23, accessed 08/01/2011.

Semyanov, V.P. (1986). Parasites and predators of *Coccinella septempunctata*. *Ecology of Aphidophaga* (ed. I. Hodek), pp. 525-530. Dordrecht, Dr W. Junk.

Shapiro-Ilan, D.I. & Cottrell, T.E. (2005). Susceptibility of lady beetles (Coleoptera : Coccinellidae) to entomopathogenic nematodes. *Journal of Invertebrate Pathology*, **89**, 150-156.

Skidmore, P. (1985). *Exochomus nigromaculatus* (Goeze) (Coleoptera, Coccinellidae) in Britain. *Entomologist's Monthly Magazine*, **121**, 239-240.

Sloggett, J.J. & Majerus, M.E.N. (2000). Habitat preferences and diet in the predatory Coccinellidae (Coleoptera): an evolutionary perspective. *Biological Journal of the Linnean Society*, **70**, 63-88.

Sloggett, J.J. & Majerus, M.E.N. (2003). Adaptations of *Coccinella magnifica*, a myrmecophilous coccinellid to aggression by wood ants (*Formica rufa* group). II. Larval behaviour, and ladybird oviposition location. *European Journal of Entomology*, **100**, 337-344.

Smith, E., Lee, J. & Lazenby, A. (1985). Beetles (Coleoptera). *The natural history of the Sheffield area and the Peak District* (ed D. Whiteley), Sheffield, Sorby Natural History Society.

Speight, M.C.D. (1990). Hippodamia 13-punctata (Coleoptera: Coccinellidae) and other insects from All Saints Bog, Co. Offaly, Ireland. *Bulletin Irish biogeographical Society* **13**: 200-212.

Stace, C.A. (2010). *New flora of the British Isles*, Cambridge, Cambridge University Press.

Tshorsnig, H.P. & Herting, B. (1994). The Tachinids (Diptera: Tachinidae) of Central Europe. Identification keys for the species and data on distribution and ecology. *Stuttgarter Beiträge Zur Naturkunde, Serie a (Biol.)*, **506**, 1-170.

Ware, R.L. & Majerus, M.E.N. (2008). Intraguild predation of immature stages of British and Japanese coccinellids by the invasive ladybird *Harmonia axyridis*. *Biocontrol*, **53**, 169-188.

Ware, R.L., Ramon-Portugal, F., Magro, A., Ducamp, C., Hemptinne, J. & Majerus, M.E.N. (2008). Chemical protection of *Calvia quatuordecimguttata* eggs against intraguild predation by the invasive ladybird *Harmonia axyridis*. *Biocontrol*, **53**, 189-200.

Webberley, K.M. & Hurst, G.D.D. (2002). The effect of aggregative overwintering on an insect sexually transmitted parasite system. *Journal of Parasitology*, **88**, 707-712.

Webberley, K.M., Buszko, J., Isham, V. & Hurst, G.D.D. (2006). Sexually transmitted disease epidemics in a natural insect population. *Journal of Animal Ecology*, **75**, 33-43.

Weir, A. & Beakes, G.M. (1996). Correlative light- and scanning electron microscope studies on the developmental morphology of *Hesperomyces virescens*. *Mycologia*, **88**, 677-693.

Weir, A. & Hammond, P.M. (1997). Laboulbeniales on beetles: Host utilization patterns and species richness of the parasites. *Biodiversity and Conservation*, **6**, 701-719.

Appendix 1: How to make a sweep net

You will need:

- an old white or cream pillowcase
- two wire coat hangers
- a piece of wood (e.g. shortened broom handle, about 70cm long)
- some duct tape
- two jubilee clips

The wire coat hangers are straightened out, twisted round each other, and then formed into a loop, leaving a short straight section at either end (around 7cm). The pillowcase should be cut so that it is slightly longer than wide, and a hem sewn into the top, leaving an open section (5-7cm) for the twisted wire to be threaded through. The twisted wire is then threaded through the material loop created by the hem, until the short lengths of wire that are sticking out protrude from the unstitched area. The jubilee clips are used to attach the protruding wire to the end of the piece of wood, and duct tape is wrapped round the handle to cover all sharp edges.

Appendix 2: Protocol recommended for structured ladybird surveys

The text below is taken from a UK Ladybird Survey letter sent to recorders who express an interest in carrying out ladybird surveys.

Take part in the UK Ladybird Survey!

Background

Thank you for your interest in the UK Ladybird Survey. As you may have heard, a new ladybird species called the harlequin ladybird, *Harmonia axyridis*, arrived in Britain in 2004. It is a large, fast-breeding, aphid-eating species which threatens to out-compete some of our 47 native ladybird species. The Harlequin Ladybird Survey (see www.harlequin-survey.org) was launched in March 2005 to track the progress of the alien species in Britain. We now need to gather as much information as possible on the presence and abundance of native species, so that the impact of the harlequin on them can be assessed. We are looking for people to help us by recording ladybirds.

Ladybird habitat preferences

Ladybirds are present in virtually all terrestrial habitats in Britain. Some species are found in a limited range of habitats, but others (such as the 2-spot and 7-spot ladybirds) are generalists and may be found almost anywhere that there are aphids. Most ladybird species are aphid-eaters, but some eat scale insects and others (such as the 22-spot and Orange ladybirds) feed on mildew.

Survey methods

In addition to sightings of individual ladybird species (which can be recorded online at www.ladybird-survey.org/recording.htm), we would like people to undertake slightly more detailed surveys several times a year. Especially if repeated over a period of several years, this will provide some extremely valuable data on the impact of the harlequin.

There are three main survey techniques for recording ladybirds – walking survey, tree beating and sweep netting.

- **Walking survey** – simply a slow walk (distance is up to you) looking for ladybirds, mostly on low vegetation.
- **Tree beating** – an open umbrella (or beating tray*) is placed under tree branches or bushes that are given a few sharp taps with a stout stick. The umbrella or tray will catch the ladybirds that fall out.
- **Sweep netting** – used in grassland, heathland and low growing vegetation. Walk slowly through the vegetation sweeping the net from side to side, collecting ladybirds in the sweep net*.

We are looking for ladybird surveyors to use any or all of the above methods. The walking survey and tree beating can be done easily without the need to buy or make anything.

* Beating trays and sweep nets may be purchased from entomological suppliers but are relatively expensive (around £20 to £60 each). An umbrella (ideally white or a pale colour) is a good replacement for a beating tray. Sweep nets can be made using heavy gauge wire, strong white canvas material and wood dowelling. For further information, please contact the UK Ladybird Survey.

Where to do your survey

Your survey site may be your garden, a local walk, or a park or woodland – it's up to you. Please try to survey at the same site(s), in a standardised manner, so that we can analyse changes there over time.

When to do your survey and for how long

How long you spend on the survey is also up to you (30 to 60 minutes each time would be good). Ideally you would do a total of six to eight surveys in the spring, summer and autumn when ladybirds are active (one in April, two in May, two in June, one in July, one in August and one in September) – but if you do fewer, that is fine. Surveys should be done between approximately 10:00 and 17:00 hours.

Weather conditions

Ladybirds are active during the day, especially on warm, dry sunny days. As a guideline, the temperature should be at least 13°C if sunny and slightly warmer if not sunny. It is important that you note weather conditions when filling in your Recording Form.

How to identify ladybirds

Our survey is concentrating on 26 main ladybird species, but at any given site you may find just a few species. Ladybirds can usually be identified with the naked eye (although a hand lens is helpful) by looking at the size, basic colour, spot colour, number of spots and other patterning of the ladybird. The following sources of information should help you to identify your ladybirds:

- www.ladybird-survey.org/UKladybirds/UKladybirds.htm for pictures and information on the species.
- Ladybirds of the UK identification sheet – colour A4 sheet available from us if not already included with this letter. Also available to download at www.ladybird-survey.org/UKladybirds/UKladybirds.htm
- A Guide to the Ladybirds of the British Isles (fold-out chart) by Michael Majerus, Helen Roy, Peter Brown, Remy Ware and Chris Shields (Field Studies Council, 2006) £2.75 – available from FSC.
- Ladybirds: Naturalists' Handbooks 10, by M. Majerus & P. Kearns, (Richmond Publishing, 1989) £9.95. This is a very good book with excellent colour drawings. It is currently being updated for publication in 2011.

How to submit records

Please submit your records in either of the following ways:

1. Complete the online form at www.ladybird-survey.org/recording.htm ('All species records from a site survey'). You can save entry time by ticking the box by 'Remember my personal details next time I visit this page'.

2. Send in paper copies of the UK Ladybird Survey Recording Form (one form per survey please). It will be clearest if your records for the whole season could be sent to us in one go, after you have carried out your last survey for this year. Please let us know if you need further copies of the form.

3. Records may also be sent in spreadsheet format. Please contact us for a template.

Summary

Thank you once again for your interest in the UK Ladybird Survey. If you can help us by doing surveys at a site of your choice, we will be very grateful and you will be helping to conserve an important part of Britain's wildlife. Remember, within the rough guidelines, how you survey your site is up to you. **The important thing is that whatever you do, you do it consistently each time.**

In summary, these are the main things to do if you take part:

- Decide on your survey method and route.
- Carry out your survey (identifying the ladybirds you find – see 'How to identify ladybirds' above)
- Fill in a UK Ladybird Survey Recording Form for each survey that you do.
- Post or email completed Recording Forms to us.

Best wishes and good luck looking for ladybirds!

Helen Roy, Peter Brown and Remy Poland

UK Ladybird Survey

CEH Wallingford, Maclean Building, Crowmarsh Gifford, Wallingford OX10 8BB.

Email: ladybird-survey@ceh.ac.uk

www.ladybird-survey.org

www.harlequin-survey.org

The survey is a collaboration between Anglia Ruskin University, Clifton College and the Biological Records Centre (within the Centre for Ecology & Hydrology).

UK LADYBIRD SURVEY RECORDING FORM (version 1.6)

Year		Date		Start time		Recorder name	
Site name				Finish time			

Grid ref. or post code of site

Site description (e.g. garden, deciduous woodland, etc)

Weather conditions

Coleoptera: Coccinellidae - Ladybirds 6455

Species no.	Ladybird species name	Walking survey Number seen	Tree beating Number seen	Sweep netting Number seen	Total	Comments
59501	2-spot, *Adalia 2-punctata*					
59502	10-spot, *Adalia 10-punctata*					
60001	Eyed, *Anatis ocellata*					
59201	Water, *Anisosticta 19-punctata*					
59301	Larch, *Aphidecta obliterata*					
59901	Cream-spot, *Calvia 14-guttata*					
58801	Heather, *Chilocorus 2-pustulatus*					
58802	Kidney-spot, *Chilocorus renipustulatus*					
59602	Hieroglyphic, *Coccinella hieroglyphica*					
59601	Scarce 7-spot, *Coccinella magnifica*					
59603	5-spot, *Coccinella 5-punctata*					
59604	7-spot, *Coccinella 7-punctata*					
59605	11-spot, *Coccinella 11-punctata*					
99201	Bryony, *Epilachna argus*					
58901	Pine, *Exochomus 4-pustulatus*					
60301	Orange, *Halyzia 16-guttata*					
59702	Harlequin, *Harmonia axyridis*					
59701	Cream-streaked, *Harmonia 4-punctata*					
59001	13-spot, *Hippodamia 13-punctata*					
59101	Adonis', *Hippodamia variegata*					
60101	18-spot, *Myrrha 18-guttata*					
60201	Striped, *Myzia oblongoguttata*					
59801	14-spot, *Propylea 14-punctata*					
57801	24-spot, *Subcoccinella 24-punctata*					
60501	22-spot, *Thea 22-punctata*					
59401	16-spot, *Tytthaspis 16-punctata*					
	Total					

Notes

Website: **www.ladybird-survey.org** Email: **ladybird-survey@ceh.ac.uk**
Post: **UK Ladybird Survey, CEH Wallingford, Maclean Building, Benson Lane, Crowmarsh Gifford, Wallingford, OX10 8BB**

Appendix 3: Plant names

Alder *Alnus glutinosa*

Angelica *Angelica sylvestris*

Apple *Malus* spp.

Ash *Fraxinus excelsior*

Aspen *Populus tremula*

Beech *Fagus sylvatica*

Birch *Betula* spp.

Bitter-cress *Cardamine hirsuta*

Black pine *Pinus nigra*

Blackcurrant *Rubus nigrum*

Blackthorn *Prunus spinosa*

Bracken *Pteridium aquilinum*

Brambles *Rubus fruticosus*

Broom *Cytisus scoparius*

Buddleja *Buddleja davidii*

Burdock *Arctium* spp.

Buttercup *Ranunculus* spp.

Camellia *Camellia japonica*

Canadian goldenrod *Solidago canadensis*

Cherry *Prunus* spp.

Common reed *Phragmites australis*

Corsican pine *Pinus nigra* ssp. *laricio*

Cow parsley *Anthriscus sylvestris*

Creeping thistle *Cirsium arvense*

Dandelion *Taraxacum officinale*

Dead-nettle *Lamium album, L. purpureum*

Dock *Rumex* spp.

Dogwood *Cornus sanguinea*

Douglas fir *Pseudotsuga menziesii*

Elm *Ulmus* spp.

False oat-grass *Arrhenatherum elatius*

Fat-hen *Chenopodium album*

Field beans *Vicia faba*

Field maple *Acer campestre*

Firethorn *Pyracantha coccinea*

Foxglove *Digitalis purpurea*

Gorse *Ulex europaeus*

Hawthorn *Crataegus monogyna*

Hazel *Corylus avellana*

Heather *Calluna vulgaris*

Hebe *Veronica* subgenus *Pseudoveronica*

Hogweed *Heracleum sphondylium*

Holly *Ilex aquifolium*

Honeysuckle *Lonicera periclymenum*

Hornbeam *Carpinus betulus*

Horse-chestnut *Aesculus hippocastanum*

Ivy *Hedera helix*

Knapweed *Centaurea* spp.

Larch *Larix* spp.

Lavender *Lavandula angustifolia*

Leyland cypress *Cupressus macrocarpa* x *Xanthocyparis nootkatensis* (x *Cuprocyparis leylandii*)

Lime *Tilia* x *europaea*

Lucerne *Medicago sativa*

Maples *Acer* spp.

Melon *Cucumis melo*

Monterey cypress *Cupressus macrocarpa*

Mugwort *Artemisia vulgaris*

Nettle *Urtica dioica*

Norway maple *Acer platanoides*

Norway spruce *Picea abies*

Oak *Quercus* spp.

Peony *Paeonia officinalis*

Pine *Pinus* spp.

Poplar *Populus* spp.

Ragwort *Senecio* spp.

Red campion *Silene dioica*

Reed sweet-grass *Glyceria maxima*

Reedmace *Typha latifolia*

Reed *Phragmites australis*

Rhododendron *Rhododendron ponticum*

Rosebay willowherb *Chamerion angustifolium*

Roses *Rosa* spp.

Rushes *Juncus* spp.

Salad burnet *Poterium sanguisorba*

Sallow *Salix caprea, S. cinerea*

Scots pine *Pinus sylvestris*

Sea radish *Raphanus raphanistrum* ssp. *maritimus*

Silver maple *Acer saccharinum*

Sitka spruce *Picea sitchensis*

Spurrey *Spergula arvensis*

Sycamore *Acer pseudoplatanus*

Tansy *Tanacetum vulgare*

Teasel *Dipsacus fullonum*

Thistle *Cirsium* spp.

Viburnum *Viburnum* spp.

Wallflowers *Erysimum cheiri*

White bryony *Bryonia dioica*

Wild carrot *Daucus carota*

Wild parsnip *Pastinaca sativa*

Willow *Salix fragilis, S. alba*

Yarrow *Achillea millefolium*

Yew *Taxus baccata*

Index to species and families

Synonyms are given in *italics*. Start of main sections and maps are given in **bold**.